INFORMATION
AND ERROR

INFORMATION
AND ERROR

AN INTRODUCTION TO
STATISTICAL ANALYSIS

Solomon Diamond
LOS ANGELES STATE COLLEGE

BASIC BOOKS, INC., NEW YORK

© 1959 BY Solomon Diamond

Library of Congress Catalog Card Number 59-7942

MANUFACTURED IN THE UNITED STATES OF AMERICA

FOURTH PRINTING

PREFACE

Whoever wishes to explore the mysteries of modern psychology must carry with him an equipment of statistical techniques that were esoteric novelties twenty years ago. At that time, a student armed with the critical ratio in one hand and the product moment correlation in the other could wander freely through the contemporary literature and fear no dragons. Occasionally the shadow of factor analysis would fall across his path, but he could quiet any feeling of apprehension by incanting the pronouncements of eminent authorities that this particular young phantom would never have teeth or claws. Thus carefree might he roam through many fertile fields of discussion where only an occasional statistic marred the otherwise serene landscape of rhetoric.

The student today faces a very different situation. Turn any page, and he may find himself face to face with a variance ratio, a chi-square, or even a set of oblique axes erected in hyperspace. These disconcerting experiences inhibit adventure beyond the safe confines of textbooks, and they also encourage a dangerous kind of sectarianism which looks upon "statistical psychologists" as a breed of invaders who threaten to subvert our interest in "the individual" with their interest in "the mass." The reverse is true. The newer techniques of statistical analysis are instruments of exploration which are opening new frontiers to psychological conquest. Today there are important areas of clinical psychology and the theory of personality, for example, which must remain out-of-bounds to those whose statistical preparation does not go beyond what was considered quite adequate not many years ago.

This situation calls for a new approach to the teaching of statistics. It does not do to teach the older methods as a beginning, and to leave the newer ones to be learned in advanced courses, almost as a separate subject. Pedagogic efficiency requires that the viewpoint which is fundamental to the newer techniques, which may be called an *analytic* as opposed to a *descriptive* viewpoint, should be introduced at the start. Fortunately, this does not demand a great deal of mathematical preparation. The underlying concepts are accessible to proof in terms of elementary college algebra, and anyone who has grasped these principles can learn to understand and apply methods whose development required a good deal of mathematical genius.

It would be misleading to say that the subject can be made easy even for those who have hitherto found mathematics difficult. However, the problem is not to make the content easy, but to keep the learner alert and interested. To do this, it is important to give concrete support to the process of concept formation: a neat proof may be wasted without an apt analogy or an enlivening bit of humor. These have always been the province of the class instructor, but I have taken the liberty of including them in these pages. They are not intended to bring the subject down to what might be called a sub-mathematical level, but to keep the student's intelligence from "freezing" in a way that is all too common in statistics courses for the social sciences.

The selection and sequence of topics are unusual, but not haphazard. The student learns to compute eta-square, and to give it a meaning, before he is introduced to the standard deviation! Analysis of variance and chi-square precede product moment correlation. The instructor is free to rearrange these topics into a more traditional order, but if he can tolerate the suspense, the development will seem quite natural to the student. In the end, the latter should comprehend that each major statistical technique can be regarded as one form of answer to a general problem: how to abstract from the sum of squares, which is a mélange of error, that portion which represents useful information relative to the question of the moment.

ACKNOWLEDGMENTS

Every book of this sort owes much to the generosity of authors and publishers who permit the reproduction of indispensable tables. I am indebted to Sir Ronald A. Fisher, Cambridge, to Dr. Frank Yates, Rothamsted, and to Messrs. Oliver and Boyd Ltd., Edinburgh, for permission to reproduce the major portion of Table III and all of Table IV from their book, *Statistical Tables for Biological, Agricultural, and Medical Research*. I am also indebted to Professor George W. Snedecor and to the Iowa State College Press for permission to use the "additional values" of Table III and all of Table V, which are taken from *Statistical Methods*, 5th edition, 1956. For Table VII, I am indebted to Professor Merle W. Tate, University of Pennsylvania, and Professor Richard C. Clelland, Wharton School of Finance and Commerce, and to The Interstate Printers and Publishers, Inc., Danville, Illinois, who have permitted me to consolidate materials from several tables in their book, *Nonparametric and Shortcut Statistics*. Professor William H. Kruskal and Professor W. Allen Wallis, both of the University of Chicago, and the American Statistical Association, have permitted use of the material presented in Table VIII. For Table IX, I am indebted to Professor Milton Friedman, University of Chicago, and to *The Annals of Mathematical Statistics*. Finally, The RAND Corporation of Santa Monica, California, and The Free Press of Glencoe, Illinois, have permitted the reproduction, in Table XII, of 10,000 digits taken from their book, *A Million Random Digits with 100,000 Normal Deviates*. The exposition of factor analysis in Chapter 12 is based in part on a briefer exposition in my earlier book, *Personality and Temperament*. I am indebted to the publishers, Harper and Brothers, for their kind permission to reuse some of this material.

Other acknowledgments occur at appropriate places in the text, but they are admittedly inadequate. It is true of this book, as of most introductory textbooks on statistics, that few words are used to give credit to those who have invented the methods described. When a name is mentioned in discussion, it is not so much by way of salute as by way of introduction, because the name may commonly be encountered as a label for a given technique, and therefore the reader should become familiar with it. Surely the principal reason which has permitted the development of this practice of wholesale borrowings without specific acknowledgments is that personal modesty is an occupational characteristic of mathematical statisticians. The writer has succumbed to the practice, but confesses it as a sin. There are few paragraphs which should not be embellished by a credit line addressed to one or more members of the great company of statisticians, past and present, whose labors tend to be merged in a vast anonymity.

However, I must mention here my friends and colleagues whose freely given suggestions (often including unpublished data from their own research or from class experiments, to serve as exercise problems) I have deeply appreciated, but can never acknowledge in detail. Among them, in my own department, are Richard S. Balvin, Dale N. Dunlap, Ralph G. Gunter (now at San Fernando Valley State College), John V. Haralson, Ronald D. Hutchinson, Alvin Marks, Charles K. A. Wang, and Howard E. Wilkening. Raymond G. Pitts, in the Division of Education, read the entire manuscript and made many useful suggestions. The most arduous task was generously performed by Charles L. Clark, head of the Department of Mathematics, Los Angeles State College, and William B. Michael, Director of the Testing Bureau of the University of Southern California. Their expert assistance in reading the galley proofs has helped to reduce the errors due to my own mistakes and oversights. For errors that remain, I am alone responsible. Such there must surely be, but I hope that they will not obstruct the reader's understanding.

S. D.

CONTENTS

INFORMATION
AND ERROR

1

A FRAME OF REFERENCE

Let us begin with a conundrum: in what way is the work of a psychologist like a game of poker? The answer, of course, is that in both, important decisions must be based on incomplete information. The same thing is true of most important life decisions. The general who is only partly informed about the strength and plans of his enemy, the innocent who is planning to buy a second-hand automobile, the young man who is wondering if he has found the right girl to be his wife—each must reach a decision on the basis of information which is inadequate for a sure conclusion.

The problem of how to evaluate incomplete information is seen in its purest form at the gambling table. Indeed, our conundrum was suggested by an article about blackjack, or "21," in a statistical journal.[1]* As this game is played in the gambling casinos of Reno and Las Vegas, the player sees two cards which he has received from the dealer, and one of the dealer's cards, which is upturned. He does not see the dealer's other card nor can he know, of course, what will come next from the deck. With this scant information, he must decide whether to "stand" or "draw," in the effort to bring the point total for his hand close to the optimal total of 21 without overshooting the mark. The article outlines a detailed strategy which, over the long pull, would result in net losses of only 6 bets per 1000, which is almost as good as not playing at all! There is no doubt that the statistical analysis of a game of chance pays off, even if it does not lead to a stable livelihood.

---

* Superior numbers refer to references which will be found at the end of each chapter.

The problem of the blackjack player is not essentially different from that of a psychologist who is shown a young man's scores on two or three aptitude tests and is asked to make a judgment as to his probable success in a profession. In both cases, the decisive cards are still hidden in the deck. Let us take a typical example. Suppose that the young man is entering a school of law and that he has taken a test of aptitude for legal studies. His score on that test is exceeded by 80 per cent of entering students, and experience over a number of years indicates that approximately one-fourth of the entrants will fail to make the grade academically. What are his chances? To answer this question correctly one should first know certain technical facts about the test, of a kind which we shall have no opportunity to discuss for many pages to come. Suffice it to say that if the test is about as good as the usual well-regarded instrument of this general kind, the young man's chances of success are about even. It would be an error to interpret the poor score as indicating a very low likelihood of success. It would probably be very nearly correct to say that the student faces a 50 per cent likelihood of failure, instead of the 25 per cent likelihood which is faced by the average entrant.

The typical clinical psychologist is ready to recognize the weakness of tests when they are interpreted in an actuarial manner, and he is more pleased than surprised to learn that vocational counselors often exaggerate the prognostic significance of test scores. But he also believes that tests can be made more useful by the leavening of intuitive judgment. One must have an eye, he says, for those rare and especially revealing responses, one or two of which occur in almost every record, which defy statistical analysis because of their unusual, very personal nature. Unfortunately, there is no evidence to support this view. Intuition has its place in the development of hypotheses, but the trend of experimental evidence clearly indicates that it cannot rival the efficiency of cold statistics. In a review of studies which compare the effectiveness of statistical and so-called "clinical" predictions, Meehl found that 17 of 27 studies indicated superiority for the statistical method, while none showed it to be inferior.[2,3] As poor as the actuarial approach may be, the intuitive approach is even less satisfactory. As clinicians or proto-clinicians we may find these facts distressing, but we cannot dare to ignore them.

There are some kinds of decisions which every man has the right to make after his own taste. The young man may reject as distasteful a statistically-oriented approach to the problem of choosing his wife, and the girl may with equal justice object to being chosen by such a procedure. But when the problem is to interpret a test score for a client, or to prepare a clinical report which will be used as the basis for a plan of therapy, there is no justification for the exercise of finicky personal preferences. Whoever enters a profession cannot ethically evade the task of learning how to acquit himself of its responsibilities in a manner consistent with the best interest of his clients, rather than in the manner most compatible with his own temperament and self-image.

Since the use of tests enters into the work of most psychologists, competence in dealing with them is regarded as an essential part of their professional training. However, this is only the most obvious need which psychologists have for statistical training. Every psychologist is also expected to be a competent research person, even—one might almost say especially—when his job is of a distinctly "applied" nature. Many large business organizations and governmental agencies have learned that a psychologist is a handy man to have around the office, because he has the know-how to quickly set up a plan of investigation to deal with almost any type of practical problem. Even the psychologist who most resolutely disclaims any interest in performing research, and who intends as a matter of principle to restrict his professional horizon at any one time to the phenomenal world of just one person, will find that he cannot keep abreast of new developments unless he understands the statistical language in which research designs are described and research results are summarized.

There is good reason to anticipate a steadily increasing emphasis on the statistical training of psychologists. In a recent survey sponsored by the American Psychological Association, psychologists were asked to state in what techniques or areas of knowledge they lacked proficiency to such a degree that it interfered with their professional work.[4] For 25 per cent of those who had been classified as Significant Contributors, and for 29 per cent of Psychologists-in-general, the most serious deficiency was stated to be in the area of statistics and experimental design. Another 9 per cent of Psychologists-in-general, and another 28 per cent of Significant Contributors, said that what they felt most keenly was lack of preparation in advanced mathematics. No other broad area of training rivaled these as a major focus for feelings of professional inadequacy. All of the respondents in this study were holders of a doctoral degree earned before 1945. If since that time there has been any increased rigor in the statistical training of doctoral candidates, it is evident that this has been in response to realistic needs.

In short, anyone who is earnest in the study of psychology must also be earnest in the study of statistics. One can no more be a psychologist in the middle of the twentieth century and be ignorant of statistics than one might have laid claim to the same title 60 years ago, being ignorant of reaction times and the uses of nonsense syllables.

INFORMATION AND ERROR

Suppose that, late one summer evening, as you enjoy the companionship of congenial guests, you suddenly hear, or think you hear, an unusual sound at the back of the house. Was that a stealthy step on the gravel path? You listen intently for a moment, wondering if it will be repeated. Uncertain, you raise your hand in a gesture which stills the conversation. You strain your ears, sorting out the random noises of the night: the creaking of a tree limb, the motor starting up down the block, the insistent clamor of the crickets. It was none of these—or was it? You heard it—but then how could you be sure, when there were all those other sounds? You are searching for a twig of meaning in a forest of sound.

Whenever there is a question of receiving or transmitting information, the problem of *noise level* is crucial. If the phonograph had been playing a hot jazz number and the voices of your guests had been raised accordingly, someone might have walked down that gravel path quite boldly without a chance of being heard. After your guests leave you may become aware of a mosquito in the room, with a vicious hum that will then seem as loud as the rumble of a jet plane. In just the same manner, whenever we wish to evaluate the information which is contained in a set of scientific observations, we are forced to contend with the confusing effects of many other concurrent phenomena. Is the incidence of mental illness increasing? Or do the records only reflect greater awareness of the problem and greater availability of treatment facilities? Possibly both are true, but how shall we distinguish between the effects of one influence and another? By how much does college education increase a man's earning power? The pay envelope in itself does not tell us, because part of the difference is due to the fact that college students as a group have greater native ability than the population at large. Can readings be made more quickly and more accurately on a pressure gauge with a circular or a vertical scale? Before we accept an apparent advantage of one type of scale over the other, we will want to consider if the numbers are equally legible, if the lighting is equivalent, if there has been equal familiarity with both scales, etc. The most carefully controlled laboratory observations do not escape the contaminating influence of extraneous factors, which introduce into the data variations other than those which reflect the influence of the experimental variable which is the object of our study.

In information theory, all this is called *noise*. That is, noise is defined to include every bit of light or sound or movement, every signal from whatever source that may be perceived by us, which does not serve to convey the particular message with which we are at the moment concerned. In statistical terminology, it is called *error*. Error embraces every sort of variation in the phenomenon which we are observing, except what results from the one source which is the object of our study at the moment, and which we try to bring into prominence by the design of our investigation. It includes all the accumulated effects of other influences, whether suspected or unsuspected, understood or not understood. Error is, of course, no prerogative of the research worker. There is an element of error present in every individual test score and in every clinical judgment. Information and error are commingled in every set of observations.

Consider, as an example, Blodgett's demonstration of latent learning in the rat.[5] He showed that if a rat is given the opportunity to acquaint himself with a maze during exercise periods for several days prior to the time when it is put to him as a problem, on a learn-or-go-hungry basis, his subsequent learning will be faster than that of rats who have not had similar advantages. The rat evidently learned something during his preliminary ambles and explorations, even though they were unmotivated by hunger and the learnings not punctuated by rewards of food. This conclusion rests on the comparison of the learning scores of two groups of rats, only one of which had the opportunity for preliminary exploration, while the other group served as control. No one would trust a demonstration of this sort unless moderately large groups of rats were involved, drawn from similar stock. This is because one recognized source of error (or "noise") in such an experiment is the existence of individual and strain differences in maze-learning ability. Match one sample of randomly selected rats against another, under similar conditions, and the almost inevitable outcome is that one group will *seem* superior to the other. How can we know, then, to what extent such a difference reflects the influence of the experimental variable—which was in this case the preliminary exploration—and to what extent it is a side-effect of extraneous factors which should be dismissed as "noise"?

Error does not carry any recognizable badge, for when we change our point of view, to focus on a different problem, what had been error may become information, and what had been information may become error. For example, a source of error in the use of the Rorschach test for personality appraisals is the variability introduced by the sex and other personal characteristics of the examiner. It is an established fact that some examiners tend to educe longer and more fanciful records than others.[6] When we turn to the study of such examiner-effects, these very differences become the information bearing on our problem, and the differences in respondent-behavior which result from personality differences among the examinees become "noise" or error, which tends to obscure the results.

Statistical method is only one of several ways by which we strive to isolate information—the perceived effect of the experimental variable—from error—the contamination which enters our observations because of the uncontrolled effects of other influences. The first, and no doubt the most important way, is by the clear formulation of our problem, which tells us what kinds of data most deserve our attention. Then come the efforts at experimental control, by which we hope to eliminate some extraneous factors and to limit the scope of others. For example, we may regulate the intensity of hunger motivation in animal subjects, not simply by feeding them once daily for 15 minutes, but by feeding measured amounts, carefully regulated to maintain a given body weight. The consequent reduction in the amount of error due to individual differences in hunger motivation will permit the effect of the experimental variable to appear more clearly. Furthermore, we try to design our experiment in such a way that uncontrolled extraneous influences, even those unknown to us, will operate more or less equally on all groups of subjects. One way to do this is by assigning subjects randomly to the different groups or treatments. Another way is to equalize the groups on the basis of certain characteristics which can be expected to influence the results. For example, if we are making an attitude survey, we may try to reduce potential disturbing influences by taking care that the distribution of subjects in our sample, by age, by sex, by social class, and the like, corresponds to that in the general population. In an animal experiment, we may attempt to equalize the effects of heredity by assigning litter-mates to different groups, rather than using the animals of one litter in the experimental group and those of another in the control group.

If we succeed uncommonly well in our efforts to eliminate error, the outcome of our investigation may be so clear that there will be no need for statistical analysis. This result is so rare in practice that when it occurs it often arouses a suspicion that the groups were not properly comparable in the first place. Usually it is necessary to make an assessment of noise level, and to estimate by statistical procedures the likelihood that what seems to be a meaningful departure from its over-all hum and buzz may be no more than a chance fluctuation in its intensity—a wholly imaginary footstep on the gravel path. In other words, the correct appraisal of information must be preceded by an appraisal of potential error. *Experimental technique and research design strive to reduce error; statistical technique measures the error which remains.*

AN EMPIRICAL ESTIMATE OF CHANCE

What is meant by appraising the potential error in a set of observations may be illustrated by a relatively crude and laborious example of statistical method. Suppose that in a class of 10 women and 14 men the grades of the women are, on the average, higher than those of the men. We may wonder if this indicates that women generally do better in this subject, or if it is just a matter of chance that many of the better students in this particular section of the course are women. One way to approach an answer to this question is to write the grade of each student on a card, shuffle the 24 cards into a chance order, and then deal off 10 of these cards to represent "women" chosen at random. The 14 cards remaining are to be regarded as "men." Do this, say, 20 times, and each time compare the grades of these mythical "women" with the grades of the mythical "men." If the difference between such randomly sorted groups is never so clear-cut as the difference between the grades of the actual men and the actual women, we may reasonably conclude that the advantage of the women in the class distribution of grades was not an accidental occurrence. (We still do not know whether it arises from a feminine talent for the content of the course, or from the grading dispositions of the professor.) If, on the other hand, several of these comparisons yield differences which are as great as the difference first noted in actual grades, we would lean toward the interpretation that the superiority of the women in this class is a chance phenomenon, in the sense that we could not expect it to reappear consistently in other sections of the same course.

The procedure outlined in the preceding paragraph was carried out, and the results are shown in Table 1.1. The actual grades are recorded

TABLE 1.1

Record of Random Sorting Experiment*

Actual Grade Distributions					
	A	B	C	D	GPA
Men ($n = 14$)	1	2	10	1	1.21
Women ($n = 10$)	3	4	3	0	2.00
Total	4	6	13	1	1.54

Chance Grade Distributions					
Trial	A	B	C	D	GPA
1	3	2	5	0	1.80
2	3	3	4	0	1.90
3	2	2	5	1	1.50
4	2	3	5	0	1.70
5	2	1	7	0	1.50
6	1	3	6	0	1.50
7	2	1	6	1	1.40
8	2	3	4	1	1.60
9	3	2	4	1	1.70
10	2	3	4	1	1.60
11	1	2	6	1	1.30
12	2	0	7	1	1.30
13	3	2	4	1	1.70
14	0	4	6	0	1.40
15	3	4	3	0	2.00
16	1	5	4	0	1.70
17	1	2	7	0	1.40
18	2	3	4	1	1.60
19	2	2	5	1	1.50
20	2	4	4	0	1.80
Sums	39	51	100	10	

* See text for explanation.

in the upper portion of the table, together with the grade point averages (GPA) for men, for women, and for the class as a whole, based on 3 points for each A, 2 points for each B, 1 point for each C, and no point credit for D's. The record of the 20 chance grade distributions follows. None of these yielded a grade point average higher than that earned by the women in the class, but on Trial 15 "chance" equalled their performance. Therefore it must be recognized that it would not be a very unusual event for 10 women in such a class to excel over 14 men to the extent observed, even though women students in general are not better than men students in general. On the other hand, it is not a very commonplace event, either, for apparently it would occur by chance only about once in 20 times.

Although such a *randomizing test* is tedious to perform, it enables us to base a conclusion on the experience of one class, instead of having to wait some years to accumulate additional experience. It provides a rough empirical standard of expected error, which permits us to judge whether the observed difference between two groups must be dismissed as all or mostly error, or whether it is so much in excess of this error standard that it should be regarded as including some clear information relative to the question being asked. Statistical techniques perform this same function with greater efficiency.

THE NULL HYPOTHESIS

Such a procedure as the one which was described in the preceding section never permits us to conclude with certainty that chance was not a factor in determining the observed result. It only permits us to state a conclusion in the form that "Even if the difference was wholly determined by chance, there is a strong likelihood that it would have been as large as observed," or "If the difference was wholly determined by chance, there is only a very remote likelihood that it would have been as large as observed." This conditional assumption—"if the difference was wholly determined by chance"—constitutes the framework of thinking within which we make our appraisal of the situation. This conditional dismissal of the effect as merely a chance phenomenon is called the *null hypothesis* because, as applied to an experimental situation, it implies that the experimental variable is without effect—null in effect.

When we first look at the results of an experiment, our judgment is likely to be influenced by our inclinations. To the extent that the results conform to our expectations, we are prone to see them as expressing essential relationships underlying the experimental arrangements which we so cleverly designed. To the extent that they do not so conform, we lean toward interpreting them as the consequences of accidental extraneous influences, and they provoke us to the invention, *post facto*, of ingenious supplementary hypotheses. This is not a process of wilful misinterpretation. It is the inevitable result of the way our minds work, as we try to fit empirical reality into a known conceptual framework.

Let us compare this ambivalence with the result of a bet that is placed on the turn of a roulette wheel. Does such a comparison seem out of place? Yet every experiment is a gamble: the words are synonyms. If the outcome were not in doubt, it would be a demonstration, not an experiment. At the gambling table, while the wheel spins, the outcome remains in teasing doubt. When it stops, whatever our feelings of elation or disappointment, we know that this was just a matter of chance, which might have had a different outcome. Unless the wheel was "fixed" in some manner, no one with less than infinite knowledge could have predicted where it would come to rest. It is exactly so with an experiment. Whatever the outcome, our interpretation must always be based on a realization that it was influenced by many chance factors, and that in a repetition of the experiment the results would surely be different, at least in small degree. We must not permit ourselves to entertain a double standard, which chooses either to emphasize the role of chance or to disregard it, according to whether the results run counter to our theory or tend to vindicate it. The only consistent point of view which we can take is to regard all results as *solely* the outcome of chance, or, more precisely, to ask about any result whether it may not reasonably be regarded as solely the result of chance. This point of view is fundamental to most statistical methodology, and it is referred to as the use of a *null hypothesis* (often symbolized H_0). Where, for example, the theory basic to an experiment points to the likelihood of a clear difference in the performance of two groups, the null hypothesis asserts, on the contrary, that there is no predictable difference between them, and hence that any apparent difference will be mere "noise," the result of chance factors. The null hypothesis defines the experiment as nothing but a gamble. For example, we carry out an investigation to test the hypothesis that depressed patients will respond favorably to an hour of music daily. But we look at the results with a skeptical eye, averring (in the null hypothesis) that the amount of improvement detected could very well have been a merely incidental phenomenon.

We abandon this nihilistic frame of mind only when the nature of the results is such that it is unreasonable to assume that they can be explained solely by the operation of chance. Then we say that "the null hypothesis is rejected," and this technical phrase, which is often met in research reports, is equivalent to stating that the possibility is not excluded that the experimental hypothesis which was basic to the design of the experiment is true. This modern scientific jargon is a very restrained substitute for Archimedes' exultant *"Eureka!"* It is cautiously hedged by a sophisticated awareness that we do not know, and never can know, precisely what we have discovered. We only know, and soberly declare, that "it ain't nuthin'." We are certain that there is some information audible, above the hammering of the boiler factory, the crackling of static, the hubbub of social conversation, or—less figuratively—the confused variation of individual differences which constitute the major source of error in most psychological investigations. Statistical analysis does not presume to translate that information into meaning, but a well-conceived series of null hypotheses may, as in the game of 20 questions, leave us very confident in our final guess.

PROBLEMS

1. *Describe an experimental investigation reported in a recent issue of a psychological journal, clearly stating in your account both the experimental hypothesis and the null hypothesis, and listing sources of error which were controlled and others which were not controlled.*

2. *Suggest a psychological experiment which could be conducted in the classroom, using the students as subjects. State the experimental hypothesis, the null hypothesis, and sources of error which would have to be taken into account.*

REFERENCES

1. Baldwin, R. R., Cantey, W. E., Maisel, H., and McDermott, J. P. The optimum strategy in blackjack. *J. Amer. Statist. Ass.*, 1956, **51**:429–439.

2. Meehl, P. E. *Clinical versus statistical prediction*. Minneapolis: Univ. of Minnesota Press, 1954.

3. Meehl, P. E. When should we use our heads instead of the formula? *J. counseling Psychol.*, 1957, **4**:268–273.

4. Clark, K. E. *America's Psychologists*. Washington, D. C.: Amer. Psychological Ass., 1957.

5. Blodgett, H. C. The effect of the introduction of reward upon the maze performance of rats. *Univ. Calif. Publ. Psychol.*, 1929, **4**:113–134.

6. Sanders, R., and Cleveland, S. E. The relationship between certain examiner personality variables and subjects' Rorschach scores. *J. proj. Techniques*, 1953, **17**:34–50.

2

THE REPRESENTATIVE SCORE

SCORES, SAMPLES, AND POPULATIONS

In the beginning there is the datum: the simple "given" fact, the record of a single observation. This may take many forms, but for the greater part of this book we shall assume that it is a *score* which can have only integral values. Perhaps it is the number of "yes" answers which are given to the items of an adjustment inventory, all of which are so phrased that each "yes" is indicative of an area of poor adjustment. Perhaps it is a verbal fluency score which consists of the number of unrelated words that are written down in an allotted period of time. Perhaps it is an interviewer's count of the number of times that a subject fidgets, or swallows, or blows his nose, or gives some other somatic evidence of uneasiness.

Most psychological scores are not really measurements but, like these examples, consist of enumerations of items which we choose to interpret as having similar significance. This raises some knotty problems for theoreticians, but they are problems which are commonly ignored in practice and we would profit little from concerning ourselves with them at this point. We shall deal with scores, therefore, as if they were measurements on psychological dimensions, stated in terms of equal linear units. And as long as we limit our conclusions to statements regarding scores (which really do occur in equal units) the possible lack of correspondence between scores and the phenomena they measure need not concern us.

The symbol* for a score in its original or *raw* form is X. This innocent symbol is sometimes a source of needless confusion to students who carry over their old habits of looking upon X as the symbol of the unknown. Whenever they see an algebraic symbol, they are seized with an excitement like that of a hound dog that is put upon the scent of a fox, to "find X." This can be very misleading in a statistical context, where the value of each X is ordinarily the one thing of which we are certain from the beginning.

A *set* of scores which is based on a number, *n*, of similar observations is called a *sample*. We may think of them as so many markers on the linear dimension, like clothespins on a line, each marking the spot which corresponds to a certain observation. It is from the sample that all statistics flow, for a *statistic* is simply a number which is computed from the data of a sample, or from other statistics, by any generalized procedure.

The sample is only a part, and usually a very minor part, of all the similar observations which might have been made. We refer to all these similar but largely unmade observations as the *population* of the sample, or as its *universe*. These terms are often used interchangeably, but later in this chapter we shall differentiate them for our own purposes. For a sample to be properly representative of its universe, it must have been made under conditions which are called *random*, that is, each element of the universe must have had an equal chance to be included in the sample. This condition is often very difficult to satisfy, even in an approximate manner. The *Literary Digest's* pre-election poll of 1936 is a monumental reminder that the size of a sample cannot compensate for lack of randomness in its selection. Two million voters were polled, but they were all telephone subscribers or automobile registrants, and in that year of economic depression and political uprising by the Common Man the opinions of these relatively affluent citizens proved to be quite unrepresentative of the national picture.

The purpose in making a set of observations is always to learn something about a population. This focus of our interest is called the *target population*. The statistics which summarize our observations are a statement of facts or information about the sample, but when the same statistics are used to describe the population they must be regarded as only estimates, and we must recognize that they contain some error, the extent of which it is important to appraise.

The basis of this error is the fact that a sample, even when it is random,

---

* Symbols will be defined at the time of their first occurrence. Whenever the reader feels unsure about the meaning of a symbol in a given context, he should refer to the Glossary of Symbols, starting on page 263. These are the *dramatis personae* of our play, and all the action of the plot follows inevitably from the definition of their characters!

is virtually never perfectly representative of its population. If we had really exhaustive knowledge of a population, we would be able to describe it in terms of certain mathematical values, or *parameters*, which would have exact values. For example, the population of unemployed agricultural workers in the United States can be exactly defined, in the sense that it is possible to set up a series of rules for deciding whether any given person does or does not belong to that population. When we have done this, we know that there is some precise number of individuals who are members of the defined population, but it would be quite impossible to determine that number exactly. The true number is called a parameter, while our estimate, which is based on more or less adequate sampling adjusted by more or less reasonable guesswork, is a statistic. Leaving aside trivial cases (including artificially constructed problems), the exact values of parameters are always beyond our ken, and hence *statistics are always wrong*. They may be very useful, nevertheless.

The Organization of Data

The first step in handling any set of scores is to organize it into a tabular form which will facilitate further handling. We begin, perhaps, with a simple listing, such as this listing of scores made by 30 students on a class examination:

30	29	33	24	20	16	18	13	22	44
31	17	17	29	35	14	40	23	20	22
15	14	22	33	22	26	19	18	25	24

To get a better overview of the data, we may organize them into a *frequency distribution*, thus:

44	1	36	0	28	0	20	2
43	0	35	1	27	0	19	1
42	0	34	0	26	1	18	2
41	0	33	2	25	1	17	2
40	1	32	0	24	2	16	1
39	0	31	1	23	1	15	1
38	0	30	1	22	4	14	2
37	0	29	2	21	0	13	1

To achieve a still higher degree of surveyability, even at the sacrifice of some detail, we may organize the data into a frequency distribution *by classes*, as shown in Table 2.1. In this table, the essential characteristics of the score distribution are far more evident than in the frequency distribution without classes. Here the possible scores have been grouped in a systematic manner, and the frequencies of the observed scores are shown for the groupings, or classes.

TABLE 2.1

Scores of 30 Students on a Class Examination, Set Forth in a
Frequency Distribution by Classes

Score (X)	Frequency (f)
42–44	1
39–41	1
36–38	0
33–35	3
30–32	2
27–29	2
24–26	4
21–23	5
18–20	5
15–17	4
12–14	3
	30

Notice that to set up the classes we adopted a *class interval, i,* which in this case equals 3. The score values which are used to state the limits of each class will be referred to as *working limits* of the class, to distinguish them from the theoretical limits, which will be defined shortly. Notice that in the table the lower working limit of each class is a number divisible by the interval, 3. Therefore the lowest class starts with 12, although the lowest score in the sample is 13. We shall observe this rule strictly whenever we set up classes for frequency distributions, in order to avoid the possibility that we might influence the statistics ever so slightly by an arbitrary choice of limits. For, as we continue our discussion, we shall see that the highest score, a 44, is now the equivalent of a 43, since that is the *mid-value* of the class in which it falls. If we had defined the top class as 44–46, we could have made this score equivalent to a 45! Decisions like this must be left to the great god Chance, and not to the whim of mortals. We protect our statistical morality by holding firm to the stated rule: the lower working limit of each class shall be divisible by *i*.*

* Some authors use the rule that the *upper* working limit of each class shall be divisible by *i*. This is no less correct, but it is a matter of some moment to the instructor, or his reader, that all the students in a class shall observe the same rule. Our preference is determined largely by the circumstance that under the rule we have chosen scores of zero, which are not uncommon in psychological observations, fall at the lower limit of one of the classes, whereas under the other rule the writing of working limits for the interval which includes zero scores becomes awkward.

The upper working limit of each class is one score unit below the lower working limit of the next higher class. The difference between the upper and lower working limits of any one class is therefore not i, but one score unit less than i. Thus, if we are tabulating measures of height which were originally recorded to the nearest half-inch, the difference between the upper and lower working limits of any class would be $i - \frac{1}{2}$. If we were dealing with a set of data in which possible scores occur only as multiples of 5, then only such values would be used to define the class limits, and the difference between the working limits of any class would be $i - 5$. In short, there is in any frequency table the same sort of discontinuity which exists in the scale of measurement that was used to record the observations.

For some problems, in later chapters, we shall find it necessary to define *theoretical class limits*, which do not reflect the discontinuity of the scale of measurement. For the data in Table **2.**1, the theoretical limits would be stated thus:

41.5–44.5
38.5–41.5
35.5–38.5, etc.

These are limits in a strict mathematical sense: the lower theoretical limit of each class is a limit approached from above, and the upper theoretical limit of the class just below is the same point, approached from below. The mid-value of each class remains the same under both systems, and therefore it is convenient to define the interval, i, as *the difference between the mid-values of successive classes.*

In a frequency distribution by classes, some of the information in the original data has been sacrificed in order to gain compactness and visibility. The grouping of adjacent scores into classes involves a blurring of fine distinctions, and therefore it constitutes an additional source of error. The nature and extent of this error will be discussed in Chapter 3, but it may be remarked at this point that if at least 12 classes are used, and if the sample is moderately large, the loss of information is usually negligible. The proper interval to select is one which gives a convenient number of classes.

GRAPHIC AND PROPORTIONAL REPRESENTATION

It is often helpful to represent a sample of scores in a graphic form. Figure **2.**1 is a *histogram*, or bar diagram, which shows at a glance the salient features of the distribution of scores in Table **2.**1. To heighten its effect, the number of classes has been reduced below what would be permissible for purposes of numerical analysis. The working limits of these classes are shown on the horizontal axis, or *abscissa*, and the relative

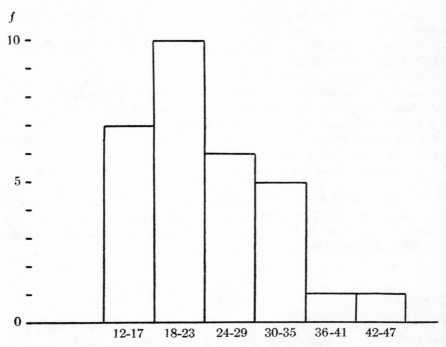

f

FIG. 2.1. Histogram of the data in Table 2.1.

frequencies on the vertical axis, or *ordinate*. Although such a graphic presentation plays no direct part in the analysis of data, it often points up characteristics which might otherwise escape notice.

An alternative method of achieving the same purpose is the *frequency polygon* (Figure 2.2). To construct a graph of this type, first mark off the class limits on the abscissa, and then use the ordinate scale to mark a point directly above the mid-value of each class, corresponding to the frequency of scores in the class. These points are then joined by straight lines. It is customary to close the polygon by including a class with zero frequency at each end of the distribution. A frequency polygon which is prepared in this manner gives an illusion of continuity which may not be justified. The risk of perceptual deception is less with the histogram.

It is sometimes useful to construct a *cumulative frequency distribution*. The first and second columns of Table 2.2 present such a distribution for the data which appear on page 15. Each cumulative frequency is the sum of frequencies for all scores equal to, or less than, the given score. One use of such a table is to facilitate the computation of *centile scores*, which are shown in the third column. An individual's centile score states what percentage of the sample he equals or excels. To obtain it, the cumu-

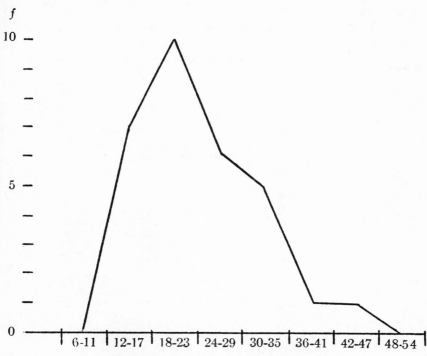

FIG. 2.2. Frequency polygon of the data in Table 2.1.

lative frequency is divided by n (which in this example is 30). In symbols:

$$C = \frac{f_{cum}}{n}$$

Notice, however, that it is customary to round each centile *upward* to a whole number, rather than up or down to the nearest whole number. This nonmathematical generosity arises from the circumstance that the principal use of centiles is for interpreting test performances. For example, if a student whose score on this examination is 18, asks the instructor how he made out, the answer may be given in terms of a centile score: "You did as well or better than 30 per cent of the class." The centile score also enables us to compare the relative standings of the same individual on different tests. To illustrate: this same student may have a raw score of only 12 on a later test, but if the general level of the scores in the class is substantially lower than on the first test, his centile score may have risen, to show that he has advanced his relative standing. Later we shall learn a better way to make such comparisons, but this device is useful whenever we wish to interpret a set of test scores to someone who lacks statistical sophistication.

TABLE 2.2

Cumulative Frequency Distribution of the Data Given on Page
15, Together with Centile Scale

X	f_{cum}	C
44	30	100
40	29	97
35	28	93
33	27	90
31	25	84
30	24	80
29	23	77
26	21	70
25	20	67
24	19	64
23	17	57
22	16	54
20	12	40
19	10	34
18	9	30
17	7	24
16	5	17
15	4	14
14	3	10
13	1	4
12	0	0

Figure 2.3 presents a *cumulative frequency curve* which is based on Table
2.2. This is a type of graphic representation which is usually intended to
serve an analytic purpose, and therefore it should be constructed in fair
detail, and it should not be based on a reduced number of classes. Each
cumulative frequency in Table 2.2 is represented by a dot in Figure 2.3.
It is a matter of taste whether one wishes to connect these points step-
wise with short vertical and horizontal lines (as we have done in the lower
portion of the figure), or draw through them the smooth curve which the
empirical data seem to approximate (as we have done in the upper portion).

This particular curve may be described as a *negatively accelerated growth
curve*, because its rate of increase falls off gradually in the way which is
characteristic of many growth phenomena. This is an expression of the
same phenomenon which shows itself in the asymmetry of Figures 2.1
and 2.2, which are based on the same data. Either of these figures can
be described as *positively skewed*, meaning that the longer, more tapered
or skewer-like tail embraces the larger values. A distribution with negative
skew will produce a positively accelerated growth curve. A symmetrical

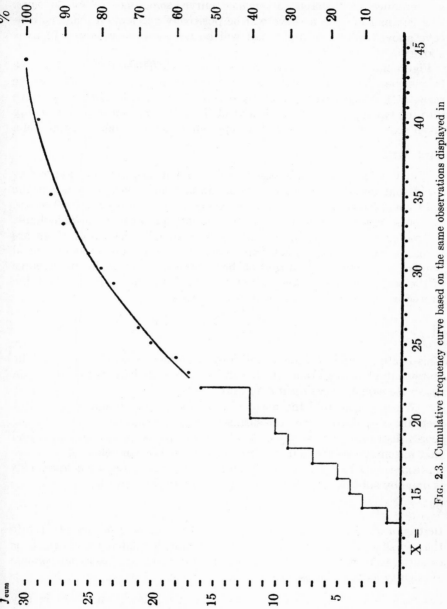

Fig. 2.3. Cumulative frequency curve based on the same observations displayed in Figures 2.1 and 2.2. Compare Table 2.2.

distribution, in which the left tail and the right tail are tapered equally, will produce an *S*-shaped or *sigmoid* curve, sometimes called an *ogive*. The left half of such a curve will be positively accelerated (that is, concave above), while the right half will be negatively accelerated (convex above).

Figure **2**.3 is provided with two vertical scales. The scale for cumulative frequencies, at the left, was used to construct the curve. The percentage scale, at the right, was formed by dividing the total height of the curve into ten equal segments. The height of the curve on this scale, above any given score value on the abscissa, represents the equivalent centile score.

THE MEAN

Had Confucius known statistics, he would in his wisdom have recognized that despite the inestimable advantages of a picture, it is not the most concise form of communication. One statistic can replace 1000 scores, compressing a vast amount of information into a few easily portable digits.

Among the statistics which are used to describe a sample there are several which are usually referred to collectively as "measures of central tendency." The most important of these is the *mean*, or arithmetic average of the scores. Everyone knows how to compute a mean. This is how the procedure is set forth in mathematical symbols:

1]
$$\bar{X} = \frac{\Sigma X}{n}$$

This is an example of a definition formula, which is simply the symbolic statement of a definition which can also be stated in words: *the mean equals the sum of scores divided by their number.*

When we are told the mean of a sample, even though we have not seen the distribution we can surmise certain things about it: that the scores distribute themselves both above and below the mean value, and that in some sense they are balanced around it. We can define this balance quite precisely by transforming each raw score into a *deviation score*. This is done by subtracting the mean from the score. In symbols,

2]
$$x = X - \bar{X}$$

that is, *a deviation score is a raw score less the mean of the sample.* (Note that small x and large X have different though related meanings. It is essential to form the habit of writing them distinctively, to avoid possible ambiguity as to which is meant.)

It can be readily shown that the sum of all deviation scores in any sample equals zero. First, we indicate the summation in this manner:

$$\Sigma x = \Sigma(X - \bar{X})$$

Notice that the parenthetic expression consists of two terms, of which the first is a variable—for X has many different values—while the second is a constant—for the sample has only one mean. Since the summation is over n such expressions, we may write:

$$\Sigma x = \Sigma X - n\bar{X}$$

That is, we make use of the summation sign to indicate a sum of variables, but we introduce n as a multiplier to indicate the sum of a constant which is to be taken once for each of the n elements in the sample. However, $n\bar{X} = n\dfrac{\Sigma X}{n} = \Sigma X$, and therefore

$$\Sigma x = \Sigma X - \Sigma X = 0$$

The fact that the deviation scores of any sample sum to zero is equivalent to a statement that if the scores are regarded as units of equal mass distributed along a linear dimension, the mean would be their center of gravity. We may think of the dimension on which the scores are placed as a see-saw plank which is balanced upon the mean as its fulcrum. Each observation is

$$\begin{array}{ccccccccc} \text{X} & & & & \text{X} & \text{X} & & \\ \hline 0 & 1 & 2 & 3 & 4 & 5 & 6 & 7 & 8 \end{array}$$

"given the same weight," that is, in the model they are regarded as having equal mass. Therefore, their moment, or tendency to impart movement to the plank, varies directly with their distance from the fulcrum. One youngster can balance two others, each as heavy as he is, by moving farther out on his end of the plank. When such a system is in balance, the sum of the positive deviations equals the sum of the negative deviations. (To find the right position for the fulcrum in the figure, calculate the mean of the three indicated scores.)

THE MEDIAN

If the distribution of scores is quite symmetric, it follows that just as many scores lie above the mean as below it. Exceptions to such symmetry are very common. For example, data on "number of wives," whether gathered under the harem system of the Near East or the divorce system of the United States, would not lead to a symmetrical distribution. In such cases it is often convenient to speak of the *median*, which is *a value so chosen that it has as many scores above it as below it*. Certain conventions are followed in locating the medians in discontinuous distributions. When it is possible to divide the frequency distribution clearly into upper and lower halves, each containing the same number of scores, the median is given the value midway between the highest score of the lower half and the lowest score of the upper half. More often the median will fall within a cluster of scores which all have the same value, and then we give it that value. For example, for the 20 random sortings in Table 1.1, page 9, the median grade point average is 1.60, although there are 8 higher values and 9 lower values in the series. When the median is being determined for a frequency distribution by classes, it is customary to estimate its position within the class in which it falls by considering what proportion of the scores in that class must be added to all scores occurring in lower classes, to complete the lower half of the distribution. This procedure is stated in the following formula:

$$3]\qquad \mathrm{Mdn} = LL + \left(\frac{n - 2f_b}{2f_w}\right)i$$

where LL represents the *theoretical* lower limit of the class which includes the median, f_b is the sum of frequencies in all classes below that class, and f_w is the frequency within that class. Thus, for the data in Table 2.1,

$$\mathrm{Mdn} = 20.5 + \frac{30 - 2\,(12)}{2\,(5)}\,3 = 22.3$$

It is possible to define a deviation score with respect to the median, instead of with respect to the mean. When this is done, an interesting consequence is that the sum of the absolute deviations (that is, deviations considered without regard to algebraic sign) is less than the sum of absolute deviations from any other point. Therefore, the absolute sum of deviations from the median is smaller than the absolute sum of deviations from the mean, except in a perfectly symmetrical distribution, where mean and median have the same value. In symbols:

$$\Sigma(|X - \mathrm{Mdn}|) \leqq \Sigma(|X - \bar{X}|)$$

This seldom-mentioned fact may be used to support a claim that the median should be preferred to the mean as a measure of central tendency.

THE MODE

In symmetrical distributions, we also find that scores generally cluster more tightly about the mean than about any other point. When a distribution is presented graphically, this tighter cluster of scores appears as the high point of the curve or frequency polygon. In distributions which are not symmetrical, this high point of the frequency curve, or area of greatest relative frequency of scores, not only fails to coincide with the mean but it characteristically lies on the opposite side of the median from the mean. (Hence the median may be called the most central of the measures of central tendency, which is another point in its favor.) In a large sample there is usually one score which occurs more frequently than any other, and this is called the *mode*. Ordinarily the score frequencies fall off progressively in both directions from this modal value. A distribution which has two areas of relatively high frequency, is called *bimodal*, even though one of the modes may be distinctly lower than the other. In small samples this sort of distribution can usually be dismissed as accidental,* but the occurrence of two distinct modes in a large sample implies that the sample is not homogeneous and that the scores actually represent two merged distributions. In discussions of psychological "types" there will frequently be allusions to real or hypothetical bimodal distributions. For example, one sure way to get a bimodal distribution is to give a test of Masculinity-Femininity to a mixed group of men and women.

In small sets of scores, the mode is often indeterminate. It is therefore of little use in dealing with typical experimental or clinical data, although it is frequently reported in digests of economic or sociological data, which employ large samples. For example, the modal earnings of factory workers, or the modal age of females entering first marriages, as computed from frequency distributions by classes, are useful descriptive statistics.

RELATIVE STABILITY OF MEAN AND MEDIAN

Thus we see that the median, the mean, and the mode each defines the central tendency of the score distribution in a different way. The median divides the set of scores into upper and lower halves and also fixes a point with respect to which the sum of absolute deviations is at a minimum. The mean defines a point of balance at which the algebraic sum of the deviations is zero. The mode is the point where the most conspicuous clustering of scores exists. Which, we may still wonder, is the most generally useful measure of central tendency?

In seeking an answer to this question, one point to bear in mind is that we are usually interested in these statistics for what they can tell us about the universe from which the sample has been drawn, more than for what they tell us about the sample itself. Therefore we want to think of each of them as an estimate of the corresponding universe parameter, rather than simply as a descriptive characteristic of the sample. From this point of view, the mean is superior to any of its rivals. In a later chapter we shall be able to determine the amount of error which is ordinarily involved in using the mean of a sample as an estimate of the universe mean, or "true" mean. We define the true mean as the value which would be found by exhaustive sampling of the universe, and therefore we shall represent it by the symbol $\bar{X}_\infty$. The mean of a sample will usually differ from the true mean by less than the amount that the median of the sample will differ from the true median. By the same criterion, the median is a more stable statistic than the mode. In large samples which have the

* The decision is subject to a test of "goodness of fit," by a procedure to be explained in Chapter 9.

characteristic unimodal and nearly symmetrical distribution which occurs so commonly in all sorts of statistical work, the deviation of the sample median from its parameter tends to be about 1.25 times as great as the deviation of the sample mean from its parameter. In smaller samples, and in those which are distinctly nonsymmetrical, the advantage of the mean is less marked, but still present.

The greater stability of the mean is a consequence of the fact that it makes use of all the information in the sample. No score can be altered without influencing its value, nor can any minor shift in a score produce a disproportionate change. In contrast, both the median and the mode may be unaffected by the shifting of a number of scores, or they may undergo sharp changes as a result of the shifting of relatively few scores. Consider this set of six scores:

$$1, 3, 3, 4, 8, 14$$

The mean is 5.5, the median is 3.5, and the mode is 3. The displacement of one of the 3's by one unit would, depending on its direction, change the mode to 4.0 or make it indeterminate. If one of the 3's were displaced two units upward, the median would become 4.5. Meanwhile, if the 8 were changed to a 12, or the 14 to a 6, neither the mode nor the median would be influenced in the slightest! These statistics are, as it were, spokesmen for the Center, and they give no representation to the extremes of the Right or the Left. Whether they respond to the shift of a score depends on where the score is located more than on the magnitude of the shift. The mean represents a "democratic" balance, which is influenced to the same extent by the same amount of change in any score. Any one-unit shift in any score will produce a change of precisely one-sixth in the mean of this set of six scores.

However, the relative insensitivity of the median to extreme scores is sometimes an advantage. When 5 rats master a problem in 20 to 40 trials, and the sixth repeats stereotyped blunders after 400, it would obviously be absurd to use the mean score to summarize the results. Even when there is no such marked discontinuity in the score distribution, whenever lack of symmetry is one of its essential characteristics, the median seems more satisfactory than the mean as a descriptive statistic. We shall also find that under these circumstances the methods of analysis in which the mean plays a conspicuous part become less trustworthy, and we must then have recourse to other methods, in which the median holds a comparable position.

THE REPRESENTATIVE SCORE

The choice between measures of central tendency appears in a somewhat different light when we look upon them as *representative scores*.

When we choose one of these statistics to communicate to a reader, or to sum up for ourselves, much of the information in a sample, we say in effect: "This is the representative score of the sample. When you think of the universe of the sample, you may think of this as the typical score of that universe. If you have occasion to guess the score of some individual member of that universe, this is the best guess to make on the basis of the information at hand."

The concept of a representative score implies that it is reasonable to think of the universe as consisting of so many individuals who would all give the same response, other things being equal. The spread of scores in every sample is the result of the operation of uncontrolled influences, that is, of those factors which are not equal and which cannot conceivably be made equal in their entirety. From this point of view, every raw score is to be regarded as consisting of two parts: (1) the *representative score* which is the same for every individual included in the sample, and which is an estimate of performance for every individual in the population, and (2) a *deviation score* which sums up the effects of individuating influences.

Consider, for example, the data presented in Table **2.3**. These data were gathered in a statistics class which consisted of 12 men and 12 women

TABLE **2.3**

Hostility Scores of Men and Women Students

X	f_M	f_W	f_{M+W}
13	1	0	1
12	0	0	0
11	0	0	0
10	3	1	4
9	4	2	6
8	1	2	3
7	1	0	1
6	1	1	2
5	0	3	3
4	0	1	1
3	0	0	0
2	0	0	0
1	0	1	1
0	1	1	2
	—	—	—
	12	12	24
$\bar{X}$	8.33	5.83	7.08
Mdn	9	5.5	8

students. They were instructed to "write 15 words that can be used to describe a person," and the words listed were then classified as being either "hostile" or "accepting" in tone. The score for each individual is the number of hostile words in his list. For the entire class, the mean is 7.08, the median is 8, and the mode is 9. Any of these values might conceivably be used as the representative score, even though a "score" of 7.08 is, in the strict sense, impossible. Let us adopt the criterion that the most useful representative score is the one which will lead to the smallest residue of "noise," or error, in the data. At this point in our discussion we do not know of any way to measure this residue except by the sum of absolute deviations from the representative score, and therefore we must for the time being accept the median as the best representative score, since it gives rise to the smallest sum of absolute deviations. (See page 24.)

The point which we wish to make is that as soon as we have made this decision, we have in effect partitioned each individual score into two parts. At the top of the list we no longer have a "13," but an "8 + 5." At the bottom of the list we no longer have scores of "0," but scores of "8 − 8." Each individual, by virtue of being a member of this student sample, has a representative score of 8, and each individual also has a deviation score which reflects the influence of forces acting upon him in different degree than upon other members of the sample.

If we consider the men and women separately, a different picture results. The median for the men is 9, and for the women 5.5. By the act of reclassification into more homogeneous groups, we have reduced the total amount of "noise" in the table. (Find the mean absolute deviation from these medians, and compare it with the figure found for the composite group.) Each score may now be considered as consisting of *three* parts: (1) the representative score which each student has *as* a student, (2) a sex differential—which is positive for the men, negative for the women— and (3) an individual residue. Thus, a man's "6" equals "8 + 1 − 3," while a woman's "6" equals "8 − 2.5 + 0.5."

In closing this section, we wish to forewarn the reader that in the next chapter we shall discover compelling reasons why the mean, and not the median, is usually the best representative score.

LINEAR MEASURES OF DISPERSION

A very important characteristic of any set of scores is its consistency, or, conversely stated, the extent to which the scores vary among themselves. When all the scores are identical we have that Utopian situation in which the representative score appears unmasked by error. When the scores take many different values they reflect the influence of many forces, and therefore the information which they transmit regarding the operation of some *one* of these forces is obscured by the effects of the others, which we call error. The statistics which are used to indicate the relative consistency or inconsistency of scores, and hence the degree to which they are contaminated by error, are called *measures of variability* or *measures of dispersion*. In this chapter we shall consider only those measures which are *linear*, that is, those which are stated in terms of units which are comparable to lengths on the score dimension.

The simplest such measure is the *range*—the difference between the highest score in the set and the lowest.

4] $$R = H - L$$

When there is a premium on speed and ease of computation, this may be a very useful statistic. It is used in industrial quality control, which is the modern substitute for the time-consuming inspection procedures which often slowed the production line. Instead of inspecting every item which comes from a certain lathe, for example, one may take a test measurement on about one item in 20, and record these measurements in groups of 5. The range within each 5 measurements is an index of the quality of the lot or series of 100 from which they were taken. Although the range plays no necessary part in our work, we shall find it convenient for a somewhat analogous purpose, that is, to provide a rough check on the accuracy of more detailed computations. (See footnote, page 85.) It will also sometimes be convenient to "rough out" certain propositions in terms of the range, rather than in terms of a more complex measure of dispersion.

We have already made several references to another measure of dispersion—the mean absolute deviation, which is usually called the *average deviation*.

5] $$AD = \Sigma\frac{(|X - \bar{X}|)}{n}$$

Writers who dismiss this statistic as illegitimate, because it suppresses the algebraic sign of the negative deviations, insult the intelligence of their readers, for mathematicians often use this device in other connections. It is not illegitimate, but obsolete for scientific purposes, because better methods have superseded it. The average deviation was formerly widely used in scientific reports, and it still has a place in reports which are directed to a lay audience, because it is a concept which is easily grasped by the intelligent reader who lacks special training in statistics. To such a reader, the phrase "average deviation" conveys the idea of a region about the mean which embraces most of the scores, leaving distinctly high and distinctly low scores outside it. For example, if a city's annual rainfall is reported as 28 inches, with an average deviation of 4 inches, the reader immediately recognizes that anything from 24 to 32 inches should not be regarded as unusual. On the other hand, if he also draws the conclusion that the annual rainfall will be within these limits just about as often as it will fall outside them, he will be mistaken. We can expect to find distinctly more than half of all the cases inside these limits, because some of the cases outside them are the "extreme" cases which exercise greater weight. In what we shall later come to know as the "normal" distribution, about 57.5 per cent of all cases lie inside the limits fixed by one AD, or average deviation, above and below the mean. Hence the average deviation is not at all the same thing as the *probable error*, which is defined as a range about the mean which includes one-half of the distribution. That is, $X \pm 1$ P.E. includes 50 per cent of the distribution. This, too, is a measure which has become obsolete in scientific usage. (The reader will discover how it is computed in a later chapter.)

Another way to define the "middle half" of a distribution is by the *interquartile range*. The *first quartile*, Q_1, is that score which equals, or exceeds, one-fourth of all the scores in a distribution, and the *third quartile*, Q_3, is the score which equals or exceeds three-fourths of the scores. The interquartile range is the difference between these values, $(Q_3 - Q_1)$, and it therefore embraces just 50 per cent of all the scores. This statistic is often used in presenting the norms of achievement and aptitude tests, when the purpose is not so much to describe the distribution as to fix the limits of "average" scores, meaning the general run of scores. One-half the difference is referred to as the *semi-interquartile range*. In a symmetric distribution this is equal to the probable error.

Each of the measures of dispersion which we have so far described is based on *linear relationships* among the scores. The system of scores defines a linear dimension, each individual score represents a position on that dimension, and the measures of dispersion, which can be represented as lengths on that dimension, tell us something about the degree to which these positions are concentrated or scattered along it. Hence, they are at the same time indicators of the operation of chance factors which influence the different subjects in different degree. For example, the hostility scores recorded in Table **2**.3 might be influenced by age or religious attitude or an accidental encounter with a favorite enemy just before the class. In general, wide dispersion means that these uncontrolled factors are relatively numerous and powerful, but there is no known way to relate the magnitude of any of the linear measures of dispersion to the strength of the forces which produce them except in this vague manner. For this reason, linear measures of dispersion have only limited usefulness.

UNIVERSE AND POPULATION

Earlier in this chapter we defined the universe of a sample as consisting of all the observations similar to those in the sample, including those which were possible but unmade. We should like now to clarify this definition. The naive way to think about a population is to imagine some collection of tangible objects or persons, and a defined characteristic of these objects which is the focus of our attention. If, for the moment, we accept such a definition, we must take note of the fact that even a relatively small collection of objects may give rise to a truly enormous number of possible samples. Let us see how this comes about.

We shall use the symbol $\binom{n}{m}$ to represent the number of different subsets, each consisting of m elements, which can be formed out of a parent set of n elements. The order or arrangement of the elements is to be disregarded. In college algebra these subsets are usually called *combinations*, and the reader may recall that the number of possible combinations, for given values of n and m (where both n and m are integers, and m does not exceed n), is given by the folowing formula:

6] $$\binom{n}{m} = \frac{n!}{(n-m)! \, m!}$$

We shall not trouble to prove this formula, but it will not be amiss to look a little into its structure, rather than take it for granted. The numerator $n!$ (read n *factorial*) is the number of all the possible arrangements which can be made of n elements, using each of the elements once in each arrangement. (For example, 3 elements can be arranged in 6 ways.) Each factor in the divisor effects some reduction of this number. Dividing by $(n-m)!$ reduces it to the number of arrangements which consist of m elements each, omitting those which include either more than or fewer than m elements. (Thus, the number of different arrangements of 3 elements each which can be constructed from a parent set of 8 elements equals $8!/5! = 8 \times 7 \times 6 = 336$). But any combination of m elements can be arranged in $m!$ ways. Hence, dividing further by $m!$ eliminates the duplicate arrangements, and leaves only the number of distinctive combinations. (In this case, $336/6 = 56$.)

If the reader is not familiar with the operation of this formula, it would be a good idea to try it out with some small values of n and m. The results can be checked in Table I of the Appendix, which gives values of $\binom{n}{m}$ whenever n does not exceed 12. The table tells us, for example, that there are 924 ways to select a sample of 6 students from a class of 12 students. If we conduct a class experiment in which students are assigned to experimental and control groups according to one of these ways, we cannot dismiss the other 923 ways from our thinking about how the experiment *might* have turned out. Therefore it is often necessary to refer to all such possible samples collectively, and it is convenient to call them a *universe of samples*.

Let us look at two other illustrations of the application of this formula. In the previous chapter, we considered a problem dealing with the performance of 10 women students in a class of 24. By Formula 6, there are 24!/10! 14! = 1,961,256 ways to form unlike subsets of 10 elements from a set of 24 elements. We can therefore see how insignificant a proportion of the possibilities in the situation was included in the empirical test of chance which we performed by taking 20 chance samples. As another example, the number of distinctive bridge hands, each consisting of 13 cards, which can be dealt from a deck of 52 playing cards equals 52!/39!13!, which turns out to be roughly 635 billion.

The reader will perceive from these examples that statistical populations multiply faster than rabbits. We are reminded of the nightmarish accounts of how the earth would be blanketed by a seething, buzzing mass, deeper than the Empire State Building is tall, if for several generations the entire progeny of every fly should mature. Ecological factors limit the multiplication of real flies, but the members of statistical populations do not eat, neither are they eaten.

It is not always easy to recognize the nature of the universe from which a sample has been drawn, but it is a pretty safe conjecture that it is very, very large. Let us suppose that an arithmetic test has been given to a tenth-grade class in San Gabriel, California. What is the population to which we may generalize the results of this sample? Certainly they cannot be applied to tenth graders across the nation. The universe consists only of those who had an equal chance to be included in the sample, and those in Hoboken, New Jersey, are not of that number. This remains true even if the class tested was randomly chosen from a roster of all the tenth-grade classes in the nation. In fact, common sense would tell us that we cannot even generalize the result to the other tenth-grade class across the corridor in the same school, unless we know that its members were selected in the same manner. Nevertheless, the universe of this sample is vast, although, like the population of bridge games, it consists mostly of imagined members.

Consider for a moment the multiplicity of selective factors that brought just this group of youngsters together as one class. Several years back, there was a debate in the school board as to whether this junior high school should be built here or about a mile east, which would have eliminated some of these children and included others. The top grade on the test was made by Johnny Jones, who would not be here if the topsoil had not blown off his grandfather's Oklahoma fields, back in the 30's. Mary Brown's mother came to California to escape the attentions of her ex-husband who lives in Ohio. Tom Tuppin was born in this district, but the school psychologist and the vice-principal had a lengthy conference on whether he should be promoted. The full story of how these 20-odd children came together could be told only by a Balzac, in as many volumes of human comedy. How nearly infinite, then, is the number of those who might have been here if the right accidents had befallen their parents and grandparents! We can imagine conditions under which Bill Boskin, now in the ninth grade in Cedar Rapids, Iowa, might have been in this tenth grade class in San Gabriel, but if those conditions had come to pass he would be a different Bill Boskin, differently instructed.

Furthermore, the universe of this sample does not really consist of youngsters at all, but of test scores. There is a small population of possible scores for each member of the class, and which one of these was recorded depends on a series of distractions, momentary confusions, fortuitous guesses, and clerical errors by the grader. In short, the statistical population which this sample represents is not a population of real children at all, but a population of might-have-beens. This is a very "iffy" population, but as we continue our discussion we shall see (most clearly when we come to the subject of sampling variance) that it is the only kind of population to which the results of the sample can be generalized without risk—or, more exactly stated, without risks in addition to those which are assessed by statistical methods.

From this point forward, for greater clarity, we shall use the unqualified word *population* only to refer to collections of real persons or objects. Most often these will be the target populations which we are interested in studying. When we have occasion to speak of such a hypothetical population as those which we have described, we shall call it a *universe*. Thus, we may say that the population of playing cards gives rise to a universe of bridge games. The word *set* is a general term which can be used to designate any collection of elements, whether it be a sample, a population, or a universe. Using this terminology, we can restate the conclusion of the previous paragraph as follows: when we use the statistics of a sample to estimate the parameters of a target population, we are making the assumption that the universe of the sample does not differ from that population in any respects which would lead to different results. For example, conclusions about "people" which are based on experiments with college students, or conclusions about "students" which are based on experiments with Princeton men, are based on assumptions that college students are representative people, and that Princeton men are representative students, from the point of view of the behavior being studied in the experiments. The validity of any conclusion which is based on statistics depends on the degree of correspondence between the universe of the sample and the target population.

PROBLEMS

As part of a research project on characteristics of effective college teachers, students were asked to rate their instructors on 40 diverse characteristics. The individual ratings were made on a five-step scale, where 1 was defined to mean that, compared with college instructors generally, this one was "worse than most" on the trait in question, and 5 was defined to mean that he was "the best, or equal to the best." Table 2.4 gives the mean ratings of 35 instructors on 3 traits.

TABLE 2.4

Mean Ratings Given by Students to 35 College Instructors, on Three Traits*

Instructor	Trait			Instructor	Trait		
	(A)	(B)	(C)		(A)	(B)	(C)
1	4.4	2.6	4.4	19	3.8	3.9	3.0
2	4.0	3.3	4.6	20	3.4	3.2	3.0
3	4.0	3.8	3.9	21	4.2	4.3	2.3
4	3.6	3.7	4.3	22	2.3	2.5	2.2
5	4.0	3.6	3.5	23	3.7	3.1	2.7
6	4.6	3.3	4.4	24	2.5	3.6	2.1
7	4.4	3.5	4.2	25	3.1	2.2	3.4
8	3.9	4.0	3.6	26	4.4	2.5	2.7
9	3.5	3.8	3.6	27	3.6	2.9	2.8
10	3.5	2.8	2.6	28	4.7	3.2	2.6
11	4.0	2.5	2.8	29	4.1	2.2	2.8
12	3.7	3.7	3.0	30	2.9	4.7	3.0
13	4.0	2.3	2.7	31	4.3	3.4	3.4
14	3.9	3.1	3.3	32	4.7	4.0	3.9
15	3.9	2.8	2.8	33	2.6	3.7	2.0
16	4.0	3.0	2.3	34	4.5	3.8	4.2
17	3.0	2.3	2.3	35	3.1	4.0	2.9
18	3.3	1.8	2.2				

* (A) Has a good sense of humor; (B) Has a clear plan of work for each meeting; (C) Seems to be proud of his class.

1. *Form a frequency distribution by classes for the mean ratings on each trait. (Use $i = 0.2$ for trait A, and $i = 0.3$ for traits B and C.)*

2. *Draw a histogram of the mean ratings on one trait.*

3. *Form a cumulative frequency distribution of the mean ratings on one trait, and compute centile scores.*

4. *Find the mean and the median for all the instructors on each trait.*

FIRST INTERLUDE

WHY THE SLIDE-RULE IS INDISPENSABLE

This is a good time to initiate our acquaintance with the slide-rule, which is indispensable for later work. "Indispensable" is a word of elastic meaning. Many innovations of yesterday are indispensable today, for modern living. In this sense, the student of statistics who learns to operate a slide-rule will soon find it indispensable because it will free his mind and his work papers from a cumbersome clutter of numbers.

Consider what is involved in a simple problem of division such as may occur in almost any statistics problem. To find the mean of 27 scores whose sum is 185, we might proceed in this manner:

$$
\begin{array}{r}
6.85 \\
27 \overline{)\ 185.00} \\
162 \\
\hline
230 \\
216 \\
\hline
140 \\
135 \\
\hline
5
\end{array}
$$

This is a process which involves three multiplications and three subtractions, and half a dozen separate judgments, even if we do not count the annoying false trials which are omitted from the record. (Students usually show their annoyance with this task by placing it askew on the page, as if it did not really belong to the problem. But this form of unconscious denial, like most neurotic mechanisms, only brings more grief, because the departure from strict columnar rectitude leads in turn to arithmetical blunders.) This is an extravagant waste of mentation which can be afforded only by those to whom figuring comes easy. On the slide-rule, as we shall soon see, it is only necessary to set up the problem and look directly for the answer. If arithmetic is what we do not like, the slide-rule is indispensable. Colonel Mannheim, the Frenchman whose invention of the slide-rule added to the fire-power of the world's artillery, was probably motivated chiefly by an innocent dislike of arithmetic.

If these esthetic considerations are not convincing, let it be remarked on the practical side that the use of a slide-rule will save a good deal of calculating time on a typical final examination. It will take an investment of time to gain this skill, but 30 minutes in June may be worth two hours at the start of the semester.

These instructions (and later hints which will appear throughout the book) will be confined to the use of the simple Mannheim slide-rule, with Scales A, B, C, and D. They should be read with the slide-rule in hand. Learn first to use Scales C and D, which have identical markings. Notice that there are three kinds of rulings on each scale. The *primary rulings* are the longest, and they are numbered from 1 to 9. There is no zero on the slide-rule. This means, for example, that 8, 80, and 0.008 are all located at the same point on either the C or D scale. Perhaps, before going any farther, you would like to try to discover for yourself how to perform a division on the slide-rule. Place the 2 on one of these scales opposite the 3 on the other, and look around to see where you can find the decimal equivalents of 2/3 and of 3/2. Neat, isn't it?

The space between two primary rulings is marked off into tenths by smaller *secondary rulings*. These are not numbered, except perhaps between primary 1 and primary 2. The secondary ruling which marks off five-tenths of the distance between primary rulings is usually just as long as the primary ruling, but it is not numbered. Finally, the space between secondary rulings is divided by still shorter *tertiary rulings* into tenths, fifths, or halves, according to convenience.

To locate a number on Scale D we move the *cursor* from left to right until the hairline lies over the first significant digit, that is, the first digit not a zero. We continue to move it to the right, to the secondary ruling which corresponds to the second significant digit. (If that digit is a zero, we may think of the corresponding ruling as zero distance from the primary ruling.) Then we move to the right to the tertiary ruling which corresponds to the third significant digit, if we are working in a portion of the scale where the tertiary rulings indicate tenths. If not, we must estimate the proper position. Follow this procedure to locate the number 185 on Scale D, and let the hairline rest there, to serve as a sort of mechanical memory.

To locate the divisor, 27, on Scale C, we shall move the slide under the stationary hairline. First we bring primary 2 under the hairline, and then secondary 7 which follows it. Now 27, on Scale C, lies opposite 185 on Scale D, and the *index* of Scale C lies directly over the answer, 6.85, on Scale D. (We call either end of any scale an index, because it is so often used to point to an answer on another scale.) This technological triumph is a simple application of the rule that

$$\log \frac{a}{b} = \log a - \log b$$

Because the scales of the slide-rule are marked in logarithmic proportions, this becomes

$$\text{length } \frac{a}{b} = \text{length } a - \text{length } b$$

By mechanically substracting "length 27" from "length 185" we have in effect performed a logarithmic computation, and we are left with a length which corresponds to the desired answer.

The slide-rule, like a table of logarithms, only keeps track of the decimal part of the logarithm, which is called the mantissa. It does not tell us whether to read the answer as 6.85, or 0.685, or 6850. The least confusing way to determine this is to perform a parallel mental computation, with numbers of one significant figure. In this case, since $200/20 = 10$, we select 6.85 as the answer. A compulsive person may be uneasy with such rough approximation, and may figure $180/30 = 6$. But such refinement is unnecessary. Numbers with a single significant figure, but the right number of places, will always suffice.

In Figure **2**.4, the use of Scales C and D for division is shown schematically, using for illustration the formula $\bar{X} = \Sigma X/n$.

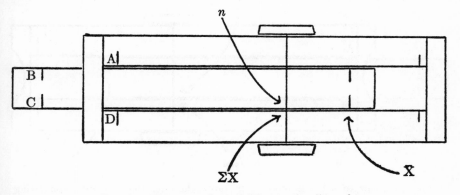

Fig. **2**.4. How to perform division on the slide-rule.

Notice that it would have been just as easy to solve 185/27.6, although this problem would have been measurably more difficult with pencil and paper. Indeed, it is just as easy to solve 185.314/27.62. Do not permit yourself to be driven to pencil and paper. For our class purposes, we shall consider as "accurate" any answer which errs by only one unit in the third significant figure. In this instance, the approximation 6.71 will do very well, and it will also do well enough in almost any practical situation unless there is reason to think that the scientific value of the result justifies a resort to the greater precision of a calculating machine or a table of logarithms.

The rule for multiplication by logarithms is:

$$\log ab = \log a + \log b$$

On the slide-rule, therefore,

$$\text{length } a + \text{length } b = \text{length } ab$$

To add length 27 to length 185, we place the index of Scale C under the hairline which has been positioned over 185 on Scale D, and then push the hairline along until it lies over 27 on Scale C. At this point, it also lies over the answer on Scale D. Since 200 (20) = 4000, we must write the answer with four digits. Only three of these can be read with assurance. But whether we write the answer as 4990 or 5000, it will be sufficiently accurate for our needs. (The correct answer, 4995, can be inferred from a knowledge that a final 5 and a final 7 were involved in the problem.)

Another computational problem which arose in the course of the preceding chapter and which can be very efficiently handled with the slide-rule, is to obtain a series of proportions, or centiles. Figure 2.5 shows how this is done. When the index on Scale C is placed opposite n on Scale D,

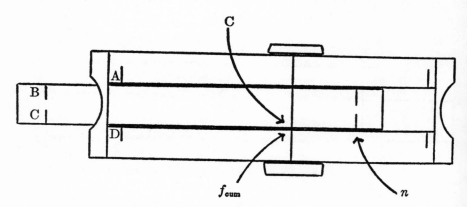

FIG. 2.5. How to solve a problem in proportions on the slide-rule: converting cumulative frequencies into centiles. ($C/f_{\text{cum}} = 100/n$.)

the opposing values on Scales C and D all stand in similar proportion. For any value on Scale D, one can read its "proportion of n" on Scale C. Thus the centiles for the entire series of cumulative frequencies are read from a single setting of the slide-rule. (This will be literally true in all cases only if the slide-rule has "folded scales," marked CF and DF. Otherwise it may be necessary to use two settings, one with each index.)

While practicing with Scales C and D, learn to "squeeze" the slide and the hairline cursor, as the good marksman squeezes the trigger, rather than trying to push or pull them short distances. This technique is explained in the caption to Figure **2.6**.

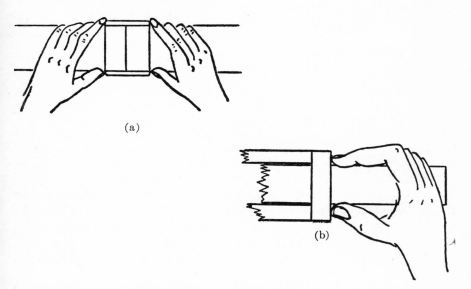

(a)

(b)

Fig. **2.6**. How to make fine adjustments on the slide-rule.

(a) The cursor is moved smoothly in either direction by squeezing against the rule with the thumb and forefinger of the opposite hand. Do not push!

(b) The slide is pulled smoothly by pressing on it with thumb and forefinger held close to the stock of the rule. As pressure causes the flesh to swell, the fingers and the slide together move outward from the rule. Do not pull!

3

THE SUM OF SQUARES

The beginner in statistics has no difficulty in following the logic of the representative score, and he also readily sees the need to take the dispersion of scores into account. However, unless he has some mathematical sophistication he will at first be puzzled by the step which we are about to take. In this chapter we shall begin to work with *squared deviations*, that is, we shall replace each score, for certain purposes, with the square of its deviation value. It is not possible to give any *a priori* justification for this procedure, and so we simply draw the reader's attention to the fact that the most economical forms of expression of many natural phenomena, as they are condensed in scientific laws, often involve the use of squared magnitudes. For example, the intensity of a light varies inversely as the square of the distance from its source, the area of a circle equals πr^2, and the distance traversed by a freely falling body is a function of the square of the elapsed time. We should not be surprised, therefore, to learn that squared deviations enter into some important statistical relationships. In our later work we shall have ample opportunity to verify the fact that it is the square of the deviation, rather than the deviation itself, which is a measure of the magnitude of those individuating forces which are responsible for the dispersion of scores about the mean value of their population. Therefore it is the squared deviation, rather than the linear deviation, which leads to the most useful measure of score variability. The sum of the squared deviations for a set of scores is called the *sum of squares*.

Take careful note of the distinction which has been suggested in the preceding paragraph: measures of variability which are based on the linear displacements of scores are concerned only with the *effects* of chance influences, whereas the sum of squares, and the statistics which we shall learn to derive from it, measure the effective *strength* of the chance influences which produce such effects.

The difference between a score, in its linear aspect, and the squared deviation which is associated with that score, may be illustrated by a figurative analogy. If you were going down to the railroad station to meet someone whom you had never seen before you would find it useful to have a good surface description of that person, something which included highly visible characteristics, like the color of the eyes or a mole on the left cheek. Under other circumstances, you would be interested to learn of "deeper" aspects of the person, which are related to underlying motivating forces. It is the linear aspect of the score (its raw value X and its linear deviation x) which corresponds to the surface description. These identify the individual performance, and they tell us how to pick the individual out of a crowd. These are the terms in which we are likely to discuss the performance with a layman. But the score also has a dynamic aspect, to which such superficial observation does not penetrate. Experience will show that it is the analysis of squared deviations which can ultimately bring us to an understanding of dynamics—of the reasons for individual differences in scores, and the relative strength of different factors which influence a set of scores. We shall discover that the sum of squares contains a good deal of information on such matters, which can be salvaged from the limbo of error.

COMPUTING A SUM OF SQUARES

First, we must learn how to compute a sum of squares. This would be a very onerous task if it were necessary to find each deviation score, square it, and total the squares. Fortunately, there is a way to find the sum of squares quite exactly without ever determining any of the deviation scores. To develop this formula, we go back to the definition of a deviation:

$$x = X - \bar{X}$$

Squaring both sides (which is easy, if we remember that $[a - b]^2 = a^2 - 2ab + b^2$), we obtain this:

$$x^2 = X^2 - 2X\bar{X} + \bar{X}^2$$

Now express the summation of such values, term by term, for a set of n scores. (The function of n in this summation was explained in a similar instance on page 23.)

$$\Sigma x^2 = \Sigma X^2 - 2\Sigma X\bar{X} + n\bar{X}^2$$

$$= \Sigma X^2 - 2\Sigma X \frac{\Sigma X}{n} + n\left(\frac{\Sigma X}{n}\right)^2$$

Simplifying within terms,

$$\Sigma x^2 = \Sigma X^2 - 2\frac{(\Sigma X)^2}{n} + \frac{(\Sigma X)^2}{n}$$

7] $$= \Sigma X^2 - \frac{(\Sigma X)^2}{n}$$

Stated verbally, *the sum of squares is the sum of squared scores less the squared sum of scores divided by their number.*

Table **3.**1 illustrates the application of this formula to a set of scores

TABLE **3.**1

Computation of the Sum of Squares, Directly and by Formula

	X	X²	(X − X̄)	(X − X̄)²
	2	4	−3	9
	6	36	1	1
	7	49	2	4
Sums	15	89	0	14

$$\bar{X} = 15/3 = 5$$
$$\Sigma x^2 = \Sigma X^2 - (\Sigma X)^2/n$$
$$= 89 - 15^2/3 = 14$$

which is purposely kept small, so that the structure of the problem is more readily grasped. The first two columns give the sum of scores and the sum of squared scores. Only these values, and n, are used in the solution by formula at the foot of the table. The third and fourth columns give the deviations and the sum of squares directly. A moment's thought will show the reader that when a large number of scores is involved the solution by formula is much more economical than the direct solution, especially when the mean is not an integer, so that the deviations and the squared deviations are also not integral amounts.

Look carefully at the part played by the last term in the formula, which we shall call the *correction term.* Since every squared value is positive, the effect of the correction term must always be to diminish the term preceding it. This means that the sum of squares is always smaller than the sum of squared scores, except in the limiting case when the mean of the distribution is zero, so that the original scores *are* deviation scores. This leads to the important conclusion that *a sum of squares taken with respect to the mean is smaller than a sum of squared deviations taken with respect to any point other than the mean.* That is,

$$\Sigma(X - \bar{X})^2 < \Sigma(X - A)^2$$

where A represents *any* value other than $\bar{X}$.

We pointed out earlier that one advantage of the median as a measure of central tendency is that the sum of linear deviations has its minimum value when it is taken with respect to the median. But the fact which we have just established, that the sum of squares has its minimum value when it is taken with respect to the mean, is far more important. This is the decisive reason why the mean is the most useful representative score whenever we are striving to understand the *sources* of score variation. The median and the mode have their virtues as descriptive statistics, but whenever possible we shall prefer to use the mean as the representative score for purposes of analysis, because it is the natural point from which to compute the sum of squares, which will occupy a key position in every method of analysis which we shall study.

Formula 7 is a convenient computational formula for which we shall have frequent use. However, it has an interesting variant which gives added insight into the nature of the correction term. If that term is multiplied by $\dfrac{n}{n}$ which of course does not change its value, it becomes $n(\Sigma X)^2/n^2$, or, simplifying, $n\bar{X}^2$. The complete formula may therefore be written thus:

7a] $$\Sigma x^2 = \Sigma X^2 - n\bar{X}^2$$

In words, the sum of squares is the sum of squared scores, *less the squared mean taken once for each element in the set.* This shows us that the correction term is simply an allowance for the fact that the zero point of the score dimension has not been placed where it should be, at the mean.

When Formula 7a is applied to the problem in Table **3**.1, the computation takes the following form:

$$\Sigma x^2 = 89 - 3\,(5^2) = 14$$

This computation is shown graphically in Figure **3**.1. The solid horizontal line represents the score dimension, and the small crosses placed on this line represent the three scores in the set. Each of the squares above the line has as its base the distance from one of the scores to the zero point of the scale. Let us call these "raw squares," since they correspond to the squared values of the raw scores. The base for each of the squares below the line is the *deviation* value of one of the scores, that is, the distance from the score to the mean of the set, which is 5. Let us call these "true squares," since they correspond to the squares which enter into the sum of squares,

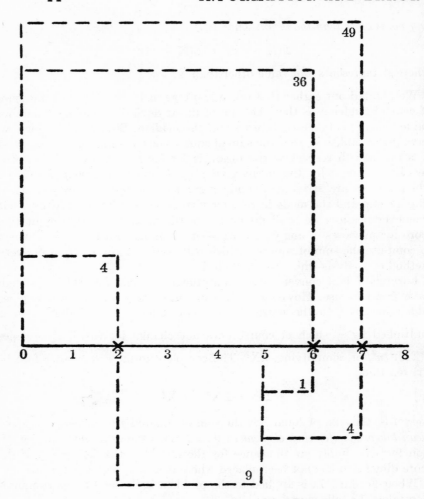

FIG. **3**.1. Graphic illustration of the formula for the sum of squares.

$$4 + 36 + 49 - 3\bar{X}^2 = 14$$
$$9 + 1 + 4 \qquad\quad = 14$$

as defined. The difference between the total area of the raw squares and the total area of the true squares is equal to n times the area of a *correction square* (not shown) which has a base equal to the distance separating the two reference points—the zero point of the scale and the mean of the set of scores.

This relationship holds whenever we compare the sum of squares around a mean with the sum of squared deviations computed with respect to any other reference point. In Figure **3**.1, the arbitrary reference point was zero, so that each raw square is based on the full numerical value of the corresponding raw score. Figure **3**.2 illustrates the computation of the sum of squares when the lowest score of the set, which in this case is 2, is taken as the arbitrary reference point. Then the magnitude of the numbers

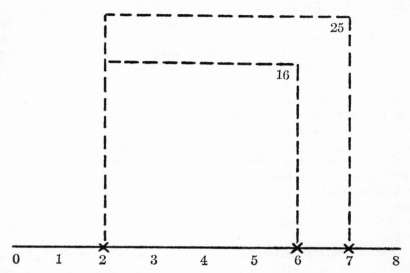

Fig. **3**.2. Illustration of the use of an arbitrary origin to compute a sum of squares. Here M′, the arbitrary origin, equals 2, and $\bar{X} = 5$.

$$0 + 16 + 25 - 3(5 - 2)^2 = 14$$

entering into the computation is reduced, because each of the deviations is smaller by 2 units, and one vanishes altogether. The size of the correction square is also reduced, since the arbitrary reference point has been brought closer to the mean. It remains true that the sum of the raw squares exceeds the sum of the true squares by n times the correction square (which is not shown).

We are tempted to call this almost magical procedure, by which the scores wax and wane in perfect counterpoint, "the dance of squares." The esthetic satisfaction which it offers is almost in itself justification for preferring the mean as the representative score of the sample. However, it also has immense practical significance, for in mathematics more surely than in poetry, beauty is the guide to truth. In the next section we shall see how this geometric choreography opens the way to a procedure which will lighten our computational burdens, and before the end of this chapter we shall begin to see how it also provides the basis for the most sensitive techniques of statistical analysis.

THE USE OF LINEAR TRANSFORMATION

Statisticians have no fondness for arithmetic. They dream, like American housewives, of a dawning wonder world of electronic gadgetry in which all drudgery will be eliminated and tasks that were once too forbidding to contemplate, like scrubbing all the floors or solving a set of equations with 17 unknowns, will be accomplished with push-button ease by those who can afford the necessary capital investment. At the student level, and for most researchers engaged in small-scale projects, it is not reasonable to look beyond the ordinary desk-model calculating machine. If such a machine is available to you, it would be wise to familiarize yourself with it. (The manufacturer provides a manual for basic statistical procedures on any particular model. It is not practical to give such instructions in a textbook, because the efficiency of the operation depends on the mastery of details which differ from one model to another.) We shall assume, however, that the student has nothing but paper, pencils, a ruler, and the usual reference tables. It is often convenient to have pencils in different colors, and the ruler is essential for keeping columns straight to avoid needless blunders. (*Please* don't let your work drift into diagonals! This is probably the most common source of arithmetical errors, but students who dislike arithmetic seem to suffer from persistent linophobia.)

Whenever we wish to measure any length or distance, we first make an arbitrary choice of what seems to be the most convenient unit of measurement for the purpose. We measure a waistband in inches, the height of a flagpole in feet, the length of a sprint race in yards, and the distance between two cities in miles. It would be possible to measure a waistband in hundred-thousandths of a mile, or the distance from New York to Los Angeles in inches. Either procedure would be silly, not because it would be inaccurate but because it would place such an extra burden of comprehension on the mind. We like to work in a comfortable range of small numbers, whose meanings we grasp readily.

Sometimes we find it convenient to shift from one unit of measure to another, even while we are dealing with the same subject matter. Having measured a room as 12 feet wide and 15 feet long, we may prefer to figure how much carpeting it needs in square yards, since that is the way it is priced. Or, having been told that an irregular plot of land measures 72,500 square feet, we may ask to have its area expressed in acre units, for readier comparison with some other plot. When we change 12 feet to 4 yards, or 72,500 square feet to 1.66 acres, we are effecting a *linear transformation* of scores which does not change the values, but states them in a more convenient form.

In all sorts of investigations, it happens repeatedly that the unit of measurement which was used in making the original observations is needlessly fine for purposes of statistical summary and analysis. For example, if we are making measurements of the height of 12-year-old boys, we may record the height of each boy in the sample to the nearest quarter-inch. If the range of heights is from 4'2" to 5'6", a frequency table without classes would require 65 rows. If we record their heights only to the nearest inch, we will need to handle frequencies in only 17 classes. This is no different from reporting your age in years rather than in days, or your take-home pay in round dollars rather than to the penny. And although such approximations may seem inaccurate when we have the individual case in mind, we shall see that they introduce very little inaccuracy into the statistics which we use to summarize a large sample of data.

Statisticians are very practical folk. Their business is error, and they are not the ones to turn away a little extra business. Therefore they often elect to add a little more error to the brew rather than to burden themselves with needless arithmetic. They like to assure themselves, however, that the errors which they so permissively introduce are of a random nature, falling sometimes in one direction and sometimes in the other, and tending for the most part to cancel each other out. That is the case, for example, when heights are recorded to the nearest inch rather than to the nearest quarter-inch. The minor variations in sample statistics which result from such random errors of approximation are no different from the sampling errors which are due to the fact that the group of boys studied included Tom, Dick, and Harry instead of Bob, Chuck, and Jim. It is with such broadminded tolerance for minor errors, and with our eyes fixed on the realistic goal of speed and ease in handling data, that we must study the following procedure for the computation of statistics from class data.

We have already described the method of organizing data into classes (see pages 15f.), but we did not at that time indicate how or why we chose a particular value for the interval. The *how* is quite simple: take the range, divide by 10, and consider whether the integral part of the quotient would make a convenient interval. In this way we insure ourselves of having at least 11 classes, if there are that many in the original data, and not more than 20. The *why* rests upon the fact (which the student may wish to test empirically) that when we group the squares of a sample into 12 or more classes the amount of error introduced into the computation of sample statistics is slight. (We are assuming that the n of the sample is at least 30; for samples smaller than this, grouping into classes is not advisable.) The procedure which we have recommended is only a method for approximating i from scores with integral values. One should not feel bound by the result. For example, if the range of scores were 195, the trial value for i would be 19. This would be a very clumsy figure to work with, and it would lead to a very unusual set of class limits. In practice, we would then choose between an interval of 20, which might reduce the number of classes to 10, and one of 15, which would probably increase their number to 14. Since it is better to have more than 12 classes rather than fewer, the latter choice is to be preferred. However, a table with only 9 or 10 classes might be satisfactory for many purposes, including class exercises.

By selecting an interval, we have in effect chosen a new unit of measurement, into which we propose to transform all of the original scores. At this point it is well to prepare a table with six columns, which will provide space not only for the transformation of scores, but also for much of the detail involved in computing sample statistics. (See Table **3.2**.)

TABLE **3.2**

Computation of Basic Sums for a Sample of 30 Scores

X	Tallies	f	x'	fx'	fx'^2
42–44	/	1	6	6	36
39–41	/	1	5	5	25
36–38		0	4	0	0
33–35	///	3	3	9	27
30–32	//	2	2	4	8
27–29	//	2	1	2	2
24–26	////	4	0	0	0
21–23	/////	5	−1	−5	5
18–20	/////	5	−2	−10	20
15–17	////	4	−3	−12	36
12–14	///	3	−4	−12	48
Sums		30	*	−13	207

* The sum of this column, which may be called a memorandum column, would have no meaning. Do not make the error of taking its sum and using it in place of $\Sigma x'$.

The working limits of the classes are entered in the first column, as described on page 16. (Notice again, if the point has been forgotten, that the lower working limit of each class is divisible by i. If all original scores are integral amounts, the working limits will be integral; if the scores are not necessarily integral, then some of the working limits should be nonintegral.)

The individual scores are tallied in the second column. This is a phase of the work during which it is well to make haste slowly, for there is no way to detect errors except by repeating the process. If we are striving for accuracy, that is just what we should do, using a colored pencil, or ink, over the pencil marks of the original tallies.

The class frequencies, taken from the tallies, are written into the third column, headed f. Sum this column immediately as a partial check. Its total must equal n.

Now we look over the distribution of tallies, which offers a sort of graphic presentation of the data, and we guess the class in which the mean lies. The mid-value of this class is designated the *assumed mean*, M'. This is the zero point for the scale of transformed scores. Accordingly, we enter a zero on that row in the column headed x', the symbol for a score which has been transformed in this manner. (Not X', because this symbol has a quite different meaning, as we shall see in Chapter 10.) On the rows above, we write successive positive integers, and on those below, successive negative integers, as shown in the table. These are the transformed score equivalents for the raw scores on the same row.

If we expect to use a calculating machine for some of the subsequent calculations, we place the zero, and hence the assumed mean, on the bottom row of the table, opposite the class which includes the lowest recorded scores. This is because calculating machines are very nimble with large numbers, but very awkward in handling negative numbers, which require them to put their machinery into reverse gear. For a paper-and-pencil operation it is more important to keep the numbers small than to avoid negatives. If we succeed in placing the assumed mean in the same class as the actual mean, that will hold the sum of transformed scores, $\Sigma x'$, to a minimum. As a result the correction term will be small, a circumstance which will reduce not only our expenditure of cortical energy but also the likelihood of arithmetical blunders. It should be understood, however, that the accuracy of the final result, if we overlook the human factor, is in no sense dependent on this exercise of judgment. With sound arithmetic, the final result will be just as accurate if we give the lowest class a transformed score value of 1492, or 1776, and then assign successively higher values to the other classes. But if we do this we will find ourselves dealing with millions or hundreds of millions. The purpose of the transformation is ease and convenience, to save time and reduce blunders. Therefore, if we are working with pencil and paper, the assumed mean should be placed in the middle of the distribution, near the natural mean, and not in the base of the table, in the trailing lower end of the distribution. In this way, we trim a good deal of unnecessary fat off the scores.

In column 5, which is headed fx', we enter on each row the product of f and x' for that row. The sum of this column is recorded as $\Sigma x'$. (It would be redundant to write $\Sigma fx'$, since in such an expression the f adds nothing to what is already implied by the summation sign.)

In column 6, headed fx'^2, we enter on each row the product of x' and fx'. This is usually more convenient than squaring x' and multiplying that value by f. (CAUTION: If the columns have been arranged in a different order, as may happen when the same scale of transformed scores is being used for two or more parallel distributions, it is not difficult to slip into the mistake of computing f^2x' instead of fx'^2.) The sum of this column is recorded as $\Sigma x'^2$, the sum of squared transformed scores.

For some purposes, it is satisfactory to proceed from this point just as if the transformed scores were the original scores. In later chapters, we shall frequently do just that, for we shall be interested primarily in the computation of certain ratios, which are not changed by linear transformations of the scores. However, there are other times when we want to return to the units of the original scale, which carry more meaning for us. This is readily achieved by reversing the steps of the transformation. What has been taken away must be restored, and the i which has served as a thinning agent must now play the role of fattener. To find the mean in original score terms, the mean of transformed scores must be multiplied by i, and then added to the assumed mean, which was previously substracted from each of the scores. This is all summed up in the following formula:

8] $$\bar{X} = M' + \frac{\Sigma x'}{n} i$$

Applying this formula to the problem in Table **3**.2,

$$\bar{X} = 25 + \left(\frac{-13}{30}\right) 3 = 23.7$$

For the sum of squares, the reverse transformation is even simpler. We compute the sum of squares in the units of the transformed scores, and then multiply by i^2. It is exactly as if, having determined how many square yards of carpeting we want, we now prefer to go back to talking about square feet. Since there are 3 feet in a yard, there are 9 square feet in each square yard. Therefore the formula for the sum of squares, computed from transformed scores, is:

9] $$\Sigma x^2 = \left[\Sigma x'^2 - \frac{(\Sigma x')^2}{n}\right] i^2$$

Applying this formula to the problem in Table **3**.2,

$$\Sigma x^2 = \left[207 - \frac{(-13)^2}{30}\right] 9 = 1812.3$$

Formula 8 gives an unbiased estimate of the sample mean. Each score has been treated as if it were equal to the mid-value of its class, and therefore some have been overvalued and others undervalued. In the aggregate, these many shifts tend to cancel each other out, so that their net effect is small and as likely to be in one direction as the other.

The situation is different with respect to Formula 9. This procedure does introduce a certain amount of bias into the computation of the sum of squares. The bias arises chiefly from the fact that the half of each class which is nearer to the mean tends to be more populated than the half of the class which is farther from the mean. Therefore overvaluations of the deviations are more common than undervaluations, and, since all squared values are positive, the effects on both sides of the distribution do not tend to cancel each other as in computing the mean, but accumulate. It is possible to make an allowance, called Sheppard's correction, for the bias in this formula. Introducing this correction, the formula for a sum of squares based on grouped scores becomes:

9a] $$\Sigma x^2 = \left[\Sigma x'^2 - \frac{(\Sigma x')^2}{n} - \frac{n}{12} \right] i^2$$

Under most circumstances, the use of Sheppard's correction is a needless refinement. We mention it only to indicate that the bias involved in Formula 9 is known, and known to be inconsequential when an adequate number of classes has been used.*

ADJURATION AND PROSPECT

The procedures of the preceding section may at first seem troublesome to the student. Since, from humanitarian motives, exercise problems are generally based on fairly small sets of scores, the student may delude himself into thinking that he can get along with the direct methods of calculation which he has practiced for so many years. Be assured, in the long run this leads to mountains of extra work, and waste baskets filled with avoidable arithmetic errors. The student who concientiously follows all the details of this routine whenever it seems at all appropriate will soon find that it can be accomplished in a surprisingly short time, and that this will free his mind for the more interesting critical appreciation of the problem at hand.

The use of linear transformations, in order to simplify arithmetical computations, is not something to be half-learned and put aside for later brushing-up. Master this routine and then all other computations needed for elementary statistics will be easy. Failing to do this, persisting in more wasteful ways of handling data, will stand in the way of proper comprehension of later topics, because many of the most important formulas which will appear in later chapters of this book are simple variations of the formula by which a sum of squared scores is partitioned into two parts, of which one is the sum of squares. Learn this procedure throughly, and you have established yourself on a plateau where further progress is relatively easy.

* The "12" which appears in Sheppard's correction is not related to the fact that it is desirable to use 12 or more classes in a frequency distribution. The formula is applicable as given, whether grouping is into few or many categories.

... Let us assume that we stand on this plateau. We understand the sum of squares, we understand its relation to the mean as a representative score, and we know how to compute it for the ordinary set of data. From this point forward, the principal milestones of our journey will be a series of important ratios, each of which arises, though sometimes obscurely, out of the partitioning of the sum of squares. We shall learn to abstract a portion of this sum as representing, from one point of view or another, information rather than error. Again and again, in different forms, we shall establish the ratio of

INFORMATION

&

ERROR

or, as we may sometimes prefer to call it, of

DESIGN

&

CHANCE.

When we have learned enough about the behavior of error, or pure chance, we shall be able to judge whether, in the segment of life which we are studying, Chance or Design (that is, the experimental design which has been pitted against chance in the null hypothesis) has the upper hand.

THE DIFFERENTIATION RATIO

At this point in our discussion, it is already possible for us to define one of these ratios which, although it is not in extremely common use, does represent an excellent introduction to several other widely used techniques of statistical analysis. In Table 2.3 we presented the distribution of "hostility" scores for men and women students in a statistics class. We now propose to re-examine those scores, having in mind the question whether sex is a determinant of hostility as so measured. The corresponding null hypothesis asserts that sex is not a factor which differentially influences the scores. If that is so, controlling sex as an experimental variable should not lead to any reduction of the error variance. Therefore, we shall test the null hypothesis by computing the sum of squares once with sex controlled, and again without controlling it.

Table 3.3 gives the full detail of the work on this problem, to the extent that we are able to deal with it at the present stage. Alongside the original scores there is a column of transformed scores, and it is in these terms that the computation of $\Sigma x'$ and $\Sigma x'^2$ is carried out, for men and women separately. Notice that we must use the same transformation for both sets of scores, since we wish later to merge both groups into one for the test of the null hypothesis. We therefore select an assumed mean near the middle of the combined distribution, to produce the greatest overall economy of work.

TABLE **3**.3

Computation of a Differentiation Ratio, Based on the
Hostility Scores of Men and Women

Scores			Men			Women	
X	x'	f	fx'	fx'^2	f	fx'	fx'^2
13	6	1	6	36			
12	5						
11	4						
10	3	3	9	27	1	3	9
9	2	4	8	16	2	4	8
8	1	1	1	1	2	2	2
7	0	1	0	0			
6	−1	1	−1	1	1	−1	1
5	−2				3	−6	12
4	−3				1	−3	9
3	−4						
2	−5						
1	−6				1	−6	36
0	−7	1	−7	49	1	−7	49
Sums		12	16	130	12	−14	126

Group Summaries

	Men	Women		Combined
m	12	12	n	24
$\Sigma x'$	16	−14	$\Sigma\Sigma x'$	2
$\Sigma x'^2$	130	126	$\Sigma\Sigma x'^2$	256
$\dfrac{(\Sigma x')^2}{m}$	21.3	16.3	$\dfrac{(\Sigma\Sigma x')^2}{n}$	0.17
Σx^2	108.7	109.7	Σx^2	255.83

The Differentiation Ratio

$$\eta^2 = \frac{255.83 - (108.7 + 109.7)}{255.83} = 0.146$$

The sums obtained in the upper part of the table have been copied out below. The corresponding entries for the combined groups are simply the sums of sums, as indicated by the double summation of signs. Three different correction terms are calculated—one for men, one for women, and one for all subjects combined. Notice that the correction for the combined

groups is not the sum of the group corrections. Since the sum of squares
for men is taken around the mean of the men's scores, it is necessarily less
than the contribution which these same scores make to the sum of squares
taken around the mean of the combined groups. The same is true for the
women. This implies a very important *inequality*, namely, that the sum
of group corrections must be greater than the correction for the combined
groups, except in the unlikely case when the means of the groups coincide
exactly. In symbols:

$$\Sigma \frac{(\Sigma x')^2}{m} \geqq \frac{(\Sigma \Sigma x')^2}{n} \ , \quad \text{where} \quad n = \Sigma m$$

(This has been our first opportunity to use an inequality sign with the
meaning "is greater than." We must learn to read and write both inequality signs, $<$ and $>$, unhesitatingly, for they are used frequently
in conventional abbreviations for reporting the results of experimental
studies. Reading from left to right, as we do in the usual context, one is
translated "is less than" and the other "is greater than." In either case,
the greater value of the two being compared is contiguous to the spreading
side of the inequality sign, and the lesser value is contiguous to the pointed
or diminishing side. See the definitions of these signs in the Glossary,
page 263.)

In this case, the sum of squares for the 24 scores considered together
equals 255.83, while the two sums of squares for the separate groups total
218.4. The difference is 37.4. What does it represent? If the reader will
for the present take on faith the statement that the sum of squares is a
measure of the strength of the influences which produce variability in the
scores, then this difference may be said to measure the strength of sex as a
differentiating factor in this situation. If the total sum of squares is to be
regarded as a measure of the strength of all uncontrolled influences when
we pay no attention to the sex of the subjects, then this reduction represents the amount of error which is eliminated when the matter of sex is
given special attention. By the act of segregating the scores of men and
women we have taken sex out of the category of uncontrolled variables,
demonstrating that it is sometimes possible to achieve statistical control
over factors which are very resistant to control by other means.

We may think of this as a kind of bookkeeping process, by which we
establish the fact that part of what has been credited to the "error" account should have been credited to an "information" account. This is,
however, single-entry bookkeeping, for we do not debit the "error" account to keep the books in balance. Instead, we merely take note of the
ratio of this discovered information to the total sum of squares, which had
been labeled error. From the size of this ratio we can judge the strength
or importance of the variable over which we have obtained statistical

control, relative to all the other variables which remain in the limbo of "chance." In this case the ratio, 37.4/255.8, is approximately one-seventh.

The denominator of the ratio we have just constructed, like the denominators of many other ratios we shall study in later chapters, is based strictly on the null hypothesis, which asserts that *only* chance influences are operating. The numerator consists of that portion of the sum of squares which, from a given point of view, is non-chance. In short, the ratio 37.4/255.8 = 0.146 represents that proportion of the determinants of hostility scores, under the conditions of the experiment, which is associated with the sex of the subjects.

We ordinarily compute this ratio by the following formula:

$$10] \qquad \eta^2 = 1 - \frac{\Sigma\Sigma x'^2 - \Sigma\frac{(\Sigma x')^2}{m}}{\Sigma\Sigma x'^2 - \frac{(\Sigma\Sigma x')^2}{n}}$$

Applied to the present problem, this becomes

$$\eta^2 = 1 - \frac{256 - (21.3 + 16.3)}{256 - 0.17} = 0.146$$

The symbol η^2, eta-square, has a history with which we shall not concern ourselves. The exponent is an essential part of this symbol, and of a number of other symbols with which we shall become acquainted later. Written without an exponent, η has a convenient name: the *correlation ratio*. But η is not so directly meaningful as η^2, and "squared correlation ratio" is a cumbersome phrase. We shall therefore permit ourselves a neologism, while warning the reader not to expect that it will be understood by strangers. We shall call η^2 the *differentiation ratio*, because it tells us with what success the groups in our experiment have been differentiated by the principle which underlies their classification.

It is important to grasp the reasoning which lies behind the differentiation ratio. The sum of squares can be found in two ways: once without regard to the group classification, and again by building up a grand sum from the sums of squares found "within" the groups. The latter procedure eliminates the variation which is introduced into the scores by virtue of factors associated with group membership. When men and women are considered separately, the fact of being a man or being a woman no longer makes any contribution to the sum of squares. We have therefore partitioned the total sum of squares into two parts: A *within-sum* which reflects uncontrolled or chance factors which are still effective under these conditions, and a residue, which is also called the *between-sum* of squares. It will sometimes be convenient to distinguish between the total sum of squares for merged groups, the within-sum of squares, and the between-sum of squares, by the use of subscripts, as follows:

$$\Sigma x^2{}_t = \Sigma x^2{}_w + \Sigma x^2{}_b$$

Remember that subscripts are only identification tags, and they do not ever represent values which enter into computations.

The magnitude of the between-sum, relative to the total-sum, depends on the degree of separation of the group means. It will drop to zero if the group means coincide exactly, for then the two correction terms are identical. However, this is the improbable limiting condition of what is fundamentally an inequality. It is equally unlikely that the within-sum shall drop to zero, for this would mean that the sole influence which produces variability in the scores is the experimental variable. If that condition did exist, the ratio of between-sum to total-sum would be unity, indicating that the entire determination of scores was assignable to factors associated with the principle of classification into groups.

The differentiation ratio gives a direct answer to a plain question. We ask: to what extent do factors associated with sex (or with whatever variable underlies the classification into groups) influence the scores? The answer is stated as a proportion. In the present case, it states that factors associated with sex are responsible for about 15 per cent of the variability in scores, under the conditions of our observations. Notice, first, that we must say "factors associated with sex," rather than simply "sex," and second, that we must limit our conclusions to comparable situations. For on the one hand, the result does not tell us whether hormones or social pressures are responsible for this aspect of *la différence*, and on the other, we have no assurance that the result would be the same if the subjects were, for example, students majoring in architecture rather than in psychology.

Let us remind the reader that the differentiation ratio, being only a statistic, is subject to error, and that we have not yet considered any technique for estimating the degree to which a statistic may be misleading. We must look at our result, therefore, with some skepticism, particularly since it is based on a very limited experience. In general, one should not place much reliance on a differentiation ratio unless it is based on fairly large samples which can be considered to be adequately representative of the target populations. Under such conditions, it can be a very useful statistic. Although it appears infrequently in psychological reports, there are some circumstances under which it is indispensable, and an understanding of its structure—how it grows out of the partitioning of the sum of squares—is an excellent introduction to the principle which underlies all modern statistical analysis. In Chapter 8 we shall consider certain safeguards which can be introduced into the computation of the differentiation ratio in order that it shall not be misleading.

It should be noted that nothing we have said implies that the subjects shall be classified into only two groups, as in our illustrative problem. The differentiation ratio is more commonly used in problems where the subjects have been classified into at least four groups on the experimental variable.

PROBLEMS

1. *Find the mean and sum of squares for the data in Table* **3**.2, *page 48, using a different assumed mean.*

2. *Find the mean and sum of squares for each set of scores in Table* **2**.4, *page 34, using linear transformation of scores.*

3. *Find the differentiation ratio for the following fictitious data, which are supposed to represent scores on a test of emotional excitability, for 15 subjects belonging to 3 different national groups.*

National Origin

French	English	Chinese
12	8	6
14	5	4
5	7	4
9	4	3
10	11	8

4. *In the illustrative problem, Table* **3**.3, *we might have found the difference between the two sums of squares by taking* 24 $(1.25)^2 = 37.5$. *Why? This suggests the formula*

$$\eta^2 = \frac{\Sigma[m_k(\bar{X}_k - \bar{X})^2]}{\Sigma\Sigma X^2 - \dfrac{(\Sigma\Sigma X)^2}{n}}$$

10a]

where m_k *and* $\bar{X}_k$ *represent the number of scores in a group, and the mean of the group, respectively, and* $n = \Sigma m$. *Solve problem 3 by this formula.*

SECOND INTERLUDE

SLIDE-RULE HINTS

If you are confident in the use of the slide-rule for simple problems of multiplication and division, on Scales C and D, you are ready to apply its magic to more complicated problems. We often have occasion to multiply and divide in the same series of computations. Of course, we can move along on the slide-rule from one partial answer to another, using the end of one simple computation, which is marked by the hairline, as the starting point for the next. However, it is usually possible to combine these operations advantageously, so that a division and a multiplication can be joined in a single operation. For example, the calculation of the mean from transformed scores requires the solution of the term $\dfrac{\Sigma x'}{n} i$. When we perform the division on the slide-rule in the usual manner, locating $\Sigma x'$ on Scale D and then placing n on Scale C in opposition to it, the quotient appears on Scale D opposite the index of Scale C. Simultaneously, however, the value for the entire term appears on Scale D opposite i on Scale C. The solution to the second part of the task comes as a bonus, without extra labor.

Now let us raise our sights to Scales A and B. Notice that each of these Scales consists of two halves. Each half is a duplicate of the D scale, except for some changes in the tertiary rulings, because of the greater compression. Notice also that the construction of the slide-rule is such that the position of Scale A is always fixed in relation to Scale D, and the position of Scale B is fixed in relation to Scale C. The values on Scales A and B are the *squares* of those on C and D, in obedience to the rule that

$$\log a^2 = 2 \log a$$

To take full advantage of this, and avoid the countless square-root errors which are epidemic in elementary statistics classes, we must always carefully distinguish between the right and the left halves of Scales A and B.

On the left half we have, for example:	On the right half we have, by contrast:
127	12.7
1.27	.127
.0127	.00127

The rule: The left half of these scales represents numbers which have an odd number of digits before the decimal, or an odd number of zeros after the decimal and preceding the first significant digit. The right half represents numbers with an even number of digits before the decimal, or an even number of zeros which follow the decimal and precede the first significant digit. Here is another way to state the rule: Imagine the number written with only one significant digit before the decimal; if, to achieve this, it was necessary to move the decimal an even number of times (or not at all), the number appears on the left hand side of the scale; if it was necessary to move the decimal an odd number of times, the number appears on the right hand side of the scale.

Careful observance of this rule will insure that when we have located a number on Scale A or B it will lie opposite its square root on the coordinate scale, C or D. For example, 16 lies opposite 4, but 160 lies opposite 12.65. If this complication makes you unhappy, do not blame it on the slide-rule. Exactly the same complication exists in any table of squares and square roots. It imposes the necessity for a degree of alertness and an occasional pause to consider the plausibility of an answer before recording it as a fact.

The slide-rule is therefore a compact substitute for a table of squares and square roots. This is unimportant, for such tables are inexpensive and convenient. What is immensely important is that it enables us to perform such an operation as $\dfrac{(\Sigma X)^2}{n}$ without stopping to square ΣX. This particular operation occurs frequently in our work, and it is illustrated in Figure **3**.3. When n on Scale B is placed opposite ΣX on Scale D, the answer appears on Scale A, opposite the index of Scale B.

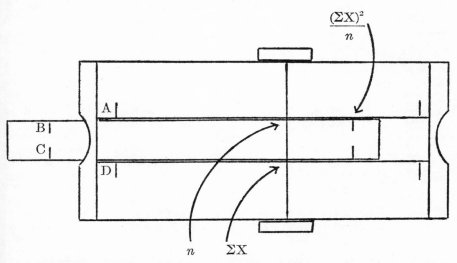

FIG. **3**.3. Combining two operations—squaring and division—on the slide rule.

Other opportunities to take advantage of the cleverness built into the slide-rule will appear from time to time in the following chapters. Table **3**.4 gives instructions for the solution of a number of formulas, or terms of formulas, selected to illustrate a variety of combined operations. This would be a good place to leave a bookmark!

TABLE **3**.4

Problem		Procedure				Answer	
		Step 1		*Step 2*			
To evaluate	Operations	Set hairline over	on	Bring this value under the hairline		Read	Opposite
$\dfrac{\Sigma x'}{n} i$	Divide and multiply	$\Sigma x'$	D	n, on C		D	i, on C
$\dfrac{(\Sigma X)^2}{n}$	Square, then divide	ΣX	D	n, on B		A	index
$\left(\dfrac{\Sigma X}{n}\right)^2$	Divide, then square	ΣX	D	n, on C		A	index
$\sqrt{\dfrac{\Sigma x^2}{n}}$	Divide, then take root	Σx^2	A	n, on B		D	index
$\dfrac{\sigma}{\sqrt{n}}$	Divide by a square root	σ	D	n, on B		D	index
$\sqrt{\dfrac{pq}{n}}$	Multiply, divide, take root	p	A	n, on B		D	q, on B
$\dfrac{\Sigma xy}{\sqrt{\Sigma x^2}\ \sqrt{\Sigma y^2}}$	Divide by a geometric average	Σx^2	A	index of B		(Proceed with steps 3 & 4)	
(Continuation of the above problem)		*(Step 3)* Σy^2	B	*(Step 4)* Σxy, on C		C	index

4

VARIANCE

THE TALE OF THE SCATTERBRAINED BOY

A boy, walking along a road in brush-covered country, came upon a flock of migrant birds all roosting on a single shrub. For sport, he clapped his hands as hard as he could and let out his loudest shout, startling the birds into flight. In a few seconds they had settled down, but now they were scattered on many bushes, with only a few on the one where they had all been gathered before. "How I have scattered them!" the boy boasted, and he appraised the effectiveness of his alarm by noting how far each of the birds had flown.

Filled with a pleasant sense of power, he decided to repeat the experience. He clapped his hands and shouted once again. Again the startled birds took to wing, circled about, and then settled in new locations. *Scatter had been added to scatter.* Now the boy wondered whether the first alarm or the second had been more effective. He considered the imaginary circle which enclosed all the birds: it was wider after the second alarm than after the first, but surely not twice as wide. He considered the sum of the distances of all the birds from their original common roost: it was greater than after the first alarm, but surely not twice as great. Yet he had clapped his hands as hard, and shouted as loud, and seemed to create as much commotion among the birds. These observations left him puzzled and disappointed. If the second alarm was, in fact, just as effective as the first, why wasn't there "twice as much scatter" after two alarms as after one?

The truth is that our scatterbrained youngster had a correct intuitive approach to the problem, but he was lacking in statistical know-how. If one of us had been there to advise him, we might have suggested that the cumulative effect of both alarms could be measured by taking the sum of the squared distances of all the birds from their original roost. If the boy did this, he would discover that after two equally effective alarms (if we assume that the direction of flight of each bird in each instance is completely haphazard), the sum of squares would be just twice as great as after the first alarm! Furthermore, if the effectiveness of the second alarm were such that, taken by itself, it would produce a sum of squares only half as great as the first alarm, then coming after the first alarm it would add just half as much again to the sum of squares! After a series of alarms, the sum of squares would be equal to the summation of the effects which these alarms would have produced separately. This is a very remarkable fact, which opens the way to studying the separate contributions of all kinds of determinants in the production of all kinds of behavior. For the dispersion of scores of any kind is in principle not different from the scattering of birds on the heath.

It is the moral of this little tale that, although the scatterbrained can sometimes exercise power, only the scatterminded can understand it. That is why we must devote ourselves to the study of score variance, or scatter.

The Mean Square: Yardstick of Chance

We have said (and soon shall prove) that the sum of squares for any set of scores varies directly with the sum of the forces which lead to variation in the scores. However, this sum is a poor statistic for making comparisons between samples of different size. We would not compare the incomes of 100 clinical psychologists and 10 industrial psychologists by simply summing up the earnings of the clinical and those of the industrial consultants. We would make an adjustment for the fact that one group is more numerous than the other, and therefore we would compare, not the sums of incomes, but the representative or mean incomes. For the same reason, if we were interested in the relative variability of the professional incomes of clinical and of industrial psychologists, or the amount of scatter around their respective means, we would not simply sum up the squared deviations for each set of income figures. We would go one step beyond this, to take a representative value for each set of squares—the *mean square*. Another name for this very important statistic is *variance*. In symbols:

11] $$\sigma^2 = \frac{\Sigma x^2}{n}$$

It is not often convenient to find a sample variance by this definition formula. In practice, it is usually more accurate and less tedious to make use of the relationship that the sum of squares is the sum of squared scores less a correction, as stated in Formula 7. By inserting n as a divisor into that formula, we obtain the following computational formula for variance:

11a] $$\sigma^2 = \frac{\Sigma X^2}{n} - \left(\frac{\Sigma X}{n}\right)^2$$

In words, *the variance is the mean squared score less the squared mean*. We can also adapt Formula 9 in the same manner, in order to find the sample variance directly from transformed scores. Introducing n as a divisor, this becomes:

11b] $$\sigma^2 = \left[\frac{\Sigma x'^2}{n} - \left(\frac{\Sigma x'}{n}\right)^2\right] i^2$$

One should make it a practice to read the symbol σ^2 directly as *variance*, rather than to verbalize it as sigma-square. This symbol, like that for the differentiation ratio, includes an exponent which reminds us that the units of variance are not the linear units of the original scale. Neither does it make much sense to talk of "square dollars" as the units of income variance, or of "square inches" as the units of variance in height. Variance is a measure of force—the force of those influences which produce score variation. It is as if, safe indoors, we judge the force of the wind by observing the sway of the treetops. Unanalyzed variance is the measure of the multiplicity of forces which. we sum up as "chance," and the effects of which constitute "error." But the fact that this cumulative variance is the sum of contributions from different sources provides the basis for many important techniques of statistical analysis. Therefore we shall try now to get a more solid grasp on the concept of variance as a measure of cumulative effects.

The Variance Law

In this section we shall offer proof of the general principle which underlies both the figurative illustration with which we opened this chapter and the still unsubstantiated assertion that the sum of squares (and hence also the mean square, or variance) measures the aggregate strength of all the factors which are responsible for individual variations in scores.

Consider any two sets of scores, which we shall call **A** and **B**. The symbol for an individual element of Set **A** is A_i if we are dealing with the original score, and a, if we are dealing with the deviation score. From the elements of these two sets form a third set, **C**, according to the following rule: each element of **C** is the sum of one element of **A** and one element of **B**, every possible combination of this sort being taken once. Assuming that we know the parameters of **A** and **B**, what do we know about the parameters of **C**?

First, what is its size? It is clear that if **A** contains m elements and **B** contains n elements, then the number of elements in **C** is equal to the product mn.

Next, what is ΣC, the sum of scores? To construct **C**, each element of **A** was used n times, once in combination with each element of **B**; similarly, each element of **B** was used m times, once in combination with each element of **A**. Therefore $\Sigma C = n\Sigma A + m\Sigma B$.

Since we know the value of ΣC, as well as how many elements the set contains, we also know the value of its mean:

$$\bar{C} = \frac{n\,\Sigma A + m\,\Sigma B}{mn} = \frac{\Sigma A}{m} + \frac{\Sigma B}{n}$$

or

$$\bar{C} = \bar{A} + \bar{B}$$

All this has been relatively easy, but what we really wish to learn is a rule which will tell us the variance of set **C** in terms of the variances of sets **A** and **B**. It is a remarkable fact, whose surprise will scarcely be lessened by any amount of prior disclosure, that this rule turns out to be just as simple as the rule for expressing the mean of set **C** in terms of the means of sets **A** and **B**. However, although the rule is as simple, the proof will be lengthier. It is worth an effort, for this proposition plays a very central part in all our future work. It will help a great deal to understand it, rather than to accept it on hearsay.

Before undertaking the proof, let us look at a concrete illustration of what we have learned so far. Then, if the reader should falter in his understanding of later steps of the general proof, he can lean for support on this concrete illustration. Suppose that the two parent sets are constituted as follows:

$$\textbf{A: } 2, 6, 13$$

$$\textbf{B: } 3, 4, \;\; 4, 9$$

In Table 4.1 we see how these two parent sets generate their offspring, set **C**, by the pairing of their elements. Set **C**, the distribution of sums, not only has a mean which is the sum of the means of the parent distributions, but it also has a variance which is the sum of their separate variances. Let us resume the proof, to see why this must be so.

Let us think of **C** as being made up of m subsets, each of which results from the pairing of one certain element of **A**, which we call A_j, to each element of **B** in turn. (In the table, each of these subsets is represented by one column of the larger rectangle.) The mean of each subset equals $A_j + \bar{B}$. All of these subsets have the same sum of squares, which equals Σb^2, because a sum of squares is not changed by adding a constant to each

TABLE 4.1

Concrete Illustration of the Relationship Between Two Parent Distributions
and the Distribution of Sums Which They Generate

Set **A**

$A_1 = 2$	$A_2 = 6$	$A_3 = 13$

Set **B**   Set **C**

$B_1 = 3$	$2 + 3 = 5$	$6 + 3 = 9$	$13 + 3 = 16$
$B_2 = 4$	$2 + 4 = 6$	$6 + 4 = 10$	$13 + 4 = 17$
$B_3 = 4$	$2 + 4 = 6$	$6 + 4 = 10$	$13 + 4 = 17$
$B_4 = 9$	$2 + 9 = 11$	$6 + 9 = 15$	$13 + 9 = 22$

Summary of Set Statistics

Set	N	ΣX	ΣX^2	$\bar{X}$	Σx^2	σ^2
A	3	21	209	7	62	20.67
B	4	20	122	5	22	5.50
C	12	144*	2042	12	314**	26.17

* $\Sigma C = 4(21) + 3(20) = 144$
** $\Sigma c^2 = 4(62) + 3(22) = 314$

score in the set (cf. page 45). These within-sums represent only a portion
of the contribution which each subset makes to the total sum of squares,
Σc^2. In addition, each subset contributes an amount which is equal to the
square of the difference between its own mean and the set mean, taken
once for each element in the subset. (Compare Formula 7a, as well as the
discussion of Figures **3**.1 and **3**.2.) To summarize the content of the last
few sentences in a formula, the contribution of any of these subsets to
Σc^2 equals

$$\Sigma b^2 + n[\bar{C} - (A_i + \bar{B})]^2$$

Since $\bar{C}$ equals $\bar{A} + \bar{B}$, we may make this substitution, so that the expression within the brackets becomes $[(\bar{A} + \bar{B}) - (A_i + \bar{B})]$, which reduces

to $\bar{A} - A_j$, or simply $-a_j$. Therefore the contribution of any of these subsets to Σc^2 equals

$$\Sigma b^2 + n\, a^2;$$

The sum of squares for **C** is the summation of these contributions from m subsets. Hence,

$$\Sigma c^2 = m\, \Sigma b^2 + n\, \Sigma a^2$$

It remains only to take the mean square, dividing by the known number of elements in the set:

$$\sigma^2{}_c = \frac{m\, \Sigma b^2 + n\, \Sigma a^2}{mn} = \frac{\Sigma b^2}{n} + \frac{\Sigma a^2}{m}$$

$$= \sigma^2{}_A + \sigma^2{}_B$$

Let us drop the reference to Set **C**, which was merely a convenience for our discussion, and restate the rule for the variance of a universe of sums formed from two independent sets in the form in which we usually meet it:

12] $$\qquad\qquad \sigma^2{}_{A+B} = \sigma^2{}_A + \sigma^2{}_B$$

This rule may be extended, using the same cycle of reasoning as often as necessary, to the following more general form:

12a] $$\qquad \sigma^2{}_{A+B+C}\cdots = \sigma^2{}_A + \sigma^2{}_B + \sigma^2{}_C + \cdots$$

Stated verbally, *the variance of the universe of sums is the sum of the variances of the separate distributions*. This is the *variance law*, whose simplicity is a delight to the mathematical eye.*

Partitioning Variance

The variance law applies to the universe of sums, that is, to the set of all the possible sums which can be formed in the prescribed manner. We must not expect that it will define exactly the variance of any set of empirical scores, which constitute a sample of the universe. Nevertheless, it has a number of important applications, as will appear from time to time in the course of the succeeding chapters. In this section and the next we wish to illustrate two different ways in which it can be helpful in connection with the analysis of experimental data. However, the actual methods which might be used for these purposes will not be described at this time. The intent here is only to open a perspective for the reader, and not to teach a technique.

* More exactly, this is a special case of the *general variance law*, and it is applicable only when the parent distributions are independent, that is, when their elements do not exhibit a tendency to enter into preferential pairings. It will suffice for our needs.

Psychological research usually deals with aspects of behavior which have more than one important determinant. For example, if we were studying the growth of vocabulary, some of the factors which we might want to consider would be: (1) age, (2) general intelligence, (3) mother's educational level, (4) father's occupational classification, and (5) the number of older siblings. In dealing with such a complex problem, one cannot get very far if the research design is limited to permitting just one determinant to vary at a time, while all the others are kept constant. As a practical matter, it may be quite impossible to achieve this measure of control over the various factors involved. But this is not really necessary, for the variance law suggests another approach: to collect data under conditions which permit several determinants to vary, and then to partition the sum of squares for the dependent variable (in this case, vocabulary) into several parts, assigning one to each of the determinants which is taken into account in the design of the investigation. The problem is relatively simple if it can be assumed that the separate influences act independently, so that the effectiveness of one is not also a measure of the degree to which another is operative. If that assumption holds the problem is entirely similar to that which confronted the boy who wanted to know which of his alarms had been more effective in scattering the birds, for the total score variance merely summates the effects of the separate determinants. If we can allocate portions of the sum of squares in this manner, then we can draw conclusions about the relative effectiveness of the separate determinants with just as much assurance as if we had studied each in a separate investigation under conditions which kept all of the others constant.

As to how this might be done, it will suffice at this time to point out that one possible procedure would be to compute a differentiation ratio with respect to each of the variables being considered. The variance law tells us that the result of such a statistical analysis is entirely comparable to the result which would be achieved if we suceeded in isolating the determinants experimentally. When only one determinant varies, it produces a distribution of scores with a variance which is the measure of its strength. When all vary together, the variance of the scores sums these effects, if the effects are independent. Ultimately we shall see that when this assumption of independence is not justified, it is also possible to allocate a portion of the sum of squares to the effect of interaction among the variables!

Testing Independence

In the previous illustration we made an assumption that all the influences acted independently. This was necessary, because the variance law, in the form in which we have given it, applies only to independent distributions. However, the predictions based upon it may therefore be used to test whether two or more distributions are independent in fact.

Suppose that a class of students has taken two examinations, one in mathematics and the other in social studies, and that the results are summarized in these statistics:

Test	$\bar{X}$	σ^2
Mathematics	20	25
Social Studies	40	30

Each student can also be given an aggregate score, which is the sum of his scores for mathematics and for social studies. No matter what may be the relationship between the two series of scores, it is certain that the mean aggregate score is 60. We cannot foretell the variance of aggregate scores with similar assurance. However, if the pairing of scores is essentially random, the result should conform reasonably well to an expectation based on the variance law, to wit:

$$\sigma^2_{M+SS} = \sigma^2_M + \sigma^2_{SS}$$

This is a direct application of Formula 12 to this situation. It is the condition which is assumed by the null hypothesis, which asserts an absence of dependence between the two sets of scores. If, on the contrary, the relationship between proficiency in mathematics and proficiency in social studies is such that students tend to score alike in both tests, the effect will be to increase the variance of the aggregate scores. If this is not immediately evident, imagine what happens to the range when one person gets the high score on both tests, and another gets the low score on both. On the other hand it is conceivable, as some readers surely believe, that those who excel in social studies (including psychology) have a compensating inferiority in mathematics (including statistics). If this is so, high scorers on one test will tend to be low scorers on the other, and hence the variance of aggregate scores will be less than the random expectation.

At this point, we are not ready to consider how large the discrepancy between the predicted variance of aggregate scores and the empirical or obtained variance must be before we can reject the hypothesis of independence. In this chapter we only want to point to the fact that the variance law makes such comparisons possible in principle.

THE ESTIMATE OF UNIVERSE VARIANCE

The definition of variance as the *mean squared deviation* is applicable to any set of scores, whether it be a sample or a universe. Of course, we cannot expect that the variance of a sample will always be equal to the variance of its universe. Because of the uncertainties which are part and parcel of the sampling process, it is inevitable that the sample variance will be sometimes larger and sometimes smaller than the universe variance. This we expect, but what may come as a surprise is the fact that over the long run the sample variance tends to be smaller than the universe variance. We repeat: the mean variance of samples drawn from a given universe is smaller than the variance of that universe, and therefore any particular sample variance, taken at random, represents a *biased* estimate of the universe variance. The reason is not hard to understand: the bias arises because each sample variance is derived from a sum of squares which is computed with respect to the sample mean, whereas an unbiased estimate of the universe variance should be based, if that were possible, on a sum of squared deviations taken with respect to the universe mean. Since the universe mean is not known to us, that is impossible. We must therefore look for some other way to eliminate this bias, or tendency to shrinkage of the estimates, which results from the fact that the sums of squares, taken around the means of the samples, tend to be too small.

The problem is complex, but the solution is easy, or at least easy to apply. An unbiased estimate of the variance of the universe is obtained as follows:

13] $$s^2 = \frac{\Sigma x^2}{n-1}$$

from which it follows that

13a] $$s^2 = \frac{n\sigma^2}{n-1}$$

Just as we read σ^2 as *variance*, so we should form the habit of reading s^2 as *variance estimate*.

A mathematical proof of Formula 13 lies outside the limits of this book, but we shall discuss its justification briefly in intuitive terms. The n scores of a sample provide us with as many items of information, all of which can be put to use in forming an estimate of the universe mean. But when we turn to making an estimate of the universe variance, we find that we have only $n - 1$ useful items of information available. The first observation, although it tells us something about the mean, tells us absolutely nothing about variance. Not until we have two scores do we have the first useful item of information about the scatter of scores. It is this loss of information which is reflected in the $(n - 1)$ of the formula for an unbiased estimate of the universe variance. In the terminology of statistics, we designate $n - 1$ as the number of *degrees of freedom* available, for reasons which will appear in later discussions.

The difference between the sample variance, σ^2, and the estimate of universe variance, s^2, is very slight when the n of the sample is large, but it grows larger as the n of the sample becomes smaller. This is appropriate, since the mean of a large sample is probably fairly close to the universe mean, while the mean of a small sample may vary considerably from the parameter and thus introduce more error into the computation of the estimate.

PROBLEMS

1. *Find σ^2 and s^2 for the data in Table 3.2, page 48.*

2. *Find σ^2 and s^2 for each distribution in Table 2.4, page 34.*

3. *In Table 4.1, two parent sets are used to construct a universe of sums. From the same sets, construct a universe of differences, Set D, in which $D_i = A_i - B_i$. Find the variance of this universe of differences, and compare it with that for the universe of sums.*

5

PROBABILITY

Every morning, throughout history, our eastern sky has brightened with the rising sun. The mathematical statement for such unbroken regularity of occurrence is

$$p = 1$$

The small letter p stands for a *proportion*, and this simple equation states that there is no day, however clouded, which does not have its sunrise. We face the morrow, therefore, with unshakeable assurance that the sun will rise. This is stated in the equation,

$$P = 1$$

The large letter P stands for *probability*, and in this case the probability is absolute, leaving no room for uncertainty. The proportion is a statement of experience. The probability is a statement of expectation which is based on our faith that the past and the future provide quite comparable samples of the movements of the planetary bodies.

Sunshine is less inevitable than the sunrise. If local records show that 90 per cent of October days are cloudless, then the statement $P = .90$ expresses our expectation that the third Sunday in October, for which a school picnic is scheduled, will turn out to be a cloudless day. Even if the picnic should be washed out by a cloudburst, the committee which set the date would not admit that the expectation had been unjustified. The probability is a conjectured proportion, in an imagined universe of possible events which cannot all come to pass.

Suppose, however, that what we are planning is not a one-day picnic, but a three-day trip into the mountains. What is the likelihood that we shall have three fine days? Or two? Or one? Or none at all? Fortunately, these different outcomes are not equally likely, but even the most dismal does have some probability. Let us pause for a formal definition of our terms and then return to the problem of calculating the probability, or expectation, of each.

If in any population of N objects a certain number of these, A, possess a given attribute, then $A/N = p$, the proportion of objects which possess the attribute. It follows that the proportion of objects which do not possess the attribute equals $(N - A)/N$, which is equal to $(N/N) - (A/N)$ or $1 - p$. It is customary to use the symbol q to represent this value. It is axiomatic that the probability that the attribute will appear in any element chosen at random out of this population is equal to the proportion of elements which possess the attribute.

Two further axioms will provide us with all the tools we need to return to the problems of forecasting. The first is an addition axiom: *the probability that any one of several mutually exclusive events will occur is equal to the sum of their separate probabilities.* If absolutely no churchgoers are drunkards, then the chance that our neighbor is either a churchgoer or a drunkard is the sum of the probabilities which attach to these separate, incompatible distinctions. The second is a multiplication axiom, which is also called the *law of compound probability: the probability that two independent events will occur together is the product of their separate probabilities.* For example, if only one girl in 10 may be classified as "very pretty," and only one in 20 may be classified as an "heiress," then only one in 200 should qualify as a "very pretty heiress." This principle also applies with equal force to any *sequence* of independent events. If, at each birth, there were an equal chance that the infant would be a boy or a girl, then the likelihood of bearing girls at two successive births would be $\frac{1}{2} \cdot \frac{1}{2} = \frac{1}{4}$, and the likelihood of bearing girls at three successive births would be $\frac{1}{2} \cdot \frac{1}{2} \cdot \frac{1}{2} = \frac{1}{8}$.

Let us now return to the problem of forecasting weather for our mountain outing. Three days are involved, and there are eight possible combinations of sunny and cloudy days which may occur. We list them all, in Table 5.1, and alongside of each we compute P, by the law of compound probability. The probability for each possible combination is the product of the separate probabilities of the elements which enter into it, but they all add up, as can be seen, to the certainty of weather.

Notice that the 8 combinations fall into groups of 1, 3, 3, and 1. This pattern is independent of the values of p and q, and would be the same for any binomial raised to the third power. These are the *binomial coefficients* which appear in Table I of the Appendix, in the column for $n = 3$. If it is a matter of indifference to us when we get our sunshine, we will

TABLE 5.1

An Application of the Law of Compound Probability

First day	Second day	Third day	Computation of P	
sunny	sunny	sunny	$.9 \times .9 \times .9 =$	.729
sunny	sunny	cloudy	$.9 \times .9 \times .1 =$	.081
sunny	cloudy	sunny	$.9 \times .1 \times .9 =$	.081
cloudy	sunny	sunny	$.1 \times .9 \times .9 =$	.081
cloudy	cloudy	sunny	$.1 \times .1 \times .9 =$	.009
cloudy	sunny	cloudy	$.1 \times .9 \times .1 =$	.009
sunny	cloudy	cloudy	$.9 \times .1 \times .1 =$	.009
cloudy	cloudy	cloudy	$.1 \times .1 \times .1 =$	.001
				1.000

group together those combinations having an equal number of sunny days, and summarize our observations thus:

Number of sunny days	P
3	.729
2	.243
1	.027
0	.001
	1.000

Such a table of chance expectations is called a *probability distribution*.

If we were concerned about the expectations for a week of vacationing, there would be 128 combinations to consider (their distribution is given in Table I in the column for $n = 7$) and if we were planning on two weeks, the number of combinations would rise to 16,384. However, it should be clear that such a neatly patterned set of computations can be reduced to some expeditious formula. After all, we are only concerned with multiplying the values of p and q, in various combinations, and summing up the products into orderly groups.

The formula for the binomial expansion meets our need exactly. Many readers will remember this formula as the following cumbersome series:

$$(p + q)^n = p^n + np^{n-1}q + \frac{n(n-1)}{2} p^{n-2}q^2$$

$$+ \frac{n(n-1)(n-2)}{2 \cdot 3} p^{n-3}q^3 + \cdots + q^n$$

This can be greatly simplified by writing a general formula for any term in the series. In this more modern form:

14]
$$(p + q)^n = \sum_{m=0}^{n} \left[\binom{n}{m} p^m q^{n-m} \right]$$

We read this formula as follows: if p and q represent two numbers, the value of their sum raised to the nth power (where n is an integer) is equal to the sum of $n + 1$ terms; each of these terms is to be found by evaluating the expression within brackets for one of the values of m, which takes on all integral values from zero to n, inclusive. The symbol $\binom{n}{m}$ has already been defined, on page 31, as representing "the number of different ways in which a subset consisting of m elements can be formed out of a parent set of n elements."

Whenever we make use of the binomial expansion for a problem in probabilities, $p + q = 1$ by definition, and therefore $(p + q)^n$ equals 1, no matter what the values of p, q, and n. We do not use the binomial expansion in order to evaluate $(p + q)^n$, but in order to break it down into fractional parts. We know in advance that the sum of $n + 1$ terms of the expansion must equal unity, that is, that it will account for all the probabilities in the situation. It is the fracturing of this unity which interests us, for each fraction represents the specific probability of one of the distinctive possibilities in the situation. (See Table 5.2 for a concrete illustration of the meaning of the binomial expansion.)

Since the expression $\binom{n}{m}$ appears in each term of the expansion, it is convenient to have a table of these values. Such a table is called a Pascal triangle (see Table I). It has a remarkable patterned quality, which makes it an easy matter to extend the table by a few columns when one wishes to do so. In the form in which we give it, each element is the sum of the one which stands to its left and the one directly above that.

Many experimental problems deal with events or attributes which are regarded as having a 50:50 likelihood of occurrence. For example, a pre-election poll is a test of the null hypothesis that the proponents of both candidates are equally numerous. In these cases, $p = q$, and therefore the value of $p^m q^{n-m}$ in Formula 14 is always equal to p^n. Since in such cases $p = \frac{1}{2}$, this in turn equals $\frac{1}{2^n}$. This simplifies the computational work enormously.

It is only necessary to take down the figures shown in the appropriate column of the Pascal triangle, reading each entry as the numerator of a fraction which has the denominator 2^n. If desired, these fractions may be converted to proportions or percentages.

Tossing coins is the classic model for this type of problem. If we let n

TABLE 5.2

Meaning of the Binomial Expansion

The binomial expansion is only a convenient way of describing what takes place in the repeated multiplication of any two-part number. To help the student appreciate this, we here show side by side the repeated multiplication of a binomial, 12, in the ordinary procedure, in a more cumbersome manner which emphasizes the binomial structure, and in symbols.

$$
\begin{array}{ll}
\begin{array}{r}
12 \\
12 \\
\hline
10 + 2 \\
10 + 2 \\
\hline
24 \\
12 \\
20 + 4 \\
100 + 20 \\
\hline
144 \\
12 \\
100 + 40 + 4 \\
10 + 2 \\
\hline
288 \\
144 \\
200 + 80 + 8 \\
1000 + 400 + 40 \\
\hline
1728 \\
12 \\
1000 + 600 + 120 + 8 \\
10 + 2 \\
\hline
1728 \\
\\
3456 \\
1728 \\
2000 + 1200 + 240 + 16 \\
6000 + 1200 + 80 \\
\hline
20736 = 10000 + 8000 + 2400 + 320 + 16
\end{array}
&
\begin{array}{l}
a + b \;= (a + b) \\
a + b \\
\hline
\qquad\quad ab + b^2 \\
a^2 + ab \\
\hline
a^2 + 2ab + b^2 \;= (a + b)^2 \\
a + b \\
\\
\\
\\
a^2 + 2ab + b^2 \\
\qquad\quad a^2b + 2ab^2 + b^3 \\
a^3 + 2a^2b + ab^2 \\
\hline
a^3 + 3a^2b + 3ab^2 + b^3 \;= (a + b)^3 \\
a + b \\
\\
\\
\\
a^3b + 3a^2b^2 + 3ab^3 + b^4 \\
a^4 + 3a^3b + 3a^2b^2 + ab^3 \\
\hline
a^4 + 4a^3b + 6a^2b^2 + 4ab^3 + b^4 = (a + b)^4 \\
\\
= a^4 + 4a^3b + 6a^2b^2 + 4ab^3 + b^4 = (a + b)^4
\end{array}
\end{array}
$$

Now you might try $(7 + 5)^4$, by formula.

represent the number of coins in each sample, and m the number which fall heads up, then each column of Table I gives the probability distribution for a universe of samples of the given size. For example, if three coins are tossed into a fountain, but there is only a 50 : 50 likelihood that wishes attached to each of them will come true, then all three wishes must be denied in one-eighth of all samples, one wish will be granted in three-eighths of all samples, etc. In a more prosaic application, the column headed $n = 5$ gives the chance distribution of scores for a short quiz consisting of 5 true-false items. Whenever $p = q$, the probability distribution will be symmetrical, as each column of binomial coefficients is symmetrical.

A PROFESSOR'S QUANDARY

Suppose that a professor, having had the delightful experience of teaching a class of six interested students, feels disposed to give all of them A's. He asks himself: is it reasonable? He looks up his records of past semesters and finds that he has given A's to only 20 per cent of the students taking this course. The problem now takes this form: is it reasonable to suppose that a random sample of six students, drawn from a universe which includes 20 per cent A students, should all be of that calibre? For the null hypothesis asserts that this is a random sample, such as might be expected to occur from time to time by chance. The value of p, the proportion of A grades, is an estimate based on past experience.

The situation may be restated as a card problem. We have a deck of cards, each of which bears a letter grade, from A to F. One-fifth of all the cards are marked A, and the distribution of the remaining grades does not concern us. What is the likelihood that, dealing six cards from such a deck, all would be A's? If this deck of cards is to be an adequate model for our universe it must be very fat—so fat that even after we have dealt a great many cards out of it the proportions of the various kinds of cards remaining in the deck are unchanged. For our universe does not consist of a few dozen students among those presently enrolled in the college who have the prerequisites for the course, but of the many thousands who might have been, under all kinds of imaginable and unimaginable conditions. As a practical matter, the need for such an infinite deck can be obviated by dealing one card at a time, returning each card to the deck and reshuffling before dealing the next.

By the law of compound probability, the likelihood of dealing a six-card flush of A's from such a deck is the sixfold product of the probability of dealing one such card.

$$P = (1/5)^6 = \frac{1}{15625}$$

The professor recognizes that there is little hope that he will meet this situation before retirement age, and he regretfully concludes that his appraisals have been too generous.

It is of some interest to compute the complete probability distribution in this situation, for it bears on an oft-discussed problem, the question of grading "on a curve." This distribution consists of seven values, each of which is a term of the following binomial expansion:

$$\left(\frac{1}{5} + \frac{4}{5}\right)^6 = \sum_{m=0}^{6} \left[\binom{6}{m}\left(\frac{1}{5}\right)^m\left(\frac{4}{5}\right)^{6-m}\right]$$

The solution is given in Table **5**.3. The first column is simply a memo-

TABLE 5.3

Computation of a Binomial Probability Distribution

m	$\binom{n}{m}$	p^m	q^{n-m}	P_m	$\%$
6	1	$(1/5)^6$	$(4/5)^0$	1/15625	0.0
5	6	$(1/5)^5$	$(4/5)^1$	24/15625	0.2
4	15	$(1/5)^4$	$(4/5)^2$	240/15625	1.5
3	20	$(1/5)^3$	$(4/5)^3$	1280/15625	8.2
2	15	$(1/5)^2$	$(4/5)^4$	3840/15625	24.6
1	6	$(1/5)^1$	$(4/5)^5$	6144/15625	39.3
0	1	$(1/5)^0$	$(4/5)^6$	4096/15625	26.2
					100.0

randum, which lists the seven values of m which must be considered. The next three columns give the three factors in each term of the expansion, indicating on any given row the form which each factor takes for a certain value of m. The product of these three factors appears in the fifth column. Notice that the denominator is a constant, which needed to be computed only once, and that the addition of the numerators provides a check on the accuracy of their computation.

For convenience, the probabilities are restated as percentages in the final column. This shows at a glance that almost 10 per cent of random samples of six students would contain three or more A students; on the other hand, more than one-fourth of the samples would contain no A students. Such a distribution should discourage any propensity to "grade on the curve" in a small class, but it also sets definite limits to the professor's generosity.

The Normal Distribution

By the methods which we have been studying in this chapter, it is possible to construct probability distributions to meet the requirements of many special problems. There is sometimes no substitute for this kind of do-it-yourself methodology, but often it is possible to find a ready-made standardized product which will do the job at a great saving of time and effort. An important part of the work of mathematical statisticians consists in devising probability distributions which have a wide range of usefulness. Although higher mathematics is involved in the creation of these distributions, it is not required for their application. Anyone who understands the binomial probability distributions of the kind which we have been discussing can quickly learn to make intelligent use of the tables in which more generalized distributions are presented.

The most generally useful probability distribution is the one whose bell-shaped symmetrical outline is familiar to everyone who has read an elementary textbook of psychology. This is a "picture of expectation" which has wide but not universal application, and we should try to understand the special conditions under which it represents a useful model of chance.

We remarked earlier that most psychological scores are not really measurements, but enumerations. This is not a peculiarity of psychological data. Almost any type of quantified data can be interpreted in this manner. A wage consists of so many increments of earning power; a child's weight is the resultant of many separate growth processes; "age at first marriage" is influenced by many kinds of personal and social facilitating and inhibiting stimuli. Virtually any distribution of scores reflects the operation of numerous causal influences. One can see this, in part, by considering the range of scores. A phenomenon which has only one determinant must always come out either "heads" or "tails," like the toss of a single coin. A phenomenon which has two determinants has four possible outcomes, but if the two determinants act quite similarly two of these outcomes are indistinguishable, and the distribution is like that which results from the repeated tossing of two coins. This is the case with the simple Mendelian inheritance of a recessive gene which is present in both parents: one-fourth of their offspring, receiving the gene from both parents, exhibit the recessive characteristic; two-fourths, receiving it from one parent, are able to transmit the gene but do not exhibit the characteristic; one-fourth do not receive the gene from either parent. As the determinants increase in number, the possible combinations of determinants also increase, and the range of scores widens.

When a phenomenon has many possible outcomes, that is a sure indication that it is complexly determined. Therefore, if the expansion of $(p + q)^n$ is to generate a probability distribution which will be suitable for the study of complex social and biological phenomena, it will be necessary to increase the size of n very substantially above the moderate values with which we have been working. If this had to be done separately for each problem, it would involve a great deal of tedious work. However, it is possible to create a distribution which will serve our need whenever the value of n is very large. Mathematicians, using the methods of calculus, let n increase "without limit." What happens under these conditions is intimated by the succession of distributions shown in Figure 5.1. For each distribution in this Figure, $p = \frac{1}{2}$, but the value of n varies. The size of each polygon is arbitrary, for they have been drawn to different scales to avoid the confusion of overlapping lines. Imagine them as all of the same area, and standing one behind the other. As n increases, the base of the distribution grows relatively broader, reflecting the increased range of possible scores. This gives rise ultimately to long flattened tails, which cover a great many score values but include only a small proportion of the area under the curve. Thus, if you toss 15 pennies, you will be more than mildly surprised if you get 15 or even 14 heads. The probability distribution tells us that such extreme results (and we include the case of 14 or 15 tails as equally extreme) are to be expected less than once in 1000 trials—a situation which is better described as an improbability than as a probability. In recognition of this fact, we shall dub the long tails of such distributions "tails of improbability."

When we draw such a figure, it is difficult to show accurately the step-wise structure of the tails themselves. If we were to raise n to a value of several hundred, most of the steps would become imperceptible, and the outline would appear like a smooth curve. Increase it "without limit" and the steps do merge into a smooth curve, even in theory. That curve is the normal distribution, whose general outline is already rather clearly intimated by a smooth curve drawn through the tops of the columns in the binomial distribution for $p = q$, $n = 15$.

In an exact sense, the normal distribution does not apply to anything real. It is the probability distribution for something which is out of this world: a variable of infinite range which has an infinite number of independent determinants. This mathematical figment is nevertheless a satisfactory model for distributions which have a wide range and are influenced by a great many factors, none of which is predominant. It is the picture of our expectation for many biological and social phenomena which approximate these conditions.

The example which is most familiar to psychology students is the distribution of intelligence. However, we must distinguish between assumptions about the theoretical distribution of intelligence and empirical distributions of mental ages or IQ's. We feel justified in assuming that intelligence, as a sort of biological potential, does have a normal distribu-

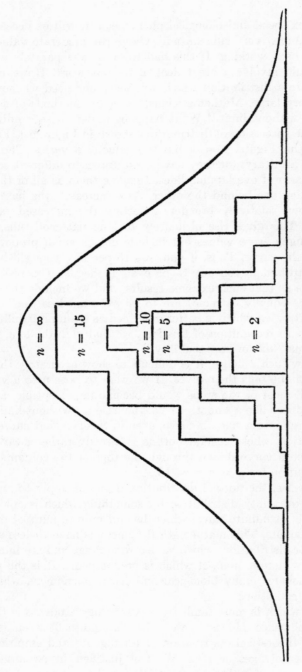

Fig. 5.1. A series of binomial probability distributions, selected to illustrate the development of "the tail of improbability." For each, $p = q$. The smooth curve, which is the limit as n approaches ∞, represents "normal" probability.

tion because we know that it has a great many developmental determinants. On the other hand, the distribution of IQ's from a standard intelligence test has a finite number of determinants: the number of items on the test. This number is large enough so that it can yield a distribution of scores which is reasonably close to normal, but it is also small enough so that we cannot assume this result. As a matter of fact, the authors of such instruments modify the scoring procedures as they find necessary so that the results shall fit the theoretical expectation of a normal distribution. The fact that the distribution of scores for children in public schools or for young men called up for military service turns out to be very nearly normal says little about the distribution of intelligence as such, but reflexts the technical skill and the theoretical convictions of the test constructors.

THE STANDARD DEVIATION

The area which lies under the normal curve is a geometric model of *normal probability*. As in any frequency curve, the height of the ordinate at any point along the abscissa defines the relative frequency of scores at that point. Let us follow this curve inward from the left, or negative, side. Sweeping in from the endless flattened tail, it rises at first slowly, but with steady positive acceleration, until it reaches a point where approximately one-sixth of the area already lies beneath it. Here there is a point of inflection, at which the curve changes from positive to negative acceleration. As it passes the mean it dips down, to mirror itself on the right. Thus, approximately two-thirds of the surface lies under the central bulge between the two points of inflection, while one-sixth is spread into each of the thinning tails.

In Figure **5.**2, this area is broken into 1000 pieces. That is, each dot in the figure represents one-tenth of 1 per cent of the normal probability area. The height of this mass of dots, relative to its width, is quite arbitrary, and is fixed according to convenience. But whether we make it tall and slender, or broad and squat, its essential form is unaltered. (Compare Figure **5.**3, which shows three normal curves, any of which might be used to depict the expected distribution of intelligence quotients, or scores on a neuroticism inventory, or the yield of corn, in bushels per acre, on 1000 Iowa farms.) As one moves away from the mean, the relative frequency of dots (that is, the ordinate of the curve) falls off in strict obedience to a mathematical law which we shall relegate, in its exact form, to a footnote.* Even the verbal statement of this law may sound confusing:

* The ordinate of the normal curve:

$$y = \frac{N}{\sigma\sqrt{2\pi}}\,e^{-x^2/2\sigma^2}$$

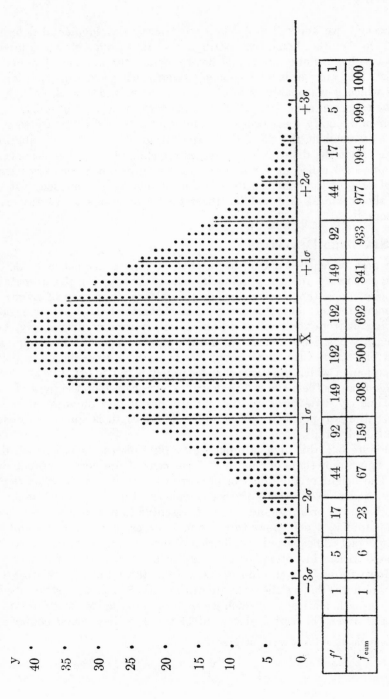

FIG. 5.2. A quasi-normal distribution of 1000 dots.

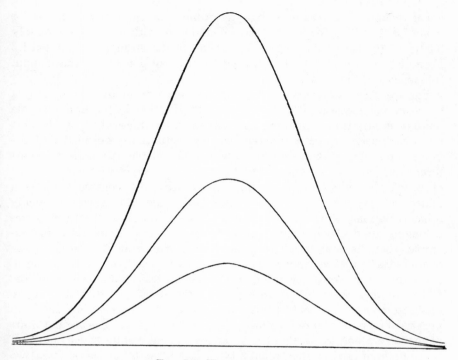

Fig. 5.3. Three normal curves.

the logarithm of the frequency of any score in a normal distribution declines as the square of the score's deviation value increases. However, this comes down to the fact that there is a simple linear relationship between the ordinate of the curve, stated as a logarithm, and points on the abscissa, when this is a scale of squared deviations. If we are willing to forego the exactness which cannot be attained without the incommensurable constants π and e, we can restate the formula for the ordinate of the normal curve in the following computational form:

15]
$$\log y = A - .217 \frac{x^2}{\sigma^2}$$

where y is the height of the ordinate, and A is the common logarithm of the ordinate at the mean of the distribution. If we like, we can give the ordinate at the mean a value of 1.0; in that case, A equals zero, and Formula 15 will give other ordinates as proportions of the central ordinate. However, since we intend to use the normal distribution as a distribution of probabilities, it is more usual to set the area under the entire curve equal to unity; this requires that the ordinate at the mean shall have a value of $1/\sqrt{2\pi}$, for which the common logarithm is approximately 9.601 − 10. Using this method, the values of the ordinates computed by Formula 15, when multiplied by 100, will correspond with the column frequencies in Figure 5.2.

For any frequency curve, the position of each ordinate is located by a score on the abscissa. This may be expressed either in the original scale units or in any transformation. In order to make practical use of the normal distribution in many different concrete situations, we must first devise some system of transformation which will enable us readily to transform any given set of scores into the units of a *standard scale*, in terms of which the tables of the normal distribution are constructed. As a matter of fact, the need for a standard scale also exists in many other situations, whenever we wish to make comparisons between scores belonging to different distributions. Who has not complained, for example, that "it is as tough to get a *B* from Smith as it is to get an *A* from Jones." Just as grades vary from class to class, so the meaning of the same score varies according to the mechanical characteristics of the test or other scoring device. In Chapter 2 we mentioned that one way to facilitate comparisons is to transform each score into a centile. This is an unsatisfactory procedure for most purposes, because centiles are not units of measure along the scale of the dimension, but points which mark off equal units of area on the probability surface. The difference between two adjacent centiles near one end of a distribution will usually be much greater, in original score units, than the difference between adjacent centiles near the middle of the distribution. Although Bill excels Bert in measured units of performance by exactly as much as Bert excels Bob, the gap between Bill and Bert may be very much greater (or less) than the gap between Bert and Bob, in centile scores.

A more satisfactory standard linear unit is obtained by taking the square root of the variance. This is a representative deviation, in the sense that it is the deviation value of the score which makes a representative (i.e., mean) contribution to the sum of squares. It is called, appropriately, a *standard deviation*. Its symbol is simply the symbol for variance, without the exponent. It is usually defined thus:

$$16] \qquad\qquad \sigma = \sqrt{\frac{\Sigma x^2}{n}}$$

Although the standard deviation is a linear measure of dispersion, we did not mention it in Chapter 2 because we restricted ourselves there to statistics which are based on linear scores.* The standard deviation is like

* The standard deviation of a sample will ordinarily be from about one-third to one-sixth of the range, tending to be relatively smaller as sample size increases. This

the shadow of the variance, and it owes its special virtues to this relationship. The reader will recognize, from the symbols employed, that the
standard deviation is the older concept, but this should not be allowed to
obscure the fact that variance is more fundamental. Relationships which
are stated in terms of variance have a simplicity which imprints them on
the mind, while the parallel relationships stated in terms of standard
deviations lack this clarity. However, the standard deviation does have
this remarkable quality: in the normal distribution, it is precisely equal
to the deviation between the mean and either point of inflection in the
frequency curve. It is helpful to keep this fact in mind when sketching
the curve, as well as in many other situations.

The standard deviation is all but indispensable when we wish to make
comparisons among linear scores, as we do whenever we discuss the relative standings of individuals on the same test, or the relative standings of
the same individual on different tests. For these purposes, any score can be
transformed into a *standard score*, or *z* score, by expressing it in terms of
standard deviation units. This is readily accomplished, thus:

17]
$$z = \frac{x}{\sigma}$$

That is, *a standard score is a deviation score divided by the standard deviation
of its distribution.* When all the scores of a set are transformed in this
manner, the distribution is said to be *standardized*. The set of standard
scores will not only have zero mean, which is true of any set of deviation
scores, but it will also have unit variance (i.e., $\sigma^2 = 1$). The circumstance
that the words *normal* and *standard* are sometimes synonyms, in nonmathematical uses, may trap us into the error of supposing that standardizing a set of scores also *normalizes* it. That is not the case. Standardization does not change the form of the distribution at all, but merely effects
a linear transformation of its scale, which either stretches it or shrinks it
uniformly over its entire length. This facilitates comparisons among
distributions having the same form.* If the set of original scores has
approximately normal distribution, standardization enables us to use the

provides a rough convenient check against gross errors of computation. We may expect
the range to embrace about 4σ when $n = 30$, 5σ when $n = 100$, and 6σ when $n = 450$.

* To make comparisons among scores from distributions of different form, or to
combine scores from such distributions, it is necessary to *normalize* them. This is a
more complicated process than standardizing. One way to accomplish it is to establish
a cumulative frequency distribution, transform that into a distribution of cumulative
proportions, and then look to the normal table for deviation values which correspond
to those proportions. The procedure is not difficult, but it is not relevant to our present
purpose. There are also several other special techniques, such as square-root transformation and logarithmic transformation, which may be used to normalize a set of
scores. These will be discussed in Chapter 13.

normal probability table as a table of proportional frequencies for the distribution.

If the reader will now look back to Figure 5.2, he will see that distances along the abscissa have been marked off in standard units, as defined in the preceding paragraph. This device permits us to use the normal distribution as a probability distribution for any set of scores which is normally distributed. Indeed, counting dots on Figure 5.2 will give us all the accuracy we can obtain from a table which gives proportional frequencies to three decimal places, for z values by tenths of standard deviations. The values of f', which appear in the the box at the base of the table, represent the count of dots for intervals of one-half σ. In the row beneath, these numbers are cumulated. From these counts we can state, for example, that the proportion of scores in a normal distribution which can be expected to fall below the value -1σ is .159, and that the proportion which can be expected to fall between the values -1σ and $+1\sigma$ is .682 (that is, the difference between .159 and .841). The mathematician arrives at these same results by the methods of integral calculus, but the principle is the same: to slice the normal distribution into a series of narrow vertical strips, to determine the proportionate area which lies within each strip, and then to total these proportions inside any desired limits.

Some published tables of normal probability report the proportional area which is included in the tail which is cut off by the ordinate erected at a given standard score, while others give the proportional area which lies between the ordinate and the mean. The former method is generally more convenient in connection with the uses to which a psychologist puts the normal table, and therefore this is the form which we have selected for Table IIA of the Appendix. Let us illustrate one of the simpler uses of this table. IQ's derived from a Stanford-Binet test have a mean of 100 and a standard deviation of 16. An IQ of 87 is therefore transformed into a standard score as follows:

$$z = \frac{x}{\sigma} = \frac{87 - 100}{16} = -.81$$

Consulting Table IIA, we see that a standard score of $\pm.81$ cuts off a tail which contains approximately 21 per cent of the area under the normal curve. This implies that 21 per cent of the standardization population, on which the test norms were based, had IQ scores of 87 or below. It is this value, rather than the IQ, which we would find useful in interpreting the child's score to a parent.

Other and more important uses of the normal table will appear in later chapters.

PROBLEMS

1. *Was the professor justified in using the null hypothesis? State your reasons.*

2. *Show the chance distribution of scores from a test consisting of eight true-false items.*

3. *Show the chance distribution of scores from a test consisting of eight multiple-choice items, each with four choices, of which only one is correct. Comparing the result with that for the previous problem, which test is more discriminating?*

4. *With reference to the illustration of the law of compound probability on page 72, what would be the implication if only 1 girl in 1000 is a very pretty heiress? Assume that the basic proportions are stated correctly.*

5. *Tom, Dick, and Harry are three friends who are comparing grades received on tests in two classes. Given the following data, whose average performance is best? Who made the most outstanding score on either test? Whose scores are most consistent?*

Test	$\bar{X}$	σ	Tom	Dick	Harry
A	90	30	60	100	105
B	15	4	23	19	17

6. *Assuming that Stanford-Binet IQ's for the general population do have $\bar{X} = 100$ and $\sigma = 16$, and that they are normally distributed, what proportion of the population falls into each of the following intelligence classifications? IQ below 70; 70–89; 90–109; 110–129; 130 and above.*

7. *If an intelligence test is so standardized that it yields normally distributed scores with $\bar{X} = 100$ and $\sigma = 20$, what IQ scores would be used to define equivalent intelligence classes?*

6

SAMPLING VARIANCE

We all know the story of the three blind men and the elephant. The first took hold of the tail and thought the elephant was like a rope; the second took hold of the trunk and thought it was a great snake; the third felt one of the massive legs and declared that both his friends were mistaken, for this beast was like a tree. This is an example of *sampling variance*, or the error which is inherent in limitations of experience.

Any sample statistic is, like the blind man's concept of an elephant, the more or less fortuitous outcome of a situation which might have given different results. The ancient parable can be matched by many true tales of modern research. In one investigation, underprivileged children overestimate the size of a dime; in a replication of this experiment, they do not. In the experience of one clinician, schizophrenics have very poor scores on an object-assembly task; in that of another, they do not. Such contradictions are ultimately reconciled, as the fragments of information which build a science are made to fit together. No man's experience is broad enough to be labeled TRUTH. We grope our way, feeling for bits of reality, and trying to form a connected picture of the whole elephant.

The beginning of statistical wisdom is the recognition that statistics, when they are statements of empirical fact, are *always* wrong. However, some statistics are more wrong than others. In some, the amount of error is so slight as to be inconsequential for most practical purposes. In others, the potential error is so great that any reliance on them would be foolhardy. Fortunately, it is usually possible to distinguish between statistics which are reasonably trustworthy and those that are not. To state the matter first in common-sense terms, our decision in this respect is influenced by two factors. First, we consider *how much* experience is represented by the statistic. Other things being equal, we place more faith in a representative score which is based on 100 observations than in one which is based on 10 observations. Second, we give greater credence to statistics which are based on *consistent* experience. Large differences among the scores cause us to wonder whether the sample is properly representative of its universe; maybe the low scores, maybe the high ones, are really atypical. When all the scores are pretty much alike, it seems reasonable to suppose that a continuation of the sampling process would not lead to any marked change in the trend of the data. These are simple, common-sense considerations. They may be summed up in the following statement: *the amount of allowance for error which is appropriate to any representative score depends on the number of scores in the sample, and on the variability of the sample.*

Now let us consider the problem in a more technical manner. When we have taken a random sample from a universe, and propose to use the sample mean as an estimate of the universe mean, we have in effect made a blindfold choice of one element out of a hypothetical universe of sample means. We should not be so naive as to suppose that this is the best of all possible samples. On the other hand, it is probably not one of the worst, either. Before we can form any opinion about how much confidence to place in this representative score, we must first investigate the totality— that is, the universe—of the possible outcomes of which this result is one. With the help of the variance law, we shall establish a formula for the variance of that universe of possibilities. We shall call it the *sampling variance of the mean:* $\sigma^2_{\bar{X}}$.

Suppose that we were to take repeated samples, each containing n observations, from the same universe. Let us give our attention first to the sample sums. The variance law tells us that the universe of sums, when $n = 2$, will have a variance equal to $2\sigma^2$, where σ^2 is the variance of the parent universe. The universe of sums when $n = 3$ would have variance equal to $3\sigma^2$, and in general, for samples of size n, the variance of the universe of sums would equal $n\sigma^2$.

Sums are a rather clumsy statistic, partly because they run to large numbers and partly because they do not permit direct comparisons between samples of different size. For these reasons, we prefer to deal with sample means. However, the mean is itself equal to a sum of transformed scores which are obtained by using n as a constant divisor. That is,

$$\frac{\Sigma X}{n} = \Sigma\left(\frac{X}{n}\right)$$

When every score of a set is divided by n, the effect on the variance is to divide it by n^2. (Compare Formula 11b, which reverses the effect of a transformation in which i is used as the divisor.) Therefore, the variance of the universe of *means*, for samples of size n, is equal to the variance of the universe of *sums*, divided by n^2. In symbols:

$$\sigma^2_{\bar{x}} = \frac{\sigma^2_{\Sigma x}}{n^2}$$

However, we have already seen that the variance of sums equals $n\sigma^2$. Substituting this in the numerator of the righthand member of the above equation, and simplifying, we obtain:

18] $$\sigma^2_{\bar{x}} = \frac{\sigma^2}{n}$$

In words: *the variance of a universe of sample means varies directly as the variance of the universe from which the samples are drawn, and inversely as the size of the sample.* This is the exact statement of the rule which we had already formulated in common-sense terms.

Formula 18 defines the relationship between the parameters of two universes, but in practical situations we must be content to form an estimate, based on another estimate. It will be remembered that an unbiased estimate of the universe variance is, by Formula 13:

$$s^2 = \frac{\Sigma x^2}{n-1}$$

Dividing by n, we obtain an unbiased estimate of the variance of the universe of sample means. According to the convenience of the moment, we can use any of these equivalent forms:

18a, b, c] $$s^2_{\bar{x}} = \frac{\Sigma x^2}{n(n-1)} = \frac{\sigma^2}{n-1} = \frac{s^2}{n}$$

Confidence Limits

Now we can return to the question of how to evaluate the mean of a single sample. We have just learned that the data of the sample provide us with an estimate of the sampling variance of the mean—that is, the variance of the universe of means of all possible samples of the same n. In order to simplify our discussion, let us assume for the time being that we are dealing with a large sample, so that the universe of means is essentially normal in distribution. In finding the mean of a random sample, we have in effect made a grab-bag selection of one element out of that universe. This single element is all that we know about the universe aside from the fact that it is normally distributed. However, the variance and the size of the sample permit us to make an unbiased estimate of the variance of that universe, the universe of samples-that-might-have-been. We still do not know whether the empirical mean which we obtained is one of those relatively frequent means which lie near the middle of the distribution, or one of those relatively rare means which lie far out in the tails. It would be reasonable to wager 2-to-1 that this randomly chosen element of a normal distribution lies under that central bulge whose limits are $\pm 1\sigma$. If we did this repeatedly, and there were some way to check up on the surmise, it would turn out to be correct about 68 times in 100. This statement is a direct application of the probabilities stated in the normal table and shown graphically in Figure **6**.1.

If we cut the tails of improbability shorter, we can raise the odds that a random element lies inside the chosen limits. The odds would be 4-to-1 that a randomly chosen element of a normal distribution lies within $\pm 1.28\sigma$ of the mean, for reference to the normal table shows that at that point each tail of the distribution contains approximately 10 per cent of the area of the probability surface, leaving 80 per cent of the area inside those limits. In the same way, the odds would be 9-to-1 that the element lies inside the limits $\pm 1.64\sigma$, and 19-to-1 that it lies within the limits $\pm 1.96\sigma$. Since the element about which we are talking is a sample mean, drawn from a nearly normal hypothetical universe of sample means, we can say that the odds are 19-to-1 that it lies within $1.96s_{\bar{x}}$ of the universe mean. Here we have introduced the symbol $s_{\bar{x}}$, that is, an estimated standard deviation of the hypothetical universe of means. We read it, however, as the *standard error of the mean*, or simply as the *standard error*.

Now, we know that the distance from Paris to Rome is neither more nor less than the distance from Rome to Paris. In the colorless precision of mathematics, $|A - B| = |B - A|$. Hence, whenever the sample mean lies within $\pm 1.96s_{\bar{x}}$ of the universe mean, it follows that the universe mean lies within $\pm 1.96s_{\bar{x}}$ of the sample mean. Since these events occur with equal frequency, one being but the mirror image of the other, they also have equal probability, and we are able to assert that there is a 95 per cent likelihood that the universe mean lies within $\pm 1.96s_{\bar{x}}$ of the sample mean. In symbols:

$$(\bar{X} - 1.96s_{\bar{x}}) < \bar{X}_\infty < (\bar{X} + 1.96s_{\bar{x}}); \quad P = .95$$

where $\bar{X}_\infty$ stands for the "true" mean or parameter, which would be found by exhaustive or "infinite" sampling of the universe. More simply:

19] $$\bar{X}_\infty = \bar{X} \pm 1.96s_{\bar{x}}; \quad P = .95$$

This pair of equations is a statement of *fiducial limits* (or *confidence limits*), which define a *confidence interval*. The first equation defines certain limits

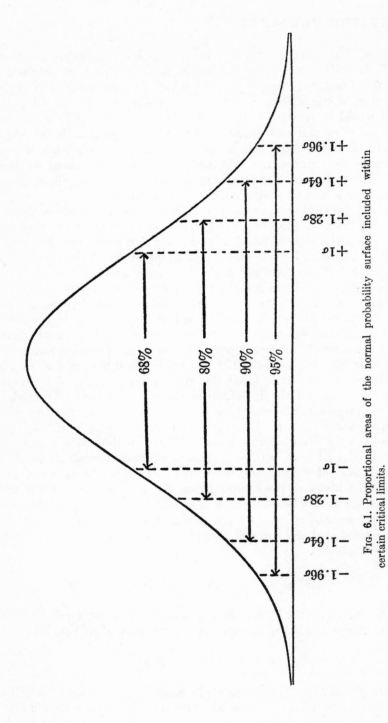

Fig. 6.1. Proportional areas of the normal probability surface included within certain critical limits.

within which the universe mean is assumed to lie; the second equation states the probability that this assumption is correct.*

The value 1.96, as it is used here, is called a *critical value*, because it serves to separate the sheep from the goats: the values which, by our standard, we accept as "probable" from those which we reject as "improbable." Another very commonly used critical value of the normal distribution is 2.58σ. At that point, only 0.5 per cent of the area under the curve is included in each tail. Hence,

19a] $\bar{X}_\infty = \bar{X} \pm 2.58s_{\bar{X}}; \qquad P = .99$

This is a statement of confidence limits which can be made with a higher degree of certainty.

Because we are usually thinking in terms of a null hypothesis rather than in terms of the positive statement of confidence limits, it is customary to speak of the 5 per cent level of confidence and the 1 per cent level of confidence, rather than the 95 per cent and 99 per cent levels, respectively. One selects either of these levels—or the still more stringent 0.1 per cent level, for which the critical value is $\pm 3.29s_{\bar{X}}$—according to the practical demands of the situation and the amount of risk which one is willing to accept. In publishing the data for any sample of observations, one should always include a statement of the number of observations and either their standard deviation or the standard error, so that the reader can form his own judgment as to whether the representative score is trustworthy.

Let us illustrate the use of Formulas 18 and 19 in a concrete application. Cottle, Lewis, and Penney[1] give the scores of 60 counselors and 60 non-counselors on an experimental scale designed to select good counselor candidates. For the counselors, $\bar{X} = 41.68$ and $\sigma = 5.01$. We estimate the standard error of the mean by Formula 18b (in modified form):

$$s_{\bar{X}} = \frac{\sigma}{\sqrt{n-1}} = \frac{5.01}{\sqrt{59}} = 0.653$$

Using this value in Formula 19, we obtain

$$\bar{X}_\infty = 41.68 \pm 1.96\,(.653),$$

or

$$40.40 < \bar{X}_\infty < 42.96; \qquad P = .95$$

* Some statistical theorists speak of *fiducial limits* (following Fisher[2]), while others speak of *confidence limits* (following Neyman[3]). Our statement has been one of *fiducial limits*, in which we asserted the probability that the universe parameter lies within a given interval. We might instead have said that if we were to take many random samples from the same universe, and compute *confidence limits* from each (by the procedure already described), then in a certain proportion of all such cases the defined interval would include the universe parameter. The distinction between these two forms of statement is not important for our purposes.

That is, we are "95 per cent sure" that the mean score for the target population of counselors, which was sampled in this study, lies within the indicated limits. This is a rather elastic definition of a "true" value, but this is an instance in which we stretch the truth advisedly, to cover a precisely calculated range of values.

We digress to make a brief comment on the use of the slide-rule. Notice, in Figure **6**.2, that when we use Scales A and B to divide variance by n, in order to obtain the variance of the universe of means, the slide-rule is simultaneously performing the division of the standard deviation by $\sqrt{n}$, to determine the standard error. That is why we have not listed the formula for the standard error independently; it is truly the same formula, in a slightly different application. Notice also that with this same setting of the slide-rule we can immediately read the value of $1.96s_{\bar{x}}$ or $2.58s_{\bar{x}}$, by reading on Scale D opposite the critical factors on Scale C.

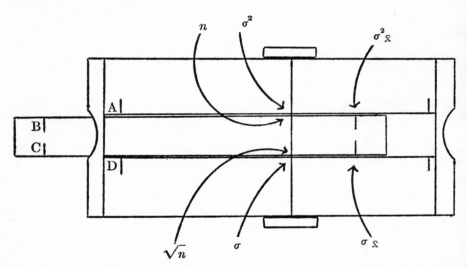

Fig. **6**.2. Computation of the standard error, or the variance of the mean, on the slide-rule.

There is another important practical application of Formula 18. When planning an investigation, we would like to know in advance how many observations will be needed in order to obtain results of some value. We can usually make a rough estimate of the expected variance of scores, based perhaps on a pilot study. If we divide this by what we regard as an acceptable value for the standard error, we obtain an estimate of the sample size which will be needed. That is, we recast Formula 18c into the following form:

$$\frac{s^2}{s^2_{\bar{x}}} = n$$

The result will sometimes save us a good deal of frustration, by providing an advance warning that there is no point in undertaking the investigation at all, unless we are able to devise additional controls which will reduce the error variance.

STUDENT'S DISTRIBUTION

The method which we have been using to define the confidence limits of the mean of an empirical sample gives accurate results only when the sample is rather large. When the sample is small, a subtle type of bias enters into the problem. One of the essential foundations of modern statistical method was the recognition of the nature of this bias and its elimination by a British statistician named Gossett, in the course of his work for the Guiness breweries. This stout contribution to science might have been suppressed by a company rule against the publication of the research of employees, but the rule was relaxed sufficiently to permit the historic article on *The Probable Error of the Mean* to appear, in 1908, under the name of "Student."

When we take a series of small samples from a normal universe, the sample means are normally distributed, but this is not true of the variance estimates. Although they are unbiased in the sense that the mean of such estimates equals the universe parameter, their distribution is nevertheless skewed. As a result, the ratio $(\bar{X} - \bar{X}_\infty)/s_{\bar{x}}$—that is, the ratio of empirical errors in determination of the mean to the estimated standard error of such determinations—likewise does not have a normal distribution. The numerical excess of small values in the denominator leads to an excess of large values, both positive and negative, for this ratio. In short, the all-important tails of improbability are heavier than normal, Under these circumstances, it is no longer valid to say that 95 per cent of the universe of sample means lies within $\pm 1.96 s_{\bar{x}}$ of the mean of the parent universe. The means of more than 5 per cent of the samples lie outside those limits. How many more depends on the precise size of the sample. Hence, if we want to accurately appraise the implications of small samples, we cannot rely on the normal probability table. Indeed, we need a different probability table for each sample size.

A knowledge of advanced calculus is needed to read the equation for *Student's distribution*, which is the basis for these individualized probability distributions. What we can all readily understand is that this equation, like the binomial expansion, gives rise to a different distribution for each value of n. In this case, however, the tails grow heavier as n grows smaller. In order to cut off the outer 5 per cent or the outer 1 per cent of the distribution, we must lop off less of the tails than in the normal distribution; that is, we must use a higher critical value, which gives a cutting point farther from the mean. It is these critical values which are given in the table of t, which may be defined as *the ratio of any statistic to the unbiased estimate of its standard error*. (Compare this to the definition of z, as the ratio of a deviation score to the standard deviation of its own distribution. When we use t instead of z or CR to designate a "critical ratio," we are vouching for the fact that we have eliminated bias from the estimate of the standard error.)

Each row of the t table (see Table III) gives a few selected values from a distribution which, if it were as fully set forth, would take as much space to present as the normal distribution. However, these few critical values suffice for almost all needs. The last row of the table is identical with the critical values of the normal distribution, and serves to remind us that the latter is only a special case of the t distribution, which arises when n is taken as infinite. In order to select the particular t distribution which will fit our need, we must enter the table with the number of degrees of freedom which were available for the computation of the standard error. For a sample of size n, there are $n - 1$ degrees of freedom available for estimating the variance of the universe, and this also represents the correct number of degrees of freedom with which to enter the table. Thus, for example, if we wish to compute the confidence limits for the mean of a sample of 10 scores, we must select a critical factor on row 9 of the table of t.* That is, we must use the value 2.262, instead of 1.960, to determine 5 per cent confidence limits in such a case. Even when $n = 30$, which is often used as the lower limit for "large" samples, critical values are substantially different from those of the normal distribution. Therefore it is becoming increasingly common to use this table even in connection with relatively large samples, up to a size of 100 or more.

We can now define the confidence limits of a sample mean in more general form:

19b] $$\bar{X}_\infty = \bar{X} \pm ts_{\bar{X}}$$

That is, the universe parameter may be assumed to lie within t standard errors of the sample mean, where the value of t is selected with attention both to the sample size and to the amount of risk which is acceptable in the given situation. In order to apply this formula to the problem which was previously used to illustrate Formula 19 (see page 93), we first turn

---

* Some authors use n to represent the degrees of freedom, rather than the sample size. When the symbol n heads a marginal column of the table of t, it is used in this manner.

to the table of t, where we find that the 5 per cent critical value, for $df = 59$, equals 2.00. Therefore,

$$\bar{X}_\infty = 41.68 \pm 2.00 \, (.653),$$

or

$$40.37 < \bar{X}_\infty < 42.99; \quad P = .95$$

The confidence interval is slightly wider than was indicated by the less exact method of Formula 19.

Every use of the t distribution assumes that the sample is drawn from a normal parent distribution. The problems that arise when the parent distribution is not normal have not yet been solved in theory, but sampling experiments (like the one which we shall perform in the next section) have shown that even when a parent distribution is distinctly skewed, the t test gives results which are satisfactory for most practical purposes. This problem will be given fuller consideration in Chapter 13.

THE MONTE CARLO METHOD

Though experience is fallible, it can also be reassuring. The principles of sampling variance are established in theory beyond any need of further proof, but we understand them better, and feel inwardly more convinced about them, when we are able to confirm them in empirical tests. To this end, students have often been required to spend hours tossing coins, in order to demonstrate that heads and tails do truly assort themselves in expected proportions. Similar experiments are performed with dice, with cards, with roulette wheels—in short, with the paraphernalia of any game of chance. Years ago, Karl Pearson, the leading statistician of his generation, used the facilities of the casino at Monte Carlo to check up on the practical validity of statistical generalizations.

All such methods have been outmoded by a modern invention: the table of random numbers. List a few thousand digits in random order (a far more difficult technical feat than it seems at first glance) and you have a kind of numerical modeling clay which can be cast into the most varied forms. Engineering problems which are too complex for theoretical solution and forbiddingly expensive to test by direct trial, often yield to the Monte Carlo method.[4] To facilitate large-scale applications of this method, the RAND Corporation has recently published a volume of 1,000,000 digits, prepared with the help of an electronic equivalent of the old-fashioned roulette-wheel.[5] (See Table XII of the Appendix.)

The Monte Carlo method can also be used to test the validity of a statistical formula. Suppose that we wish to test the practical adequacy of the binomial expansion as a statement of the probabilities in coin-tossing. One way is to toss, toss, toss, and count, count, count, patiently, patiently. Another way is to establish the rule that even digits are to be called "heads," and odd digits "tails." Then, for example, instead of tossing a sample of 5 coins, we count the number of even digits in a series of 5 consecutive digits in the random table. This was done for 320 groups of 5 digits each, representing in all the equivalent of 1600 tosses completed without a bit of grime, with the following results:

Number of "heads" in each group of 5 "tosses"

	0	1	2	3	4	5
Observed	7	47	115	95	47	9
Expected	10	50	100	100	50	10

In Chapter 9 we shall learn an easy way to test whether such discrepancies as those which appear in this experiment are within chance limits. We shall see then that the correspondence of the two series is quite satisfactory, a circumstance which reassures us not only with respect to the validity of the theory on which the expected values are based, but also with respect to the randomness of digits in the RAND Corporation tables. It may seem surprising to the reader that we should so lightly dismiss a discrepancy such as that in the third column, which shows that there were 115 instances of 2 "heads" observed, as against only 100 expected. However, gambling would be no fun if inconsistency were not the rule rather than the exception, and scientific gambles are subjected to the same mathematical hazards as those of the gaming table. This result is satisfactory because it shows evidence of being an "honest gamble." If the correspondence between the empirical result and the theoretical expectation were very close, we would have to assume that the tables we were using were not truly random, and hence did not provide a good model of chance.

We shall now design an experiment of the Monte Carlo type to test the validity of the formula for the sampling variance of the mean. We establish a universe of 1000 members, by agreeing to look upon the table as consisting, not of individual digits, but of three-place numbers. Even though the portion of the table which we use for the experiment may not include every one of the possible three-place numbers, and those that are included are present an unequal number of times, the table still represents a random sample of that universe, since every one of those numbers had an equal chance to be included. For our purposes, these numbers are not quantities, but numerical labels, each of which stands for one element of the universe. Let us pretend that they are the badge numbers of 1000 policemen, and that these men have from one to seven years of seniority on the force of a large city. Let the distribution of seniorities be as given in Table **6.1**.

The experiment consists in taking several series of samples, using a different n for each series, computing the variance of the means of these samples, and comparing this experience with the predicted variances. To

TABLE 6.1

The Universe for a Sampling Experiment to be Conducted in the Table
of Random Numbers

Badge Numbers	f	Seniority
000–024	25	7 years
025–074	50	6 years
075–174	100	5 years
175–349	175	4 years
350–574	225	3 years
575–799	225	2 years
800–999	200	1 year
	1000	

$\bar{X} = 3.00;$ $\sigma^2 = 2.45.$

make the procedure perfectly clear, we shall describe in detail the prepara‑
tion of one such sample, with $n = 10$. The first step is to randomly select
a starting place in Table XII. To do this, I open the table, close my eyes,
and bring the point of my pencil down somewhere near the middle of the
page. Opening my eyes, I read the digits 26 directly in front of the pencil
point, and 66 directly after. Accordingly, the initial digit of my first three-
place numbers is to be sought in Column *26*, Row *66* of the table. Turning
to that place, I find that the first number in the sample is *433*. In the
hypothetical universe of Table 6.1, this is the badge number of a police-
man who has three years seniority. To complete the same, I read the next
nine three-place numbers, which appear vertically below *433*, transforming
each into a seniority score according to the rules of the universe. The mean
of this sample, as it turns out, is 2.6.

Each member of the class should go through this procedure three times,
using three different values of n, which have been agreed upon by the class.
The results should then be assembled into three distributions. Each of
these will be a distribution of sample means, which should have a variance
not too far from what would be predicted by Formula 19. We should not
expect a close correspondence, but if the n's are not too much alike, the
three variances should show a clear trend. (n's of 10, 20, and 40 should
work satisfactorily.)

Whatever the results of the class experiment, we can be sure of this:
they are statistics of samples, and therefore they are in error. Before
drawing pessimistic conclusions about the futility of statistical methods,
let us extend the experiment through another stage. Each student should
make three statements of confidence limits for the mean of the parent
universe, basing each one on the results of one of his own samples. When
the results for the class are assembled, it will be seen that in almost every
case the confidence limits embrace the true value, which in this case is

known to us. If the 5 per cent confidence level has been used, it is the theoretical expectation that one sample in 20 shall be misleading. Therefore, the most desirable outcome of the experiment is that a few individuals in the class should be led into error by their samples. We do not want to be allowed to forget the eternal fallibility of experience.

The over-all result should convince us that statistical formulas can provide useful guides to decision, even though the information in a sample does not lead to a single firm conclusion. The data of one sample can be used to support an infinite number of hypotheses regarding the mean of the parent universe, but they also enable us to establish a distribution of probabilities for these hypotheses. The confidence limits are critical points in this distribution of hypotheses. They encourage us to consider some values as likely and to reject others, which lie in the "tails of improbability," as unlikely. We cut these tails long or short, according to the amount of risk which we are willing to assume in the situation.

PROBLEMS

1. *In the illustration on page 97, we computed the 5 per cent confidence limits for the mean score of a group of school counselors on a test for personal characteristics of counselors. Find the 1 per cent limits for that group.*

2. *The same authors*[1] *report that a group of 60 noncounselor teachers who took the same test had a mean of 27.98, with* $\sigma = 6.82$. *Find the 5 per cent and 1 per cent confidence limits for the universe of this sample.*

3. *Draw a figure illustrating the relationship between the universe of means inferred from the scores of the counselor group, and that inferred from the scores of the noncounselors.*

4. *Find* σ^2 *for each distribution of sample means gathered in the class sampling experiment, and compare these values with the theoretical expectations established by Formula 18.*

5. *For each of your own samples, find both* σ^2 *and* s^2. *Assembling these results for the class, which method gives the better set of estimates of the variance of the parent universe?*

REFERENCES

1. Cottle, W. C., Lewis, W. W., Jr., and Penney, M. M. Personal characteristics of counselors: III. An experimental scale. *J. of counseling Psychol.*, 1954, **1**:74–77.

2. Fisher, R. A. The fiducial argument in statistical inference. *Annals of Eugenics*, 1935, **6**:391–398.

3. Neyman, J. Fiducial argument and the theory of confidence intervals. *Biometrika*, 1941, **32**:128–150.

4. McCracken, D. D. The Monte Carlo method. *Scientific Amer.*, 1955, **192**:90–97.

5. RAND Corporation. *A million random digits with 100,000 normal deviates.* Glencoe, Illinois: Free Press, 1955.

7

COMPARISON OF TWO MEANS

The most direct test of the effectiveness of an experimental variable is to compare the representative scores of two groups which differ with respect to this variable, and in no other nonchance way. Since it is too much to hope that chance differences between the groups have been eliminated, a statistical analysis of the results is required. When we are able to reject the null hypothesis that the observed difference between the groups is wholly due to chance, we conclude that it is *significant*. As used in a statistical context, this word is not a synonym of "important," but of *trustworthy* or *replicable*. It is a frustrating truth that many inconsequential facts are labeled as "very significant" by statistical procedures, while apparently important relationships must be dismissed as "not significant" because they elude our efforts to demonstrate them by experimental methods. However, a sound knowledge of statistics should not only protect us against assuming significance where it is absent, but it should also help us to plan our experiments in such a way as to improve the chance that we may be able to earn for our pet theories the coveted badge, "very significant."

COMPARISON OF PAIRED SCORES

Under certain conditions, the sampling variance of a single mean, which was used in the last chapter to establish confidence intervals, can also be used to test whether an experimental treatment has influenced a set of scores. This would be the case if we were to compare the scores of identical twins, with one twin of each pair being placed in the experimental group, and the other in the control group, in order to eliminate "noise" which might be caused by genetic differences. In analyzing the results of an investigation in which this method of twin control has been used, we only need to consider the differences between the twins in each pair, for these *difference scores* contain all the information relative to the experimental variable. The confidence interval for the mean difference sums up this information in an effective manner. If both the upper and lower limits of the confidence interval have the same algebraic sign, this amounts to a statement that in replications of the experiment the difference, whether great or small, will consistently favor the same group. We must therefore reject the null hypothesis that the experimental variable is without influence on the scores.

Any sort of "twinning" procedure leads to a logically similar situation. For example, in studying the effects of a drug it is a common practice to use the same subjects in both experimental and control groups. A given subject receives the drug on one day and a placebo on another day, without knowing which capsule contains the active ingredient. In this manner individual differences in suggestibility, as well as differences in susceptibility to the drug, are controlled. There would be more room for error in a comparison of the effect of the drug on Subject A, and of the placebo on Subject B, than in the difference score which represents a comparison of the effects of the drug and the placebo on the same subject.

If we wish to study vocabulary-test performance of boys and girls, we might compare fairly large samples of both sexes, at the same age and grade level. Two principle sources of error in such a comparison would be the cultural level of the home and the influence of older siblings on language development. Both would be controlled if we had available a number of brother-sister pairs of fraternal twins. A sex comparison based on relatively small samples of this kind might be more informing than one based on large samples of unrelated boys and girls.

In each of these illustrations, there exists a relationship between the two series of observations which determines in an unambiguous manner that each certain element in one series is to be paired with one certain element in the other series. This natural pairing carries with it the implication that some of the chance factors which influence the scores act similarly on both members of each pair. This eliminates some of the experimental error which would be present in a comparison of two sets of scores, disregarding the pair-relationships.

In practice, we do not ordinarily establish confidence limits for the mean difference within pairs. The customary procedure is to list the difference scores and to find their mean and the estimate of the standard deviation for the universe of the sample. This permits us to establish the ratio,

20]
$$t = \frac{\bar{D}}{s_{\bar{D}}}$$

Here, as always, t is the ratio of a statistic to the unbiased estimate of its standard error—a ratio of information to error. Let us turn to an illustration of this procedure.

THE ROSE-TINTED SPECTACLES

When we see a mutilated person, our emotional response inhibits our recognition of the amount of mutilation. This is a special aspect of an old problem, that we tend to shut our eyes against unpleasant sights. Wittreich and Radcliffe[1] demonstrated this effect in an interesting manner, by fitting their subjects with spectacles which were ground so as to induce distortion of the visual field. This "fitting" was done for each subject under two conditions: while viewing either a normal person or one whose dangling sleeve and blinkered eye made him seem the victim of a double mutilation. Table 7.1 gives a score for each subject under each of these conditions. Each of these scores is the mean of several determinations of the amount of induced distortion which was necessary before the subject perceived that some sort of distortion had taken place in the visual field.

Since we have paired scores, we may test the efficacy of the experimental condition in terms of the ratio of the mean difference to the standard error of the mean difference. We first list the scores, by pairs. Then comes a column of D scores, which show the difference between the two conditions, for each subject. (Notice that it is necessary to indicate the direction of the difference. When the second listed score exceeds the first, we show this as a negative difference. A moment's thought will show that since we are investigating the consistency of a trend, the direction of each difference is important as well as its magnitude. If Tom sleeps 4 hours *more* after taking a dose of a certain sedative, and Bill sleeps 4 hours *less* under the same conditions, $\Sigma D = 0$, not 8.) In the last column, the differences are squared. At the bottom of the table, the computation is shown for the mean difference and for the variance of the mean difference, and also for t, which in this case is the ratio of the mean difference to the standard error of the mean difference.

To interpret the result, we turn to the table of t, which we enter with degrees of freedom one less than the number of pairs or difference scores. Since the empirical value of t is higher than the critical value shown for $P = .01$, we reject the null hypothesis, concluding that there is less than one chance in 100 that what has been reported is merely a chance result.

Notice that there are two equivalent procedures for carrying out this test. (1) We can select a desired level of probability and, using the corresponding critical value of t, compute the confidence interval for the mean difference. This leads to a conclusion in the form that there are 95 chances

TABLE 7.1

Differences in Thresholds for Perception of Distortion, When Viewing a
Normal and a Mutilated Person: Computation of t*

Sj	Mean Threshold Mutilated condition	Normal condition	D	D^2
1	3.08	2.41	0.67	0.449
2	3.92	2.66	1.26	1.588
3	3.67	2.50	1.17	1.369
4	4.67	4.83	−0.16	0.026
5	4.08	3.16	0.92	0.846
6	5.58	5.50	0.08	0.006
7	4.25	1.66	2.59	6.708
8	1.58	1.41	0.17	0.029
9	1.50	1.25	0.25	0.062
10	2.00	1.58	0.42	0.176
11	2.75	2.25	0.50	0.250
12	8.91	7.50	1.41	1.988
Sums	45.99	36.71	9.28	13.497

$$\bar{D} = \frac{\Sigma D}{n} = \frac{9.28}{12} = 0.77$$

$$s^2_{\bar{D}} = \frac{\Sigma x^2}{n(n-1)} = \frac{\Sigma D^2 - \frac{(\Sigma D)^2}{n}}{12\,(11)}$$

$$= \frac{13.497 - (9.28)^2/12}{132} = .0478$$

$$t = \frac{\bar{D}}{s_{\bar{D}}} = \frac{0.77}{\sqrt{.0478}} = \frac{0.77}{0.218} = 3.53; \quad df = 11, \quad P < .01.$$

*Based on Wittreich and Radcliffe.[1]

in 100 that in a replication of the experiment on an exhaustive scale the
experimental effect would be at least as great as the difference indicated
by the lower limit of the confidence interval. In this case we talk of "confidence," and not of "significance." (2) Instead of this, we can compute
the value of t, and then by reference to Table III determine the corresponding probability level. Then our conclusion takes the form that "there
are so many chances in 100 that an exhaustive replication of the experiment would show *some* experimental effect, however slight, in the observed

direction." In this case we speak of "significance," not "confidence." The latter is the more usual procedure, but it should be clear that it is not necessarily the most useful one under all circumstances.

It is convenient to have a single formula which combines all of the steps which are involved in testing the significance of a difference between paired scores. Such a formula is the following:

21] $$t^2 = \frac{(n - 1)(\Sigma D)^2}{n \Sigma D^2 - (\Sigma D)^2}$$

In the present problem, this gives us:

$$t^2 = \frac{11 \ (9.28)^2}{12 \ (13.497) - (9.28)^2} = 12.5$$

If the result is to be evaluated by the table of t, it is still necessary to take the square root of t^2. However, we also have a convenient table of t^2, although it does not go by that name. If the reader will turn to the table of F (Table V), which will not otherwise be the object of our attention until Chapter 8, he can easily verify that the entries in the first column of the table are the squares of corresponding entries in the table of t. This implies that just as the normal distribution is a special case of t, so t is a special case of F. Therefore the significance of t^2 can be evaluated by comparing it with the entries in the first column of the F table, choosing the appropriate row exactly as one would in the table of t.

STATEMENTS OF SIGNIFICANCE

The conventional form in which we make statements of significance concerning the outcome of experimental investigations is determined by the logic of the null hypothesis. The simplest scientific experiment consists of two series of observations taken under conditions which are in most respects as alike as we can make them, but in one respect are different. This deliberately planned differentiating factor is called the experimental variable or the experimental treatment, or the independent variable. We make every reasonable effort to keep other influences constant for the two groups, but we are aware that nevertheless there will be other, "chance" differences. The experiment is designed to test an experimental hypothesis, that the deliberately arranged difference will influence the outcome, as shown by the scores on the dependent variable. The role of statistical analysis is to determine, first of all, whether the uncontrolled factors may not have been responsible for whatever difference is observed. Thus, the statistical analysis is not directed toward the experimental hypothesis, but toward a null hypothesis, which is its converse. What we test is the hypothesis that the outcome may reasonably be regarded as the result of chance influences, and hence that it gives no assurance that the experimental treatment has had any measurable effect. From this point of view, a significant result is one of *low* chance probability, and it leads to *rejection* of the hypothesis being tested.

The decision to accept or reject the null hypothesis is always on the probability level which attaches to some statistic representing a ratio between the apparent strength of the experimental and chance influences. Thus, in the ratio $t = \bar{D}/s_{\bar{D}}$, the numerator, or mean difference, reflects the apparent strength of the condition which differentiates the two sets of observations, while the denominator, the standard error of the mean difference, characterizes the distribution of results which might be expected to occur by chance, when the assessment of the strength of chance influences is derived from the observed lack of consistency among the differences. It is the work of mathematical statisticians to attach probability figures to such ratios. Their conclusions are summarized in tables, which we consult.

Table **7**.2 is an abbreviated table of t, which is unconventional in form

TABLE **7**.2

An Abbreviated Table of t

df	$P > .05$	$P = .05$	$P < .05$	$P = .01$	$P < .01$
5		2.57		4.03	
10		2.23		3.17	
15		2.13		2.95	
20		2.09		2.84	
25		2.06		2.79	
30		2.04		2.75	

because we have included headings for what are usually only intercolumnar spaces. The precise value of t which we find in any problem will rarely coincide with any of the tabled values, and hence we must think of it as falling into one of those spaces. On each row, t values *in*crease from left to right, but the corresponding P values, which appear in the headings, *de*crease from left to right. Although the intercolumnar headings do not appear in the conventional table, it is in these terms that our conclusions must almost always be stated. The value of t can be interpreted as fixing a precise probability level for the observed result, but we do not ordinarily concern ourselves with that. We content ourselves with reporting that the probability is above or below a certain level. Table **7**.3 shows the different forms in which the results of a statistical test of significance may be reported, and the meanings thus conveyed.

TABLE 7.3

The Form and the Substance of Statements of Significance

| The Form | | The Substance | |
Mathematical	Verbal	Null hypothesis	Experimental hypothesis
$P > .05$	Not significant	Accepted	Disproved
$P < .05$	Significant	Rejected	Supported
$P < .01$	Very significant	Rejected	Supported

COMPARING MEANS OF INDEPENDENT SAMPLES

Although the t ratio has many uses, we meet it most often in tests which deal with the difference between the means of two independent samples— that is, samples which are chosen by separate processes of randomization. In order to fully understand its application to this situation, we shall have to imagine still another kind of hypothetical universe. Before doing that, let us look at the problem in its concrete aspect, and consider how we might deal with it on the basis of what we already know.

Table 7.4 reports the performance norms of eighth-grade boys and girls, in a certain small city, on the Differential Aptitude Tests (DAT). The data are taken from the test manual. Using the methods described in the preceding chapter, we can establish a confidence interval for each mean

TABLE 7.4

Scores of Eighth-grade Boys and Girls on the DAT (Differential Aptitude Tests), as Given in the Test Manual.*

| Subtest | Boys $n = 166$ | | Girls $n = 179$ | |
	X̄	σ	X̄	σ
Verbal reasoning	16.1	7.8	16.4	8.0
Numerical ability	14.6	7.2	15.5	7.5
Abstract reasoning	23.4	11.0	21.6	11.9
Space relations	35.4	22.4	30.7	19.6
Mechanical reasoning	30.6	11.5	18.9	9.6
Clerical speed and accuracy	44.7	8.7	51.1	9.2

* Based on Table 26 of Bennett, Seashore, and Wesman.[2]

score in this table. For example, the 5 per cent confidence interval for the mean verbal reasoning score of the boys equals

$$16.1 \pm 1.96 \,(7.8)/\sqrt{165} = 16.1 \pm 1.2$$

For three of the subtests, the confidence intervals which would thus be established are as follows:

Subtest	5 per cent Confidence Intervals	
	Boys	Girls
Verbal reasoning	14.9–17.3	15.2–17.6
Mechanical reasoning	28.8–32.4	17.5–20.3
Space relations	32.0–38.8	27.8–33.6

Because the confidence intervals for the verbal reasoning subtest overlap so extensively, we would have no hesitation about dismissing the slight advantage of the girls over the boys as a chance effect. On the other hand, because there is no overlap between the confidence intervals for mechanical reasoning, we can feel practically certain that the marked superiority of the boys reflects a real difference between the two populations. In other words, apparently the first difference is a matter of sampling variance but the second is not. It is more difficult to reach a decision regarding ability in space relations. In this case it is conceivable that the population mean for the girls (which we shall symbolize thus: $\bar{G}_\infty$) is as high as that for the boys ($\bar{B}_\infty$). Figure 7.1 shows the probability distribution of the universe of means for each group. The shaded portions of each curve lie outside the 5 per cent confidence interval.

At first glance, one might suppose that this problem is open to direct solution by the law of compound probability. If we take the value midway between the lower limit of the confidence limit for $\bar{B}_\infty$ and the upper limit of the confidence limit for $\bar{G}_\infty$, we can easily compute the likelihood that the mean for the boys falls below this point, and the likelihood that the mean for the girls falls above it. (This is the point indicated by the arrow in Figure 7.1.) The product of these two probability values would give the likelihood that simultaneously the mean for boys would fall below this point and the mean for girls above it. However, we have not taken into account the fact that the population mean for girls may exceed that for boys even though both are greater than this arbitrary value, or both are less than this value. Therefore, another approach is necessary.

Actually, we already have a formula to meet this situation. We only need to understand the situation clearly in order to see how the formula applies to it. Let us recall our first statement of the variance law:

$$\sigma^2_{A+B} = \sigma^2_A + \sigma^2_B$$

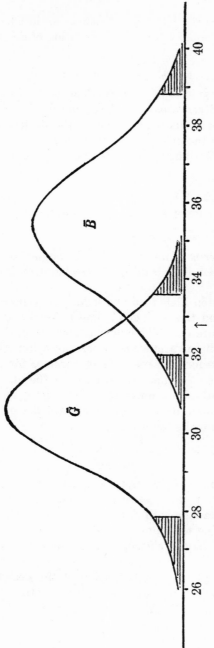

Fig. 7.1. The hypothetical universe of sample means, for Boys and for Girls, on the Space Relations test. Shaded portions of each probability surface lie outside the 5 per cent confidence interval for the mean.

If the reader will review the proof of this equation, in Chapter 4, he will see that it would apply equally well to a population of differences, instead of sums. That is,

22]
$$\sigma^2_{A-B} = \sigma^2_A + \sigma^2_B$$

The variance of a universe of differences equals the sum of the separate variances of the two parent distributions. (If the reader díd Problem 3, page 70, he has already confirmed this relationship in the illustration which was used in connection with the proof of the variance law.)

When each parent distribution is a distribution of sample means, the formula becomes:

22a]
$$\sigma^2_{\bar{A}-\bar{B}} = \sigma^2_{\bar{A}} + \sigma^2_{\bar{B}}$$

We meet this formula more often in the following form:

22b]
$$s_{\bar{X}_1-\bar{X}_2} = \sqrt{s^2_{\bar{X}_1} + s^2_{\bar{X}_2}}$$

In words: *the standard error of an obtained difference between sample means is equal to the square root of the sum of the estimated variances for the two distributions of means.*

This brings us one step higher on the ladder of hypotheses which we have been climbing, and this is a good time to review its construction, rung by rung. (See Figure 7.2.) The ladder is planted on the firm earth of an empirical sample, whose variance is a fact, not a hypothesis. The first step up the ladder is to form an estimate of variance for the universe of the sample. Next comes an estimated variance for the universe of means. Still climbing, we hypothesize a universe of differences among hypothetical means, and we estimate its variance. This provides us with the error term, or denominator, for the following ratio:

23]
$$t = \frac{\bar{X}_1 - \bar{X}_2}{s_{\bar{X}_1-\bar{X}_2}}$$

In order to interpret this ratio, we must know how many degrees of freedom are associated with it. But there's a rub! When the two samples have been drawn from populations with different variances, it is a rather complex matter to determine the number of degrees of freedom with which to enter the t table. We have a choice, therefore, among several courses of action:

(1) We can make a precise determination of the degrees of freedom, using an involved formula which we relegate to a footnote, and which we shall not attempt to explain.* (In the present problem, this yields $df = 330$.)

$$* \quad df = \frac{[(s^2_1/n_1) + (s^2_2/n_2)]^2}{\dfrac{(s^2_1/n_1)^2}{n_1 + 1} + \dfrac{(s^2_2/n_2)^2}{n_2 + 1}} - 2$$

Cf. Welch[3].

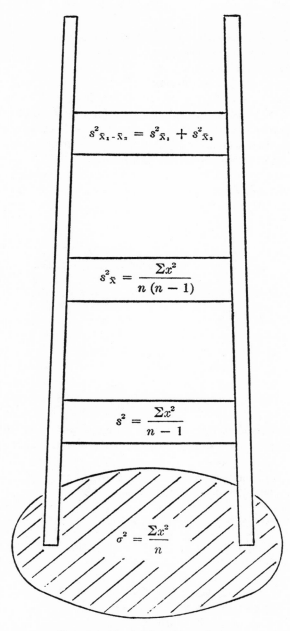

FIG. **7**.2. The ladder of hypotheses.

(2) We can restate the null hypothesis to include an assumption that the two populations have like variance. We shall study the implications of this course of action in the following section.

(3) We can acknowledge the approximate nature of our solution by labelling the ratio as z, that is, by regarding it as drawn from a normal universe, so that it can be interpreted by reference to the table of normal probability. This may be very misleading when small samples are involved, but it is admissible whenever both samples are large, as in the present case, and it is the course which we shall follow.

We are now able to fix the probability that $\bar{G}_\infty > \bar{B}_\infty$ in the problem which we have been considering. The following tabular scheme is a convenient way to organize the necessary work, when the sample $\bar{X}$ and σ are already known:

Sample	n	$\bar{X}$	σ	$s^2_{\bar{X}}$
Boys	166	35.4	22.4	3.02
Girls	179	30.7	19.6	2.15
	345	4.7		5.17

$$z = \frac{\bar{X}_B - \bar{X}_G}{\sqrt{s^2_{\bar{X}_B} + s^2_{\bar{X}_G}}} = \frac{4.7}{\sqrt{5.17}} = 2.07$$

$$P < .05$$

The result implies that it is unlikely, judging from the information in hand, that an exhaustive test of this comparison would lead to a different conclusion. We would expect future experience to confirm the finding that the representative score for boys is higher than that for girls. Hence, we call the means "significantly" different.

Assuming Homogeneous Variance

We have used a critical ratio to test the hypothesis that there is no difference between the means of the universes from which two random samples have been drawn. Furthermore, we have interpreted the result by means of a probability table which imposes another condition, amounting to an elaboration of the null hypothesis: that the two universes are alike in that both have normal form. This restriction is less crippling than one might suppose, because unless the parent universe is very unusual in form, the universe of sample means will be approximately normal even for moderate values of n. One further condition which is usually imposed is that the two parent universes have the same variance. At this point, having asserted that they have the same mean, the same shape, and the same variance, we have in effect said that they are the same universe. (Not, in our previous example, that boys are girls, but that the *scores* of boys and the *scores* of girls form a common universe.)

Such a thorough-going application of the null hypothesis calls for a refinement of method. If we are truly dealing with samples from one universe, it is logical that we should pool all of our information in a single estimate of its variance, rather than employ two separate estimates. This pooling of information, to obtain a single unbiased estimate of the universe variance, is effected by the following formula:

24]
$$s^2 = \frac{\Sigma x^2_1 + \Sigma x^2_2}{n_1 + n_2 - 2}$$

An estimate which is formed in this way gives proper weight to the data of each sample in forming a single estimate. To make use of this improved estimate, we compute the t ratio thus:

25]
$$t = \frac{\bar{X}_1 - \bar{X}_2}{\sqrt{\dfrac{s^2}{n_1} + \dfrac{s^2}{n_2}}}$$

When $n_1 = n_2$ the value of the ratio is identical with that of the procedure followed in the preceding section. However, whether the n's are like or unlike, large or small, it is now possible to determine the degrees of freedom without involved computation, because for this ratio $df = n_1 + n_2 - 2$.

It is sometimes convenient to have a single formula which permits us to vault directly from the sample data to the t ratio, without climbing, as it were, rung by rung up the ladder. Here is one form which such a formula can take, for the comparison of means of independent samples, when homogeneity of variance is also assumed:

25a]
$$t^2 = \frac{n_1 n_2 (\bar{X}_1 - \bar{X}_2)^2}{\Sigma x^2_1 + \Sigma x^2_2} \cdot \frac{n_1 + n_2 - 2}{n_1 + n_2}$$

Notice that this formula, like Formula 21, is stated in terms of t^2. This means that critical values will be found in the first column of the F table, as explained on page 105. Another point to notice about this formula is that there is no need to compute the correction factor, which is given separately at the right, unless the value in the ratio at the left passes the critical level. Since the correction for bias will always reduce the value of t^2, it need not be computed at all if a partial computation shows that t^2 cannot attain a significant value.

To use Formula 25a, one must first compute sample means and sums of squares. A cookbook formula, calling for sums of scores and sums of squared scores, can take this form:

25b]
$$t^2 = \frac{n_1 n_2 \left(\frac{\Sigma X_1}{n_1} - \frac{\Sigma X_2}{n_2}\right)^2}{\Sigma X^2_1 + \Sigma X^2_2 - \left[\frac{(\Sigma X_1)^2}{n_1} + \frac{(\Sigma X_2)^2}{n_2}\right]} \cdot \frac{n_1 + n_2 - 2}{n_1 + n_2}$$

When the two samples are of like size, n, this can be much simplified:

25c]
$$t^2 = \frac{(\Sigma X_1 - \Sigma X_2)^2}{\Sigma X^2_1 + \Sigma X^2_2 - \left[\frac{(\Sigma X_1)^2 + (\Sigma X_2)^2}{n}\right]} \cdot \frac{n - 1}{n}$$

where, of course, df equals $2n - 2$.

We shall illustrate Formula 25a by applying it to the problem that was solved on page 112. Notice that in this solution we shall obtain the sum of squares for each sample by taking n times the mean square, or variance. The computations will be set forth only with the degree of accuracy which is attainable by a casual use of the slide-rule.

$$t^2 = \frac{(166)(179)(4.7)^2}{166\,(22.4)^2 + 179\,(19.6)^2} \cdot \frac{343}{345}$$

$$= \frac{657,000\,(343)}{152,000\,(345)} = 4.3; \quad \text{whence} \quad t = 2.07$$

Table **7**.5 illustrates the use of Formula 25c by applying it to the data of Table **2**.3, which are repeated in the first columns of Table **7**.5. Notice in this case that we first compute sums of scores and sums of squared scores in transformed values, and that this greatly reduces the size of the numbers which must be handled.

THE ONE-TAILED TEST

The usual test of the null hypothesis makes no assumptions regarding the direction of the effect which will betray the operation of the experimental variable. We think in terms of a null hypothesis which states flatly, "no difference," and we are prepared to accept a difference in either direction as calling for its rejection. The critical value which is employed in such a test, at the 5 per cent level of significance, cuts off 2.5 per cent of the probability surface in each tail of the distribution. This is called a *two-tailed test* of significance.

Sometimes, however, the experimental hypothesis is of such a nature that it would be considered disproved even though there were a substantial difference in one direction. If, for example, we assert that Frenchmen are more excitable than Englishmen, and test the null hypothesis that there

TABLE 7.5

Illustrating the Computation of t for Two Samples of Like Size. Data Represent "Hostility" Scores for Men and Women.

X	f_M	f_W	x'	$f_M x'$	$f_M x'^2$	$f_W x'$	$f_W x'^2$
13	1	0	6	6	36		
12	0	0	5				
11	0	0	4				
10	3	1	3	9	27	3	9
9	4	2	2	8	16	4	8
8	1	2	1	·1	1	2	2
7	1	0	0	0	0		
6	1	1	−1	−1	1	−1	1
5	0	3	−2			−6	12
4	0	1	−3			−3	9
3	0	0	−4				
2	0	0	−5				
1	0	1	−6			−6	36
0	1	1	−7	−7	49	−7	49
Sums	12	12		16	131	−14	126

Applying Formula 25c, which is equally applicable to raw scores or transformed scores:

$$t^2 = \frac{[16 - (-14)]^2}{131 + 126 - \dfrac{16^2 + 14^2}{12}} \cdot \frac{11}{12} = \frac{11\,(900)}{12\,(219.3)}$$

$$= 3.76; \quad df = 22, \quad P > .05.$$

$$t = \sqrt{3.76} = 1.94.$$

is really no difference between them in this respect, it is not a matter of indifference whether Frenchmen or Englishmen make higher scores on the test we use. If it turns out that Englishmen make higher scores for excitability, the experimental hypothesis is disproved even though the null hypothesis is rejected. Since our real interest is in the experimental hypothesis, not in the null hypothesis, some sort of allowance should be made for this type of situation.

We do this by making a *one-tailed test* of significance. That is, we employ a critical value which cuts off 5 per cent (or 1 per cent) of the probability surface under a single tail. These values appear as the 10 per cent and 2 per cent points in tables of probability which are designed primarily for two-tailed tests.

We can justify the use of a one-tailed test only if we can show that the choice of this method was not a matter of opportunism, but was logically required by the nature of the problem being investigated. This is not the case when we simply make a preliminary guess that the result will run one way rather than the other. For in such a case, finding ourselves mistaken, we may simply think up reasons why the guess was wrong and perhaps even forget to mention it in an account of the experiment. The one-tailed test is justified when it is applied to a prediction, or better to a series of predictions, which derive logically from a clearly formulated theory. In this case, it is not so much the prediction which is at stake as the theory, and a result contrary to the prediction is even more damaging to the theory than one which sustains the null hypothesis.

As an example of such a situation we may cite Child's[4] study of Sheldon's theory of relationships between physique and temperament. Child administered a specially designed personality inventory to a large group of college men who had previously been somatotyped by Sheldon's method. He made 96 predictions about the outcomes of specific items. Any significant relationship running contrary to the prediction (there was but one) was classed as a "disconfirmation." Under these conditions, it is logical to use a one-tailed test of significance.

When using a one-tailed test, one must be rather more cautious than ordinarily about violating the assumption of normality in the parent universe. One reason why the normal table of probability gives fairly satisfactory results in connection with the sampling of skewed distributions is that the skewed distribution of sample means will lose from one tail about as much as it gains in the other. When we make a one-tailed test we cannot count on this compensating effect.

THE SOCIAL CLIMATE OF SIGNIFICANCE

The rejection of the null hypothesis does not always justify a cry of "Eureka!" It tells us that an event of low chance probability has taken place, if the assumptions of the statistical test were reasonably fulfilled. We must restrain our enthusiasm long enough to entertain a few sobering considerations.

Was the sample reasonably random? Truly random samples do not exist except in theory. The engineers of the RAND Corporation found that even their electronic computer, when they had instructed it to produce an endless series of random digits, would drift into a display of preferences after perhaps 100,000 digits. How difficult it is to avoid selectivity of experience which vitiates conclusions that are based on ideal theorems!

Next we ask the closely allied question: whether the universe of the sample is properly comparable to the target population to which the conclusion will be generalized. The statistical formulas do not deal with this question, and often it is rather inaccessible to experimental testing. It is certain that lack of normality in the parent distributions, lack of homogeneity in their variances, and many other such faults do not have nearly so much damaging effect as carelessness and unavoidable systematic influences in sampling.

Has the obtained value of P been reduced (so that its apparent significance has been heightened) by eliminating some of the "lost chances" from the record? This question does not imply wilful dishonesty in reporting results. However, it frequently happens that in the course of a single investigation the same hypothesis will be subjected to several more or less parallel tests, each of which leads to its own P value. These values are not independent in their implications. It is clear that when there are 20 such tests, one can be expected to reach the 5 per cent level of significance by chance, just as in a sampling experiment. If this is so, must we not be more severe in judging one test of even two or three? Therefore, whenever multiple tests have been made, we expect them all to be reported. It is proper, nevertheless, to compute an independent probability for each. (The evaluation of their joint probability, if they are truly independent, will be considered in Chapter 9.)

Even if the particular report deals with only one test of a single hypothesis, it must be considered against the background of ongoing research by others. The negative results which these workers obtain are rarely deemed worthy of publication; positive results are rarely suppressed by modesty. If we assume that about one research project in two brings positive results—that is, the confirmation of the experimental hypothesis—it follows that about 1 in 10 of those that are published represents a chance result satisfying the 1-in-20 criterion of significance. In a field in which a good deal of active research is going on (say, for example, investigation of the personality correlates of the California F-Scale), we must expect that a fair proportion of the published "successes" are the products of chance.

It is possible, but not economical, to protect ourselves against being misled in these ways by insisting on higher levels of significance. If we insist on a 1 per cent level, or a 0.1 per cent level, we increase the expense of conducting research, in time, money, and effort. Viewing the whole field of psychological research as a socially concerted program, it is better to accept the risk of occasional errors than to invite the paralysis of compulsive perfectionism, which has as its monument exhaustive unpublished treatises on outdated problems. It is true that a more severe criterion reduces the chance that the null hypothesis will be rejected and the experimental hypothesis confirmed, when these conclusions are in fact mistaken. (Such an error is called an error of Type I.) But it simultaneously increases the chance that we will accept the null hypothesis and say "nothing proved," when it should in fact be rejected. (This is called an error of Type II. The distinction between these errors will be discussed more extensively in Chapter 13.) People who never make a mistake end up by never doing anything worthwhile—when they do not end up in institutions. A rigid insistence on strict criteria is the road to scientific catatonia.

There is one simple way to satisfy all the varied considerations in this section. Experimental replication, or cross-validation, provides an economical means of detecting systematic sampling errors and chance results. Ideally, cross-validating replications of all experiments which yield statistically significant results should be carried out with all nonessential conditions changed: by a different investigator, in a different city, with subjects somewhat differently selected. There is increasing recognition that some form of replication provides the only effective defense against the accumulation of experimental errors.

PROBLEMS

1. *Using the data of Table* **7.**4, *page 107, test the null hypothesis for each subtest of the DAT. State the level of significance of the results in each case.*

2. *College students who are enrolled in different major sequences generally exhibit different interest patterns. Magill[5] has shown that this is also true of students who engage in different forms of extracurricular activity. Table* **7.**6 *gives the means and standard deviations of scores on the various dimen-*

TABLE 7.6

Means and Standard Deviations of Kuder Preference Record Scores for College Students Who Engage in Difference Types of Extracurricular Activity*

	Activity groups					
	Publication		*Religious*		*Athletic*	
Interest	$n = 78$		$n = 43$		$n = 218$	
Dimension	$\bar{X}$	σ	$\bar{X}$	σ	$\bar{X}$	σ
Mechanical	68.6	23.0	58.0	21.6	72.5	19.3
Commercial	33.5	13.2	32.5	12.8	34.2	12.4
Scientific	68.9	19.6	61.4	19.6	67.2	16.0
Persuasive	79.1	16.4	78.6	19.8	72.7	18.7
Artistic	42.3	12.8	39.8	13.7	47.6	15.3
Literary	58.5	17.4	53.8	18.0	46.3	12.3
Musical	20.6	9.8	20.3	9.6	17.2	9.0
Social Service	69.9	20.8	81.0	26.7	73.9	19.0
Clerical	46.7	15.2	50.6	13.1	48.2	13.1

* Based on Magill.[5]

sions of the Kuder Preference Record, for students who are active in college publications, those active in campus religious organizations, and those active in athletics. Find some significant differences, considering only two groups at a time.

3. *Miller*[6] *studied the frequency of interpolation errors, when subjects were required to estimate, in tenths, the position of a mark placed inside an interval indicated by two short vertical lines (an interpolation similar to that which is required when attempting to read the third significant figure in the answer to a problem worked on the slide-rule). Table* **7.7** *reproduces the results for 2 intervals. Does either of these intervals lead to significantly more frequent errors than the other?*

TABLE **7.7**

Frequency of Errors in Linear Interpolation, for 520 Judgments at Each of Two Intervals*

Subject	3 mm.	5 mm.	Subject	3 mm.	5 mm.
RH	1	2	EH	11	26
FH	0	2	ME	21	17
GD	0	0	JC	43	10
LO	0	3	WM	25	33
RD	11	0	HM	26	24
FB	4	4	DS	29	18
HK	4	1	ES	66	45
RR	16	2	FL	36	32
GB	6	0	BH	74	45
FF	8	6	WJ	91	90
BG	16	15			

* Data from Miller.[6]

REFERENCES

1. Wittreich, W. J., and Radcliffe, K. B., Jr. The influence of simulated mutilation upon the perception of the human figure. *J. abn. soc. Psychol.*, 1955, **51**:493–495.

2. Bennett, G. K., Seashore, H. G., and Wesman, A. G. *Differential Aptitude Tests: Manual.* 3rd ed. New York: The Psychological Corporation, 1959.

3. Welch, E. L. The generalization of "Student's" problem when several different population variances are involved. *Biometrika*, 1947, **34**:28–35.

4. Child, I. L. The relation of somatotype to self-ratings on Sheldon's temperamental traits. *J. Personality*, 1950, **18**:440–453.

5. Magill, J. W. Interest profiles of college activity groups. *J. appl. Psychol.*, 1955, **39**:53–56.

6. Miller, J. K., Jr. An exploratory study of linear interpolation. *J. appl. Psychol.*, 1950, **34**:367–370.

THIRD INTERLUDE

A BIT OF POESY

"Euclid alone has looked on beauty bare." Some who are not his disciples prefer to see her clothed in metric verse. For their amusement, the essential characteristics of the test for the significance of a difference between the means of independent groups are summarized in this interlude. Some of the meanings intended in the third stanza will not be evident before a reading of Chapter 8.

The Standard Error of a Difference

Here, by the grace of Chance, we've staked a Mean,
Uncertain marker of elusive Truth.
But have we caught a fact, or trapped a doubt
Within this stretching span of confidence—
A shadow world four standard errors wide,
All swollen by the stint of observation?
For recollect that once in twenty times
The phantom Truth will even lie byond
That span, in the unending thin-drawn tails
Which point to the infinitude of Error.

Here stands another Mean, an unlike twin,
Another child of planless Chance,
Different, as sons are differently cast
By random sorting of the parent genes.
Yet different too, it may be, by Design,
By treatments planned to conquer Chance
And weight the rolling dice in divers ways
To part these Means, as true twins may be parted
Despite a likeness in heredity
By greater strength of circumstance.

Which is the stronger variance? *Within*
The scores are tumbled by unreckoned factors;
Between, there is the mirroring of these
Plus what Design has added. We make this test:
The standard error of the difference,
Extracted from the sum of variances
Within these twin-tossed congeries of Chance,
Is matched against the difference *between*.
If twice outdone, Chance has lost the contest
To Design. We shout exultant, *It's a Fact!*

But still we're cautioned by those ominous tails,
Which point to Error, *ad infinitum*.

8

THE VARIANCE RATIO

When the three blind travelers had returned from India, they met an acquaintance who asked them about their adventures. "I had my hands on an elephant," said the first, "and he was like a rope." "Do not listen to him," said the second, "the elephant was like a snake." "They are both misleading you," said the third, "the elephant was like a tree." This was in the days before zoos or picture books, and their sighted but untraveled friend had absolutely no notion of what an elephant might be like. Moved by a desire to avoid useless argument, he said: "Evidently there is some mistake. You must have put your hands on different things." In short, he rejected the null hypothesis, since in his judgment these three accounts were simply too discrepant to have the same factual basis.

THE VARIANCE RATIO

Any statistical test of significance is basically a matter of checking one story against another. Each witness tells his story, and each story by itself is plausible. But do they hang together, or do they have such inconsistent implications that one must be thrown out of court? The basic tool of statistics for such a cross-examination is the *variance ratio:* the ratio between two independent estimates of what is, under the null hypothesis, a single universe. For one example of this, let us look more closely into the structure of the t ratio, as we have been using it to test the significance of a difference between the means of independent samples. By giving it a slightly different twist, we shall be able to recognize in it a ratio between two estimates of variance of the same universe.

Formula 23 expresses t as the ratio of

the difference between two means

————————and————————

the standard error of that difference

But this standard error is based on the sum of two separate estimates of error variance, one derived from each sample. (See Formula 22b.) Therefore, we can also write the following formula for t^2, which we have further modified by inserting 2 as a divisor in both the numerator and the denominator.

$$t^2 = \frac{\dfrac{(\bar{X}_1 - \bar{X}_2)^2}{2}}{\dfrac{s^2_{\bar{X}_1} + s^2_{\bar{X}_2}}{2}}$$

Now, it is easy to see that both the numerator and the denominator are estimates of the variance of the same hypothetical universe of means. The estimate in the numerator is based on a sample of two means from that universe. Since there are but two elements in the sample, each deviation score equals half the difference between them, and therefore the sum of squares equals

$$2\left(\frac{\bar{X}_1 - \bar{X}_2}{2}\right)^2 = \frac{(\bar{X}_1 - \bar{X}_2)^2}{2}$$

Since there is but one degree of freedom, this is also the estimate of variance.

As to the denominator, this consists of an average of two such estimates, each derived from the data of one sample. In forming this joint estimate, equal weight has been given to each sample. As we know, it is also possible to form an estimate in which each sample is given weight according to its size.

Thus, the formula for t^2 is a ratio between two independent estimates of variance of what is, according to the null hypothesis, one universe. Notice that the estimate in the numerator is based on the information which we have concerning the influence of the experimental variable, while the estimate in the denominator is based on the error which is ascribed to chance influences. The variance ratio may therefore be regarded as *a ratio of information to error*. We are not impressed by the amount of information present until it greatly exceeds the prevailing "noise level," as shown by the high value of this information:error ratio. When that happens we acknowledge that the two estimates are inconsistent, and we reject the null hypothesis. In the words of our poetic interlude, "If twice outdone, Chance has lost the contest to Design." But "twice" is only poetic license for 1.96, and in this chapter, where we deal with variance ratios rather than with standard errors, we shall have to learn a new series of critical factors.

F STANDS FOR FISHER

Once we are aware that the test of a null hypothesis consists of the comparison of two variance estimates, it is natural to consider the possibility of basing these estimates on more than two samples. Why should we not study the reactions of four dog breeds to frustration, or the responses of depressed patients to three kinds of music, or the scholastic aptitudes of students in five major fields? In such designs, just as in comparisons of two groups, the variance among the representative scores, when viewed against the background of individual differences, will reflect the influence of the experimental variable. That is, the ratio between these two independent estimates of variance can be used to provide a general test for detecting nonchance influences on the representative scores.

If such a test is to have practical value, we must know the probability distribution for variance ratios. Of course, the mean value of such ratios is unity, since over the long run the estimates in the numerator, which are based on one method, and those in the denominator, which are based on another, will have the same mean value. But the probability distribution for each estimate depends on the degrees of freedom associated with it, and the probability distribution for the *ratio of estimates* is therefore a very involved mathematical function, in which the df of the numerator and the df of the denominator must both be taken into account. Fisher's solution of this problem opened a new era, not only in statistics, but in experimental science. We shall simply have to take his results on faith, knowing that this probability distribution is not in principle different from any other. It, too, is a "picture of expectation": what we must expect to arise in repeated comparisons of two independent, unbiased estimates of the variance of one universe. We must take note of the fact that the solution, which rests on Gosset's earlier work, includes the assumption that sampling is from a normal universe, and therefore it is not strictly applicable unless this assumption is satisfied.

Critical values of the variance ratio have been put into convenient tabular form by Snedecor. It was Snedecor who introduced the symbol F, to immortalize the author of this technique. To use the table of F (Table V) we must select the proper cell according to degrees of freedom available for each of the estimates. We select a *column* in the table according to the df for the *larger* estimate. (For the sort of problem that we are considering this will always be the numerator, simply because we will immediately dismiss as chance, without reference to the F table, any ratio which has a value less than unity.) We then select a *row* in the table according to the *df* for the *smaller* estimate. (In most problems, this is the denominator.) Then we will compare the obtained ratio with the critical values in the cell thus selected. When the obtained value of F exceeds one of these critical values, we can reject the null hypothesis at the indicated level of significance.

It has already been pointed out that entries in the first column of the table are values of t^2. These are the critical values whenever $df = 1$ for the larger estimate of variance. The cell at the foot of this column represents the normal distribution, which applies to the case in which $df = 1$ for the numerator and df is taken as without limit for the denominator. We gain some appreciation of the immense scope of the table of F when we realize that within this vast scheme, in which each cell represents a universe, the "normal" distribution is relegated to one corner, just as our little sun and its planets shrink to insignificance in the vast perspective of modern astronomy.

COMPUTING F: SAMPLES OF LIKE SIZE

We shall illustrate the use of the variance ratio by looking again at the excitable Frenchmen, the stolid Englishmen, and the placid Chinese who figured in problem 3 on page 57. Table 8.1 is based on the original scores

TABLE 8.1

Computation of a Variance Ratio Between Two Estimates of the
Variance of a Universe of Means

	French	English	Chinese	Sums
m	5	5	5	$n = 15$
ΣX	50	35	25	$\Sigma\Sigma X = 110$
ΣX^2	546	275	141	$\Sigma\Sigma X^2 = 962$
$\dfrac{(\Sigma X)^2}{m}$	500	245	125	$\Sigma \dfrac{(\Sigma X)^2}{m} = 870$
Σx^2	46	30	16	$\Sigma x^2_w = 92$
$s^2_{\bar{X}}$	2.3	1.5	0.8	
$\bar{X}$	10	7	5	$\Sigma\bar{X} = 22$
$\bar{X}^2$	100	49	25	$\Sigma\bar{X}^2 = 174$

Estimate based on obtained sample means

$$s^2_{\bar{X}} = \frac{\Sigma\bar{X}^2 - (\Sigma\bar{X})^2/k}{k - 1} = \frac{174 - 22^2/3}{2} = 6.33$$

Mean of estimates based on sample variances

$$s^2_{\bar{X}} = (2.3 + 1.5 + 0.8)/3 = 1.53$$

The variance ratio

$$F = \frac{6.33}{1.53} = 4.13; \qquad df = 2/12; \qquad P < .05.$$

for the three groups of subjects. Notice the symbolism which is included in the righthand column, which includes "sums of sums," indicated as such by double summation signs. The entries on the fourth row are "sample corrections," and a "sum of sample corrections." On the fifth row, there are sums of squares computed within each sample separately, and their sum is designated as a within-sum of squares. The sixth row gives three separate estimates of the universe of means, each based on the data of one sample, and computed by the formula

$$s^2_{\bar{X}} = \frac{\Sigma x^2}{m(m-1)}$$

At the foot of the table, the variance of the universe of sample means which is assumed under the null hypothesis is computed by two different methods. The first computation consists in finding the sum of squares for the three obtained means, which can be regarded as individual elements randomly chosen from that universe, and dividing by $k - 1$, the number of degrees of freedom available when k is the number of samples. The second computation consists in taking the mean of the separate estimates based on the variance in each sample. This composite estimate has 12 degrees of freedom, that is, $n - k$. The degrees of freedom are restated alongside the variance ratio, in a conventional notation which is not to be regarded as a fraction. Guiding ourselves by these values, we turn to Column 2, Row 12 of Table V. There we see that the obtained ratio exceeds the value required for the 5 per cent level of significance, but does not reach the 1 per cent value.

The procedure which we have just carried out can be reduced to the following formula, which is applicable only when all the samples are of like size:

26] $$F = \frac{(m-1)}{(k-1)} \cdot \frac{k \Sigma \bar{X}^2 - (\Sigma \bar{X})^2}{\Sigma \sigma^2} \; ; \quad df = (k-1)/(n-k)$$

where m is the number of observations in each sample, and $n = km$.

When applied to the problem in Table 8.1, this gives:

$$F = \frac{4}{2} \cdot \frac{3\,(174) - 22^2}{9.2 + 6.0 + 3.2} = 4.13$$

Formula 26 can be used to test a null hypothesis for any number of samples of like size, when $\bar{X}$ and σ for each sample are given. Nevertheless, even under these circumstances the method of the next section will ordinarily be more convenient, when the basic data of each sample are available.

COMPUTING F: SAMPLES OF UNLIKE SIZE

In practice, we do not ordinarily form the F ratio from independent estimates of the variance of means, as in the preceding section. It is more convenient to deal with two estimates of the variance of the universe of original scores. One advantage of the method to be presented in this section is that it is applicable to situations in which the samples are of unlike size. (However, one should be wary of situations in which conclusions are based on the discrepant value of one small sample, while a false appearance of stability is gained from a large number of degrees of freedom contributed by the other samples.)

Before presenting this method, let us look in retrospect at the relationships among some of the formulas which we have been using.

$$\sigma^2 = \Sigma x^2/n$$
$$s^2 = \Sigma x^2/(n-1) \qquad s^2_w \doteq s^2_b$$
$$s^2_{\bar{X}} = \Sigma x^2/[n(n-1)]$$

The arrow at the left symbolizes the fact that in the usual procedure, when we deal with two samples, we advance progressively from the obtained variance of the sample to an estimate of the variance of its universe and then to an estimate of the variance of means. However, if the variance of means can be inferred from what is known about the variance of scores, then conversely an estimate of the variance of individual scores can be based on what is known about the distribution of means. We take advantage of this in the usual procedure for the analysis of variance, which is symbolized by the two arrows at the right. One estimate of the variance of the universe of scores is based on within-sample variance, and another is based on between-sample variance. We refer to these as the *within estimate* and the *between estimate*, respectively, and represent them by the symbols s^2_w and s^2_b. Each of these estimates is based on a sum of squares which we have already identified, in the discussion of the differentiation ratio, as a *within-sum* of squares and a *between-sum* of squares.

Accordingly, the computational scheme for the analysis of variance follows in part that for the differentiation ratio. Most of the preparatory work appears on the first four rows of Table 8.1. This work leads, in the righthand column, to the grand sum of scores, the grand sum of squared scores, and the sum of cell corrections. We also need a grand correction, based on all of the data regarded as one sample. In this case,

$$\frac{(\Sigma\Sigma X)^2}{n} = \frac{110^2}{15} = 806.7$$

These are all the values needed to compute the within-sum of squares, the between-sum of squares, and the total sum of squares, by the following formulas:

27] $$\Sigma x^2_w = \Sigma\Sigma X^2 - \Sigma \frac{(\Sigma X)^2}{m}$$

28]
$$\Sigma x^2_{b} = \Sigma \frac{(\Sigma X)^2}{m} - \frac{(\Sigma\Sigma X)^2}{n}$$

29]
$$\Sigma x^2_{t} = \Sigma\Sigma X^2 - \frac{(\Sigma\Sigma X)^2}{n}$$

Notice that the within-sum is found by substituting the sum of the cell corrections in place of the grand correction. It is the sum of the squared deviations of all scores, each with respect to the mean of its own group. It provides the basis for the within-estimate of variance of the universe.

The between-sum is simply the difference between the two forms of correction. This is the part of the total which arises from lack of uniformity among the group means. It leads to the between-estimate of variance.

The formula for the total sum of squares differs from Formula 7 only by the fact that it uses double summation signs, which show that subtotals were taken before the grand totals.

The remaining work is best set forth within the framework of a conventional analysis-of-variance table, such as one will find in many research reports. The schema for this table is shown in the upper part of Table 8.2, and its application to the present problem is shown in the lower

TABLE 8.2

Analysis of Variance Table

Schema

Source	Sums of squares	df	Mean sq.	F
Between samples	Σx^2_{b}	$k - 1$	s^2_{b}	$\dfrac{s^2_{b}}{s^2_{w}}$
Within samples	Σx^2_{w}	$n - k$	s^2_{w}	
Total	Σx^2_{t}	$n - 1$		

Application

Source	Sums of sq.	df	Mean sq.	F
Nationality	63.3	2	31.7	4.13
Individuals	92.0	12	7.67	
Total	155.3	14		

part. There, we see that the ratio of variance estimates is just the same as by the other procedure, although in one case we used estimates of the variance of the universe of means, and in the other case estimates relating to the universe of individual scores. Notice that instead of the generalization "between samples," we have specified the experimental variable as "nationality," and in place of the phrase "within samples," we have specified the source of error as "individual differences." *Error* is another term which is frequently used to designate within-variance.

AN ALTERNATE PROCEDURE

The method of the preceding section can be described as a trick which is done with mirrors, since it is a test of the significance of a difference among sample means which is performed without any determination of the means themselves. The dispersion of the sample means is reflected in the difference between the two forms of correction, and this leads to a judgment regarding the probability that the obtained differences among sample means are the results of chance influences.

It is possible, of course, to restate this procedure in a formula which uses sample means and variances, instead of sums of scores and sums of squared scores. This will generally involve extra labor, as well as a loss of precision due to the use of additional intermediate rounded values. However, it does sometimes happen that we would like to compute an F for several samples, for each of which m, X, and σ are given, although the basic sums are not accessible and would have to be recomputed from these values. This would be the case, for example, if we wanted to test a null hypothesis for any one of the interest scales in the data of Table 7.6 (on page 118). A formula which will serve this purpose is:

$$30] \qquad F = \frac{(n - k)}{(k - 1)} \cdot \frac{\Sigma[m(X - \bar{\bar{X}})^2]}{\Sigma(m\sigma^2)} ; \qquad df = (k - 1)/(n - k)$$

where m, X, and σ stand for statistics of each of k samples of possibly unlike size, $n = \Sigma m$, and $\bar{\bar{X}} = \Sigma(mX)/n$. (Notice, in the numerator, that each observation contributes to the between-sum the square of the difference between the grand mean and the mean of the sample to which it belongs; in the denominator, each observation contributes, on the average, the mean square of its sample.)

Let us apply this formula to the data on clerical interest, in Table 7.6. We first determine the value of the grand mean, which is the universe mean under the null hypothesis.

$$\bar{\bar{X}} = \frac{78\ (46.7) + 43\ (50.6) + 218\ (48.2)}{339} = 48.2$$

Using this value in Formula 30, we have:

$$F = \frac{336}{2} \cdot \frac{78 (1.5)^2 + 43 (2.4)^2 + 218 (0)}{78 (15.2)^2 + 43 (13.1)^2 + 218 (13.1)^2} = 1.13$$

which, with 2 and 336 degrees of freedom, is not significant.

THE DIFFERENTIATION RATIO REVISITED

The procedure we have just learned is called simple analysis of variance, or the analysis of variance in one dimension. It starts by partitioning the sum of squares into two parts, just as for the differentiation ratio, and then goes on to compute a mean square for each of those parts, with due allowance for "lost" degrees of freedom. The resulting F ratio tells us whether the experimental variable has had a significant influence on the scores, but it tells us nothing about the strength of that influence. Where there is little incidental error, a very slight influence may be noted with assurance; where there is much, a major influence may escape detection. On the other hand, the differentiation ratio, η^2, which is formed directly from the sums of squares, does inform us about the strength of the experimental variable, relative to the other influences which are active. If F is significant, as described above, the implication is that η^2 also is significant, for this is only another way of saying that there is greater than chance variation among the sample means. Nevertheless, the value of η^2 tends to overstate the influence of the experimental variable, since the between-sum of squares inevitably includes some error variance.

We now have the possibility of eliminating the bias in the differentiation ratio. If the null hypothesis is correct, the two estimates of variance, the within and the between, differ only by chance. This implies that the sums of squares on which they are based, if they were free from error, would stand in the same proportion to each other as the degrees of freedom associated with them. For example, if there are 2 degrees of freedom for the between-estimate, and 12 degrees of freedom for the within-estimate, then the expected chance value of the sum of squares for the former is one-sixth of the sum of squares for the latter. In other words, the within-estimate of variance, s^2_w, is a sort of unit allowance for error, which we can expect to find associated with each degree of freedom, in the between-sum of squares just as in the within-sum of squares. This means that under the null hypothesis the expected value for the between-sum, around which it fluctuates by chance, is equal to $(k - 1) s^2_w$. If we subtract this from the between-sum as obtained, whatever excess remains is an estimate of the influence of the experimental variable from which bias has been eliminated. Following this reasoning, we can find the *unbiased differentiation ratio* by the following formula:

31]
$$\epsilon^2 = \frac{\Sigma x^2_{\cdot b} - (k - 1)s^2_w}{\Sigma x^2}$$

In the problem which we have been considering, this becomes:

$$\epsilon^2 = \frac{63.3 - 2\,(7.67)}{155.3} = 0.31$$

Without this allowance, by the method of Chapter 3, we would have found $\eta^2 = 0.41$. The reduction is due to the elimination of bias. The information estimate has been decontaminated, as it were, by removing some error-effect which was masquerading as experimental effect.*

Formula 31 gives insight into the nature of the correction for bias. It is a perfectly feasible formula for computational purposes, but the form which we more often meet is this:

31a) $$\epsilon^2 = 1 - \frac{s^2_{\,w}}{s^2}$$

In the illustration,

$$\epsilon^2 = 1 - \frac{7.67}{155.3/14} = 0.31$$

In other words, 69 per cent of the score variance is ascribable to the influence of chance factors whose operation is betrayed by the dispersion of scores within each of the samples or categories. The remainder, 31 per cent, may be attributed to the operation of factors associated with the experimental variable which underlies the system of categories. Of course, these proportions obtained only under the conditions of the experiment, which may have excluded some factors which ordinarily influence the kind of behavior that is being observed.

TESTING HOMOGENEITY OF VARIANCE

It was pointed out earlier (on page 113) that thoroughgoing application of the null hypothesis implies an assumption that the parent universes have the same variance. When we are dealing with only two samples, the variance ratio provides a quick and easy test of this assumption. We need only evaluate

$$F = \frac{s^2_{\,1}}{s^2_{\,2}} \quad \text{or} \quad \frac{s^2_{\,2}}{s^2_{\,1}}$$

(whichever is greater) and compare the result with the critical values for the corresponding df's. Note, however, that for the comparison of these two variance estimates we have given ourselves *two* chances to find a significant ratio. In most uses of the variance ratio, it is determined in advance that one of the variance estimates shall be the numerator, and when this estimate has the smaller value we immediately dismiss the

---

* For a method of determining critical values of ϵ^2, see the note to Table VI.

result as nonsignificant. When we are making a test for homogeneity of variance, it does not matter which estimate is larger. Therefore, the chance of reaching the tabled critical value is doubled, and we must look upon the table of F as consisting of 10 per cent and 2 per cent points, rather than 5 per cent and 1 per cent points.

Occasionally our interest is centered on a comparison of variances, rather than on a comparison of means. For example, we might wish to test the hypothesis that boys are more variable than girls in their acceptance of authority—that is, that girls tend to approximate a single social norm more closely than their brothers. Given an attitude test or a rating scale which will yield comparable scores for boys and girls on this variable, the null hypothesis of homogeneous variance can be tested by the method described in the preceding paragraph. However, since our hypothesis does not merely assert a difference in variance, but states specifically that the boys are more variable, we are making a one-tailed test (compare page 113), and therefore the significance levels stated in the F table apply directly.

There is no equally convenient test for homogeneity of variance in several groups. In theory, the results of an analysis of variance are inexact if the condition of homogeneity of variance is not satisfied. Fortunately, this is another one of those ideal conditions which can be breached in practice without serious consequence. Experience indicates that the resulting inaccuracies are quite minor unless the variance discrepancies are huge. If the reader should ever find himself preparing an analysis of variance for publication, he will want to apply one of the standard tests (e.g., Bartlett's test for homogeneity of variance) if there is any doubt whatever on this score. When he reads the results of such an analysis, he may expect to find a mention that such a test has been made, whenever it is not obvious that the condition has been satisfied. The practical importance of these tests is not sufficient to justify including, at this point, the rather lengthy exposition which any one of them would require.

MULTIDIMENSIONAL ANALYSIS

"If you can't lick 'em, join 'em." This homely precept has an analogy in the principles of experimental design. If you cannot eliminate a major source of error, try including it in the design as an experimental variable. This will complicate the statistical analysis, but it is more than likely that the extra effort will pay off in better understanding. The traditional experimental plan, which allows only one factor to vary at a time, is inadequate to investigate dynamic interrelationships among simultaneous influences. The great importance of the analysis of variance is that it has made it feasible to conduct experiments of multidimensional factorial design. For this reason, the old complaint that the statistical approach leads to "oversimplification" is obsolete. On the contrary, modern statistical analysis encourages the investigator to deal with simultaneously interacting forces in their original context, rather than attempting to isolate them.

Let us suppose that we conduct an investigation into an interesting facet of restaurant-behavior: "decision time." We define this as the elapsed time from the moment when the waitress hands the customer his menu until he is ready to state his order. We record it for men and women, young and middle-aged. Assume that the outcome of this investigation is as shown in Table 8.3. On the basis of these results, one could not say

TABLE 8.3

Mean Decision Time by Age and Sex, in Ordering Restaurant
Meals (fictional data)

	Men	*Women*
Young	3 mins.	5 mins.
Middle-aged	5 mins.	3 mins.

that men make up their minds either more or less quickly than women, nor that young people make up their minds either more or less quickly than the middle-aged. However, the results do suggest a curious fact, to wit, that as men grow into middle-age they take longer time to decide between a roast and a stew, while women undergo an opposite evolution, and take less time to decide between a salad and a sandwich. Aging is not the same thing to men and to women, as regards their restaurant behavior. Therefore it would be misleading to compare men and women without taking age into account, or to compare the young and the middle-aged without taking sex into account. There is *interaction* between age and sex as determiners of decision-time. (Kinsey turned up some not altogether dissimilar results in another area of human behavior.)

The interaction effect is measured by the sum of squares of the deviations between the obtained cell means and the expected values which would be fixed for the cell means, on the basis of (1) a knowledge of the row and column means and (2) the assumption that the two variables are independent, that is, that there is no interaction between them. In the fictional data which we are considering, the null hypothesis states that the expected mean for each sample of subjects is 4 minutes. Accordingly, the interaction sum of squares equals 4. Its significance would have to be evaluated in relation to the error variance within the cells, which is not included in this fictional data.

Now let us consider an authentic piece of research, in which the object of the investigators was to discover the most effective way to reply to persons making antiminority remarks. Suppose, for example, that the man sitting beside you on a bus makes an unsavory remark about Negroes, when a Negro woman has just hurried to take an empty seat down the aisle. You feel impelled to talk up for tolerance, but more than likely you suppress the impulse, not knowing how to handle the situation effectively. A team of psychologists (Citron, Chein, and Harding[1]) studied the relative effectiveness of different ways of replying. We are concerned here with one portion of their experiment, in which they simultaneously studied both the *content* and the *manner* of the reply. As to content, the reply might make reference to American principles of fair play and equal rights, or it might point out that it is unscientific to judge individuals by group stereotypes or to condemn groups for the behavior of individuals. Either type of reply can be made in a calm and relatively detached manner or in an excitable and militant manner. The general plan of such an investigation is shown in Table 8.4. Each special treatment or condition on one variable is combined with each special treatment or condition on the other variable.

TABLE 8.4

Schema for the Organization of Basic Data in a Two-dimensional Experiment of Factorial Design*

	Data by Cells		Row Sums
	Treatment: R_1C_1 m ΣX ΣX^2	Treatment: R_1C_2 m ΣX ΣX^2	Treatment: R_1 n_r $\Sigma_r \Sigma X$ $\Sigma_r \Sigma X^2$
	Treatment: R_2C_1 m ΣX ΣX^2	Treatment: R_2C_2 m ΣX ΣX^2	Treatment: R_2 n_r $\Sigma_r \Sigma X$ $\Sigma_r \Sigma X^2$
	Column Sums		Grand Sums
	Treatment: C_1 n_c $\Sigma_c \Sigma X$ $\Sigma_c \Sigma X^2$	Treatment: C_2 n_c $\Sigma_c \Sigma X$ $\Sigma_c \Sigma X^2$	All treatments n $\Sigma \Sigma \Sigma X$ $\Sigma \Sigma \Sigma X^2$

* One of the experimental variables is designated as R, the row-dimension, and the other as C, the column-dimension.

This results in a rectangular pattern of cells, in each of which some observations (ideally, the same number) are recorded. In each cell there is a record of the number of observations under the given conditions, the sum of scores, and the sum of squared scores. These values are summed into marginal boxes, by rows and by columns. The grand totals are entered into a summary box which completes the pattern.

A correction term must be computed for every cell of this pattern, including each of the marginal cells. We may classify these terms as cell corrections, row corrections, column corrections, and the grand correction based on the keystone cell. These four different kinds of corrections are then grouped "like with like" to give rise to four different final correction terms, as follows:

(1) The grand correction: $\dfrac{(\Sigma\Sigma\Sigma X)^2}{n}$

(2) The within-cells correction: $\Sigma\Sigma\dfrac{(\Sigma X)^2}{m}$

(3) The sum of row corrections: $\Sigma\dfrac{(\Sigma_r\Sigma X)^2}{n_r}$

(4) The sum of column corrections: $\Sigma\dfrac{(\Sigma_c\Sigma X)^2}{n_c}$

In Table **8.5**, we see how these different correction terms are used to compute the total sum of squares (that is, the sum of squared deviations

TABLE **8.5**

Formulas for Analysis of the Sum of Squares in a Two-dimensional Analysis of Variance, and Degrees of Freedom Associated with Each Portion.

Source	Sum of Squares	df
Rows	$\Sigma\dfrac{(\Sigma_r\Sigma X)^2}{n_r} - \dfrac{(\Sigma\Sigma\Sigma X)^2}{n}$	$R - 1$
Columns	$\Sigma\dfrac{(\Sigma_c\Sigma X)^2}{n_c} - \dfrac{(\Sigma\Sigma\Sigma X)^2}{n}$	$C - 1$
Rows × Columns	Residue	$(R - 1)(C - 1)$
Within cells	$\Sigma\Sigma\Sigma X^2 - \Sigma\Sigma\dfrac{(\Sigma X)^2}{m}$	$n - RC$
Total	$\Sigma\Sigma\Sigma X^2 - \dfrac{(\Sigma\Sigma\Sigma X)^2}{n}$	$n - 1$

for all scores with respect to the one grand mean, with complete disregard
for experimental treatments of any sort), and to break this grand sum
down into its parts. The schema of this table corresponds to that of the
conventional table for reporting a two-dimensional analysis of variance.
The total sum of squares, which appears in the last row of the table, is
obtained by subtracting the grand correction from the grand sum of
squared scores. The formula is still our old friend,

$$\Sigma x^2 = \Sigma X^2 - (\Sigma X)^2/n$$

made to appear somewhat strange by being dressed up with additional
summation signs. These should not frighten us, for they merely express
the fact that the grand sum of scores, and the grand sum of squared scores,
are reached in three steps: by adding first within cells, then adding the
cell sums across rows (or down columns), and then adding the row (or
column) sums. Each summation sign expresses one of these operations.
This grand sum of squares is broken into four parts, as follows:

1. There is a portion of the variability in scores which arises from chance
factors, that is, from the operation of influences other than the experimental variables. We measure this by considering the deviation of each
score from the mean of its cell, that is, from the mean of all scores which
have received similar treatment on both experimental variables.

32] $$\Sigma x^2_w = \Sigma\Sigma\Sigma X^2 - \Sigma\Sigma \frac{(\Sigma X)^2}{m}$$

This is the sum of squares *within cells*, and the formula is the same as that
which was used to obtain the within-sum in the one-dimensional analysis
of variance, except for the use of an additional summation sign in each
term, which expresses the fact that subtotals (by rows or by columns)
were taken as a step toward the grand totals. This provides the basis for
the primary estimate of error variance—the within-estimate of variance
of the universe. For this estimate to be without bias, we must remember
that one degree of freedom is lost in each cell, by the use of its private
mean. Accordingly, the divisor used to convert the sum of squares into
a mean square equals $n - RC$, where R and C represent, respectively, the
number of rows and the number of columns in the experimental design.

2. A portion of the variance may arise from the influence of the variable
which underlies the classification into rows. We measure this by considering
the deviation of each row mean from the grand mean, and taking the
square of such deviation once for each score included on the row. This
quantity is found by taking the difference between two of the correction
terms defined above:

33] $$\Sigma x^2_r = \Sigma \frac{(\Sigma_r \Sigma X)^2}{n_r} - \frac{(\Sigma\Sigma\Sigma X)^2}{n}$$

This is the sum of squares *between rows*. (This is a linguistic barbarism which has become entrenched in statistical terminology; we say *between* rows, *between* columns, etc., even when three or more rows or columns are involved.) Its formula is similar to that for the between-sum in the one-dimensional analysis of variance, from which it differs only by the introduction of additional summation signs which trace the development of the sums through several stages. To convert this sum into a row-estimate of variance, the proper divisor is $R - 1$, that is, one less than the number of separate treatments or samples on this variable. The ratio of this estimate to the within-estimate of variance tests whether the row-variable has had a significant influence on the scores.

3. Another portion of the variability may arise from the influence of the variable which underlies the classification into columns. This situation is entirely similar to that with respect to rows:

$$34] \qquad \Sigma x^2_c = \Sigma \frac{(\Sigma_c \Sigma \mathrm{X})^2}{n_c} - \frac{(\Sigma \Sigma \Sigma \mathrm{X})^2}{n}$$

To use this portion of the total sum of squares as the basis for an estimate of the universe variance, the proper divisor is $C - 1$.

4. When we add up the several quantities which we have just defined, we will find that the within-sum, the rows-sum and the columns-sum do not match the total sum of squares. There is a residue remaining. What we have missed, in computing the sums of squares around cell means and row means and column means, is the *interaction* which takes place between the experimental variables. As we know from our "study" of decision-time in restaurant behavior, the most important finding of the investigation may depend on this portion of the sum of squares.

In the absence of interaction, cell means along each row follow a roughly similar trend, which is seen most clearly in the trend of column means. Also, cell means along each column follow roughly the same trend which is shown by the row means. This parallel proportionality of rows among themselves, and of columns among themselves, means that within each cell we have a summation of the row-effect and the column-effect, but no interaction. When there is interaction, the trend of cell means along one row may be markedly different from that along another row, because the condition represented by a particular column "interacts" with the conditions represented by a given row, to produce an effect which is not merely summative. It is this departure of the cell means from their expected trend within the rows and columns which gives rise to the interaction sum of squares. When the design is in two dimensions, it is not necessary to compute the interaction sum of squares by formula, since it can be found as the residue needed to complete the total sum of squares.

Let us now return to the problem of what is the most effective retort to bigotry. Table **8**.6 presents an analysis of variance of scores on the

TABLE **8**.6

Analysis of Variance of Attitude Change*

Source of variation	Sum of squares	df	s^2	F
Manner of answer	1.72	1	1.72	
Content of answer	2.51	1	2.51	
Manner × Content	8.24	1	8.24	3.19
Within groups	167.44	65	2.58	
Total	179.91	68		

* From Citron, Chein, and Harding.[1]

change of attitude in audiences, recruited from city sidewalks, which witnessed playlets in which the bigot spoke his piece, and received his answer. Since this portion of the experiment dealt with but two types of content, and but two manners of delivery, there is but one degree of freedom associated with each of these variables. For the interaction, $df = (R - 1)(C - 1)$, which is likewise 1 in this case. One can see that there must have been 69 subjects included in the four samples. For both manner and for content, $F < 1$, so that there is no encouragement for selecting one manner of response, or one type of content, by preference to another. However, the interaction-estimate gives rise to an F ratio which, while not quite significant, was high enough to suggest an interesting hypothesis to the investigators. Manner and content seem to interact. If you are going to use the emotionally toned argument which is based on American tradition, it is best to deliver it in a calm and unemotional manner; if you are going to answer with an argument based on the science of individual differences, do it with emotional impact! The authors found sufficient confirming evidence in the rest of their investigation to support a recommendation that the unemotional manner, coupled with the appeal to American tradition, constitute the most effective tactic.

This illustration displays a twofold strength in the analysis of variance, when it is linked with factorial design. On the one hand, it effects a remarkable economy, since it is possible to use the same subjects simultaneously to investigate different problems in the same area. On the other hand, this technique deepens both phases of the study, making it possible to discern interactional effects which might otherwise go unnoticed. To use these advantages often requires the design of experiments in three or four dimensions, rather than two. We shall not discuss the complexities of interpretation which arise in such cases. It is unusual to find significant double or triple interactions, although the possibility cannot be ruled out in advance. But even a three-dimensional design (in which we deal with rows, columns, and *blocks*) gives rise to three separate single interactions, each of which may be enlightening. When the interaction estimates are not significant, they are usually pooled with the within-estimate to create a more stable error term by which the significance of row-, column-, and block-estimates can be judged.

Multidimensional analysis of variance has played an essential part in the development of modern research designs, which have greatly increased the yield of scientific effort. The research-oriented student will want some day to read Fisher's important book, *The Design of Experiments*,[2] as well as to study such manuals of experimental design as those of Edwards[3] and Lindquist.[4]

VARIATIONS IN SAMPLE SIZE

It is theoretically desirable that there shall be the same number of observations in each cell of a multidimensional design, but in practice some variation is permissible. In laboratory experiments, an investigator may protect the elegance of his design by including alternates in each sample, in order to insure equal m's at the conclusion in spite of the attrition which comes from the uncertain life expectancy of rats or the reduced trustworthiness of college sophomores under psychological harassment. However, if one is studying the effects of environmental influences which are not under experimental control, it may not be possible to secure even approximately equal m's. For example, Hallowell's study[5] of the influence of acculturation on personality dealt with the Rorschach responses of men and women in three Indian tribes. There would have been little point to limiting the sample size according to the number of subjects available in the smallest sex-tribe category. In such a case, one should take care that any sizable variations in the number of observations per cell occur in the same proportions on all rows, or on all columns, since otherwise the test of the interaction will not be valid.

PROBLEMS

1. *Wiener*[6] *reports data on the performance of veterans receiving disability payments for various kinds of disability, on the Minnesota Multiphasic Personality Inventory. Some of his data are summarized in Table* **8.7**. *Formula 26 can be used to test whether the various categories of subjects differ significantly with respect to any one of the MMPI variables.*

2. *Referring to Table* **7**.6, *page* 118, *determine whether the scores of "religious" students are significantly more variable than the scores of*

TABLE 8.7

Scores on Major Variables of the *MMPI*, for Veterans in Five Different Disability Groups (for each group, $n = 50$).*

	Asthma		Flat feet		Heart		Skin		Ulcer	
	$\bar{X}$	σ	$\bar{X}$	σ	$\bar{X}$	σ	$\bar{X}$	σ	$\bar{X}$	σ
Hs†	53.1	9.3	58.5	10.4	62.7	11.8	56.4	11.4	62.8	11.8
D	60.5	13.2	57.4	9.5	58.2	9.2	56.1	8.9	57.3	10.7
Hy	54.2	9.0	58.0	9.9	64.0	11.0	58.5	10.1	55.4	10.0
Pd	60.3	10.3	54.5	8.6	54.6	10.7	54.4	9.4	53.9	8.7
Mf	56.2	9.7	54.2	10.2	52.2	8.2	53.6	9.7	51.0	8.7
Pa	52.3	12.3	52.7	8.4	51.4	9.2	49.3	8.2	47.9	6.8
Pt	53.2	9.6	55.5	8.2	53.9	10.3	56.6	11.2	53.5	10.7
Sc	55.1	11.1	56.5	8.8	53.3	9.3	56.0	9.0	52.8	8.7
Ma	55.2	8.5	55.5	10.0	51.9	8.1	57.5	10.2	54.5	9.7

* Data taken from Wiener,[6] but reorganized and slightly altered by further rounding of values.

† Short names for the listed *MMPI* variables, not to be construed as definitions, are: *Hs*, hypochondriasis; *D*, depression; *Hy*, hysteria; *Pd*, psychopathic deviate; *Mf*, masculinity- femininity; *Pa*, paranoia; *Pt*, psychasthenia; *Sc*, schizoid; *Ma*, hypomania.

"athletic" students on any of the Kuder interest scales. Consider each scale by itself.

3. Sines[7] reports an investigation on the differential response of subjects to different fantasy-evoking stimuli. Subjects were chosen on the basis of psychiatric opinion "that the primary source of a man's anxiety was conflict concerning the expression or control of either hostile-aggressive impulses, passive-dependent needs or heterosexual impulses." There were 7 subjects of the first kind, 8 of the second, and 5 of the third. Each subject viewed, and was encouraged to empathize with, each of three drawings: one depicting a hostile act, one depicting passivity, and one—from Esquire— showing a seductive scene. A rather complex measure of autonomic responsiveness under each condition was the score. The sums of squares reported by the author were as follows: for groups, 137.5; for treatments, 13.3; interaction, 280.2; within cells, 946.7; total, 1377.7. Of course, the author also completed the analysis of variance, and drew certain conclusions. Can you construct the analysis of variance table from the information which has been given here? First, make the schema for the table, to fit the experimental design. Enter the sums of squares which have been given in appropriate places, decide on the proper df for each, and then determine the results of the experiment.

4. *The following data are taken, with some simplification, from an article by Scott and Charles,*[8] *dealing with the responsiveness of dogs of various breeds to humans. These scores are for "approach" behavior in a standard test situation. Do the breeds differ significantly?*

Breed	n	ΣX	ΣX²
Basenji	26	200	2750
Beagle	30	380	5950
Cocker spaniel	35	620	12500
Wire-haired terrier	25	275	5100
Sums	116	1475	26300

5. *Seven subjects who had recently taken the Minnesota Rate of Manipulation Test under standard conditions were re-tested by Seashore,*[9] *on 9 days over a 3-week period. At each testing, a 25-cent bonus was offered for each full second of improvement over the previous best score. Times for the first and ninth bonus days were as follows (each score being the mean of 3 timed trials):*

Subject	A	B	C	D	E	F	G
1st bonus day	45.3	52.6	50.6	49.3	51.3	51.0	59.8
9th bonus day	42.7	42.2	44.5	40.5	44.6	47.4	49.9

Is there a significant reduction in inter-individual variability?

6. *Copies of a 350-word account of Bacon's position as a philosopher of science, containing many typographical errors, were distributed to a class. Each student also received written instructions. Some were instructed to read the passage for content; others, to look through the passage and cross out all e's; still others, to indicate all typographical errors. All were told to work as quickly as possible. Immediately after, they were given a 12-item true-false test on the content of the passage. The scores were:*

Content readers: 6, 8, 9, 9, 11, 11, 11
E-crossers: 4, 4, 5, 6, 6, 6, 7, 7
Proofreaders: 4, 5, 5, 5, 5, 5, 6, 11

Considering all three groups, do the means differ significantly? Considering the groups two at a time, which comparisons are significant?

7. *Thirty-two subjects were instructed to operate a finger ergograph to the point of complete fatigue, in time with a metronome. The ergograph and a polygraph showing the amplitude of each response were screened from view, except as noted below. Subjects worked with eyes closed, but when the level of performance had dropped to 15 per cent of the starting level, members of*

the experimental group were instructed to open their eyes and watch the recording, the screen being removed. There were two control groups. Members of C-1 were never given any instruction to open their eyes. Members of C-2 were so instructed when their performance had fallen to the 15 per cent level, but the screen was not removed. The score for each subject is the mean difference in amplitude between the 3 responses just before the 15 per cent criterion was reached and the 3 responses following.

Individual scores were as follows: Group E: 27, 11, 10, 8, 8, 7, 3, 1, −2, −7, −8. Group C-1: −2, −3, −4, −6, −8, −8, −10, −10, −11, −12, −18. Group C-2: 5, 2, 2, 1, 0, 0, −2, −2, −8, −13.

Do the groups differ significantly? Is there a significant difference between C-2 and E? Is a one-tailed test justified for this comparison?

REFERENCES

1. Citron, A. F., Chein, I., and Harding, J. Anti-minority remarks: a problem for action research. *J. abn. soc. Psychol.*, 1950, **45**:99–126.

2. Fisher, R. A. *The design of experiments.* (6th ed.) New York: Hafner, 1951.

3. Edwards, A. L. *Experimental design in psychological research.* New York: Rinehart, 1950.

4. Lindquist, E. F. *Design and analysis of experiments in psychology and education.* Boston: Houghton Mifflin, 1953.

5. Hallowell, A. I. The use of projective techniques in the study of the socio-psychological aspects of acculturation. *J. proj. Tech.*, 1951, **15**:27–44.

6. Wiener, D. N. Personality characteristics of selected disability groups. *Genet. Psychol. Monog.*, 1952, **45**:175–255.

7. Sines, J. O. Conflict-related stimuli as elicitors of selected physiological responses. *J. proj. Tech.*, 1957, **21**:194–198.

8. Scott, J. P., and Charles, Margaret S. Some problems of social and hereditary behavior. *J. gen. Psychol.*, 1953, **48**:209–230.

9. Seashore, H. G. The improvement of performance on the Minnesota Rate of Manipulation Test. *J. appl. Psychol.*, 1947, **31**:254–259.

9

PROPORTIONS AND CHI-SQUARE

THE PARAMETERS OF ATTRIBUTES

What is a quality, if it is not a measurable dimension? If you cannot agree with Lewis Carroll that one day is more brillig than another, or that one animal is less mimsy than another, then you will doubt that these words denote real qualities. The test of their meaningfulness, as that of every qualitative term, is in the demonstrated possibility of discrimination. Nevertheless, we commonly speak of the qualitative approach, as opposed to the quantitative approach, when our measurements are relatively crude, so that we can only talk of more or less, rather than just-so-much. Sometimes the best that we can do is to say yes-or-no, to indicate that the quality which interests us is present to some defined extent, or absent. It is this sort of rudimentary measurement which provides the data for the techniques which we shall study in this chapter.

These techniques are satisfactory enough so that we sometimes content ourselves with simple dichotomous classifications even when we know how to make more refined measurements on the same dimension. For example, in the early stages of research into taste-blindness it was thought that all men could be classified as either "tasters" or "nontasters," according to whether or not they could detect the bitter flavor of phenyl thiocarbamide. Later it was discovered that there is a continuous, although markedly bimodal, distribution of sensitivities to this substance. Thus, research advanced from the qualitative to the quantitative stage. Today, anyone who plans to do basic research on the nature of taste-blindness will probably utilize the more refined measurements, but someone who plans to apply our present knowledge for the investigation of another problem, as for example the study of the genetic background of an island group in the South Pacific, may find the simple dichotomous classification of persons into tasters and nontasters to be more practical. As another example, all men may be classified as either "fat" or "not fat." It is obvious that such a gross schema of classification will lead to many ambiguities and hurt feelings, but it may nevertheless have its place in an investigation of the question whether fat men are really more jolly than those who are not fat. From a practical point of view, this dichotomous classification, guided by a careful definition of the concept, may under some circumstances be preferred to a score on Sheldon's seven-step scale for endomorphy.

Let us think of a universe which has been dichotomized by some criterion, so that it consists of two classes, which we may call the "haves" and the "have-nots." The elements of one class possess a certain attribute, and the elements of the other class do not. Let N stand for the number of elements in this universe—we are reserving small n to stand for the size of a sample—and let p stand for the proportion of elements in which the attribute is present. The proportion which do not possess the attribute is then $1 - p$, or q. (Compare page 72).

Let us assign a score of 1 to each of the "haves," and a score of 0 to each of the "have-nots," reflecting our assumption that the attribute is either all there or not at all present. This does not by any means imply that the underlying trait or quality, such as taste-blindness or obesity, is an all-or-none characteristic. We make no assumption whatever about the distribution of that underlying trait, but we define the attribute as possession of "at least so much" of the quality. Less than this does not mean "none of the quality," but "none of the attribute." The result is a set of scores which has only two classes, 0 and 1.

Since the distribution of attribute-scores is so simple in form, we should not be surprised to learn that some rather simple formulas define its parameters. Table 9.1 shows that for such a set of attribute-scores the sum of scores and the sum of squared scores are both equal to pN. When

TABLE 9.1

Schematic Computation of Basic Statistics for a Set of Attribute-scores

Class	X	f	fX	fX^2
"Haves"	1	pN	pN	pN
"Have-nots"	0	qN	0	0
Sums		N	pN	pN

we substitute these values into the usual computational formulas for the mean and the variance, we discover that, for the mean, since $\frac{\Sigma X}{n}$ has become $\frac{pN}{N}$,

35] $$\bar{X} = p$$

and for the variance, since now

$$\frac{\Sigma X^2}{n} - \left(\frac{\Sigma X}{n}\right)^2 = \frac{pN}{N} - \left(\frac{pN}{N}\right)^2$$

then, of course,

$$\sigma^2 = p - p^2 = p(1 - p)$$

36] $$= pq$$

Now let us consider the results of random sampling in this simple universe. Remember that when we take random samples of n elements each out of any parent universe, the universe of sums has a variance equal to $n\sigma^2$, where σ^2 is the variance of the parent universe (see page 89). This rule admits no exception. We have just seen that in the present case the variance of the parent distribution equals pq, and therefore the sampling variance for samples of size n equals npq. Notice that the universe of samples of size n, drawn from a universe of attribute-scores, has the binomial distribution for $(p + q)^n$. Therefore, the formula which we have just derived applies to binomial distributions generally, and it deserves to be remembered:

37] $$\sigma^2_{bin} = npq$$

For example, the distribution of chance scores for a quiz which consists of eight true-false items (as in Problem 2 on page 87), has as its variance

$$8(.50)^2 = 2$$

and the variance of chance scores for a quiz which consists of eight four-choice items (as in Problem 3 on page 87), is

$$8(.25)(.75) = 1.5$$

Remember, too, that for random samples of size n drawn from any universe whatever, the sampling variance of the mean equals $\frac{\sigma^2}{n}$. Once again we write pq in place of σ^2, and thus we learn that the sampling variance for means of attribute-scores equals $\frac{pq}{n}$. Since the mean of such a sample is also the proportion of elements in the sample which possess the attribute, we call this the sampling variance of a proportion rather than the sampling variance of the mean:

38] $$\sigma^2_{p} = \frac{pq}{n}$$

38a] $$\text{whence} \quad s_{p} = \sqrt{\frac{pq}{n}}$$

This is called the *standard error of a proportion*, and it can be used, like any other standard error, to establish confidence limits for an empirical finding. For example, if 20 per cent of 65 persons interviewed state that they dislike cottage cheese so much that they refuse to eat it (thus "failing" what one author has called the most significant single item on neuroticism inventories), we can fix the proportion of persons who intensely dislike cottage cheese, in the universe of this sample, at

$$.20 \pm \sqrt{\frac{(.20)(.80)}{65}} = .20 \pm .05$$

Under most circumstances this standard error may be interpreted as a normal deviate, leading to a conclusion that the 5 per cent confidence interval for this empirically determined proportion is approximately $.10 < p < .30$. (However, normal distribution of sample proportions should not be assumed if the value of p is less than .10 or greater than .90, or if there are fewer than 5 cases of "haves" or "have-nots," whichever is the smaller class.)

THE LOVING SONS

By continuing the same line of development as in Chapter 7, we can arrive at a formula for the *standard error of a difference in proportions* in terms which are analogous to those used in Formula 22b, on page 110. That is,

39] $$s_{p_1-p_2} = \sqrt{\frac{pq}{n_1} + \frac{pq}{n_2}}$$

where p is an estimate of the universe parameter which is based on the merged experience of both samples. We shall use this formula in an illustrative problem, which we shall work with more than usual exactness so that the reader will see the precise coincidence of the result with the answer which we will obtain less laboriously by a method to be described in the next section.

The data in Table 9.2 are compiled from a report by MacKinnon[1]. His subjects, all young men, were placed in a task situation so designed that they thought they could cheat with impunity. Actually they were being observed through a peephole, in the sly manner which psychological investigators sometimes permit themselves. On the basis of their behavior

TABLE 9.2

Preference for Mother, among Violators and Nonviolators*

	+	−	Row sum
Violators	20	7	27
Nonviolators	14	24	38
	34	31	65

* Data based on MacKinnon.[1] + stands for "mother preferred," and − stands for "father preferred or no preference."

in this situation, the subjects were classified as "Violators" and "Non-violators." The two categories of subjects were then compared in several respects, including their stated attitudes toward their parents. It was found that 20 of 27 Violators, but only 14 of 38 Nonviolators, stated that as children they had been more attached to their mothers than to their fathers. These data suggested that there have been some early hard feelings between future Violators and their fathers. We restate this as a conservative null hypothesis: Violators do not differ from Nonviolators with respect to their stated parent preferences. The hypothesis implies that the Violators and Nonviolators in this investigation are random samples from a universe of college men which is homogeneous as regards their reports of early parental attachments.

To test the hypothesis, we carry out the following computations:

$$p = 34/65 \quad = .5231$$

whence $\quad q = \quad .4769$

and $\quad pq = \quad .2495$

Also $\quad p_1 - p_2 = \dfrac{20}{27} - \dfrac{14}{38} = .3723$

By Formula 39,

$$s_{p_1-p_2} = \sqrt{\frac{.2495}{27} + \frac{.2495}{38}} = .1259$$

and finally,

$$z = \frac{p_1 - p_2}{s_{p_1-p_2}} = \frac{.3723}{.1259} = 2.962$$

Our calculations have terminated in a *critical ratio*, the ratio of the obtained difference in proportions to the standard error of that difference. It would not be proper to designate this as a *t* ratio, because it does not benefit from the refinement of Student's correction for bias. Therefore we designate it as z, a deviation in standard units. The numerator in this ratio is the difference in the proportion of the "haves" and the "have-nots" in two empirical samples which are, under the null hypothesis, random samples of one universe. The denominator is an estimate of the standard deviation of the universe *of such differences*, based on the size of the samples and on what we know about the hypothetical parent universe.

To interpret the critical ratio, we make the assumption that the universe-of-differences-in-proportion has a normal distribution, and this is a reasonable assumption because neither sample of subjects is small and the value of p is evidently not extreme. We conclude that, in this case, the difference in proportions is significant at the 1 per cent level, and the null hypothesis must be rejected. Violators and Nonviolators *do* differ in the reports which they give about their early parental attachments. Whether this means that the fathers of Violators were, in general, harsher disciplinarians, or that the Violators were spoiled by their mothers, are matters of interpretation to which the statistical analysis of these data do not penetrate.

THE CHI-SQUARE TECHNIQUE

We shall now obtain the same result by another method—one which is less laborious and which also has a wider range of possible applications. Look again at Table **9**.2. Although such a table is based on a twofold dichotomization, custom ordains that it shall be called a *fourfold* table. It is the simplest form of a *contingency* table, in which coordinated observations based on two methods of classification are set forth in a manner which permits us to judge whether membership in a given class on one dimension tends to be associated with (that is, contingent upon) membership in some class on the other dimension. The sums of the columns in such a table constitute, in effect, a statement of the null hypothesis that the two systems of classification are independent. In this case, the null hypothesis asserts that each of the samples is drawn from a common universe in which $p = 34/65$. According to this hypothesis, the observations recorded on the first row constitute a random sample from the binomial distribution with $p = 34/65$ and $n = 27$, while the observations recorded on the second row constitute a random sample from the binomial distribution with $p = 34/65$ and $n = 38$.

As a first step toward testing this hypothesis, we construct a table of *expected frequencies*, f_e. An expected frequency is a mean or *representative value for a universe of chance outcomes*. These values are found by the following formula:

40]
$$f_e = \frac{n_c n_r}{n}$$

That is, the expected frequency for any cell is the product of the number of observations on the row and in the column in which the cell is located, divided by the total number of observations in the table. For example, thirty-four–sixty-fifths of a sample of 27 equals 14.125. Although fourteen and one-eighth persons may seem to be an unrealistic expectation, it is the correct representative value for the universe of chance outcomes in a random sampling procedure, where $n = 27$ and $p = 34/65$. It is the expected number of "heads" in 27 tosses of a coin with this amount of bias. (The fact that observed frequencies are always in integral amounts, and expected frequencies are usually non-integral, does lead to some inaccuracy in the results. We are using a theory based on a *continuous* distribution, and applying it to a *discontinuous* situation. In the next section we will introduce a refinement to adjust for this difficulty.)

Table **9**.3 shows the complete set of expected frequencies, arranged in

TABLE **9.3**

Organization of Data for a χ^2 Test of the Independence of Two Criteria of Categorization

	f_o (Obtained Frequencies)		Sums	f_e (Expected Frequencies)	
	A+*	A−		A+	A−
B+†	20	7	27	14.125	12.875
B−	14	24	38	19.875	18.125
	34	31	65	34.0	31.0

* Criterion A: Mother preferred (+), or Mother not preferred (−).
† Criterion B: Violator (+), or Nonviolator (−).

parallel with the obtained frequencies. The proportions which are found in the marginal sums of the obtained frequencies (27 : 38 and 34 : 31) can also be found on each row and in each column of the expected frequencies. Notice that the absolute difference between any f_e and the corresponding f_o is the same, 5.875. Notice also that it was really necessary to compute only one of the expected frequencies by formula, since the others could then have been derived by subtraction from the marginal sums, which must be the same for both sets of frequencies, since they are the source of the null hypothesis. Either of these facts carries the implication that such a table has only one degree of freedom. To state it in still another way: since the size of each sample is given, and the value of p for the null hypothesis is taken from the pooled results of both samples, the amount of the discrepancy in one sample gives us complete information about the amount of the discrepancy in the other sample.

Let us now compute the following quantity, which is called χ^2:

41]
$$\chi^2 = \Sigma \frac{(f_o - f_e)^2}{f_e}$$

This formula is in a form which will be applicable also to larger contingency tables, that is, to two-dimensional frequency tables in which there may be more than two categories on one or both of the dimensions. To apply it, we take the difference between the obtained and expected frequency for each cell of the table, square that difference, and divide by the expected frequency for the cell. The sum of such values equals χ^2. In the present problem:

$$\chi^2 = \frac{5.875^2}{14.125} + \frac{5.875^2}{12.875} + \frac{5.875^2}{19.875} + \frac{5.875^2}{18.125} = 8.774$$

The square root of this value is 2.962, which is the value of the critical ratio which we found by using the standard error for a difference in proportions. How shall we explain this coincidence?

Actually, we have elaborated the same implicit relationships by two different computational procedures. Each method takes its start from four obtained frequencies, one in each quadrant of the fourfold table. It is customary to designate these values as a, b, c, and d, according to the following schema:

a	b
c	d

This gives rise to the following identities:

$$p = \frac{a + c}{a + b + c + d}$$

$$q = \frac{b + d}{a + b + c + d}$$

$$p_1 = \frac{a}{a + b} \qquad n_1 = a + b$$

$$p_2 = \frac{c}{c + d} \qquad n_2 = c + d$$

Let us substitute these values into the formula for the critical ratio for a difference in proportions. Before the substitutions, the formula may be written thus:

$$z = \frac{p_1 - p_2}{\sqrt{\dfrac{pq}{n_1} + \dfrac{pq}{n_2}}}$$

where the denominator is taken from Formula 39. After substituting the above identities, this becomes:

$$\frac{\dfrac{a}{a+b} - \dfrac{c}{c+d}}{\sqrt{\dfrac{(a+c)(b+d)}{(a+b)(a+b+c+d)} + \dfrac{(a+c)(b+d)}{(c+d)(a+b+c+d)}}}$$

and this reduces, by steps which we shall not specify in detail, to:

$$\sqrt{\frac{(a+b+c+d)(ad-bc)^2}{(a+b)(c+d)(a+c)(b+d)}}$$

In somewhat the same manner, it can be shown that the expression under the radical is a computational equivalent for χ^2 based on a fourfold table, when it is computed according to Formula 41. In other words, χ^2 for a fourfold table is equal to the squared critical ratio for a difference in proportions. Knowing this, we can determine the P value which is associated with any given value of χ^2, when it is based on a fourfold table, by taking its square root and interpreting it as a normal deviate.

It should now be evident that χ^2 is another form of variance ratio. When it is based on a comparison of two samples (or, as we shall see later, on the comparison of one sample with a theoretical expectation), it has only one degree of freedom in its numerator. In this respect it resembles t^2. Unlike t^2, which has a specified number of degrees of freedom in its denominator, χ^2 has a denominator which is assumed to be based on completely adequate information. Therefore χ^2 does not have the exactness of the t technique.* Critical values for χ^2 with $df = 1$ are found in the bottom cell of the first column in the table of F; if we were using the t technique, we would refer to this last cell only if our sample were extremely large.

At this point, let us summarize in cook-book fashion the steps of the procedure which we have used, and which we shall want to apply to certain other types of problem as well.

1. Organize the frequency data into a contingency table, showing the marginal sums for all rows and columns.

* We shall not describe any exact statistical test for fourfold tables. However, Armsen[2] has provided exact probability tables for such tests, whenever $\Sigma n \leq 50$.

2. Using Formula 40, construct a parallel table of expected frequencies.

3. For each cell, evaluate $(f_o - f_e)^2/f_e$.

4. Add these values.

5. When $df = 1$, interpret the result as if it were a value of z^2, either through the normal probability table or by comparison with critical values for t^2 with $df = \infty$. (Later we shall discuss χ^2 with $df > 1$.)

CORRECTION FOR CONTINUITY

The exact solution of any problem of probabilities, when we deal with finite data, requires the construction of a *discontinuous* table of probabilities by the use of the binomial expansion or some similar method. We do not often feel that circumstances justify the effort which would be involved, and therefore we content ourselves with approximations which are based on *continuous* functions, such as the normal distribution, the t distributions, and the χ^2 distributions. The resulting error is negligible when the possible outcomes of the set of observations are quasi-continuous, as is the case when we deal with the mean of a large sample. Even though all the scores are whole numbers, the mean will usually have a decimal value, and the distribution of possible means—which is the distribution to which we apply the probability distribution—may be considered continuous for all practical purposes. But this is not the case when we deal with small frequencies. Under these conditions we are compelled to perform an act of translation, which can be illustrated more readily than it can be explained.

Suppose that we are checking up on the height of a young man who is a candidate for a police force, where the minimum acceptable height is 5 feet 8 inches. We find a record which gives his height as 5 feet 8 inches, but the context indicates that the measurements in this list were recorded to the nearest inch. Therefore we only know that he is at least 5 feet 7½ inches tall. To be "more than 5 feet 8 inches tall" does not mean the same thing on a continuous and on a discontinuous scale. In one case it means that he has surpassed this measurement, if only by a hair, while in the other case it would mean that his height was to be recorded as 5 feet 9 inches, with the implication that an exact measurement would have been not less than 5 feet 8½ inches.

A similar act of translation is necessary when we wish to use a continuous probability distribution in connection with a discontinuous phenomenon. Let us consider the distribution of chance scores on a quiz which consists of ten true-false items. All the scores are whole numbers, and a correct graphic representation of this discontinuous distribution would consist of a series of lines which show the relative frequencies of the various possible scores. However, we usually show such a distribution as a series of contiguous rectangles, as in Figure 9.1. There the area of each

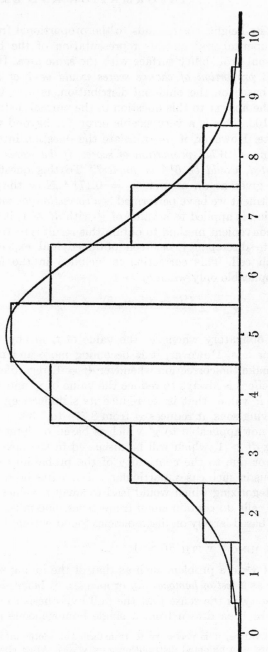

Fig. 9.1. Comparison of the binomial distribution for $n = 10$, $p = .5$, and the normal distribution with the same mean and variance. The area in the binomial distribution which represents scores of "7 and above," for example, is matched approximately in the normal distribution by the area "6½ and above." This is the basis of *correction for continuity*.

rectangle, as well as its height, corresponds to the proportional frequency of a given score. Superimposed on this representation of the binomial distribution is a normal probability surface with the same area. If we ask the question, *"What proportion of chance scores would be 7 or higher?"* the correct answer, based on the binomial distribution, is $p = 0.172$. If we attempt to find the answer to this question in the normal distribution, the result is $p = 0.103$. This is a very sizable error, far beyond what we are willing to tolerate. However, if we translate the question into appropriate terms, it becomes *"What proportion of scores, if the scores could be continuously distributed, would be 6½ or higher?"* To this question, the normal distribution gives as an answer, $p = 0.171$.* Now the error is negligible. The adjustment we have performed is a *correction for continuity*.

When this correction is applied to a value of χ^2 with $df = 1$, it is called *Yates' correction*. A convenient method to obtain this result is to reduce by one-half the absolute discrepancy between obtained and expected frequencies within each cell. This correction is included in the following formula, which is applicable only when $df = 1$.

41a]
$$\chi^2 = \Sigma \frac{(|f_o - f_e| - .5)^2}{f_e}$$

Yates' correction is obligatory whenever the value of f_e in any cell of a fourfold table is 5 or less. However, it is becoming more and more the general practice to make the correction whenever $df = 1$, regardless of the cell frequencies. Its effect is always to reduce the value of χ^2 and hence to raise the associated P value (that is, to reduce its significance). Applied to the case of the loving sons, it reduces χ^2 from 8.774 to 7.337.

The correction is not applicable to χ^2 which is based on larger contingency tables, having $df > 1$, which will be discussed in the next section. Fortunately, the error due to the continuity of the probability distribution is also less serious in such cases, particularly if care has been taken to avoid systems of categorizing which would lead to small f_e values in some of the cells. If some cells do contain small frequencies, one must discount conclusions that are based largely on discrepancies found within those cells.

TESTS OF INDEPENDENCE, WITH $df > 1$

The application of χ^2 to a problem such as that of the loving sons may be designated either as a *test of homogeneity* or as a *test of independence*. It is a test of homogeneity in the sense that the null hypothesis asserts that the two samples have been drawn from a single homogeneous universe.

* To find both these values, it is necessary to transform the scores into z scores. This is not difficult, since in a binomial distribution $\sigma = \sqrt{npq}$. After checking the above figures, the reader may wish to compute the proportions, adjusted and unadjusted, for the question: *"What proportion of scores would be 8 or higher?"*

From another point of view, it tests whether the two systems of classification are independent of each other. If the possession of attribute A makes it either more or less likely that one shall also possess attribute B, the null hypothesis must be rejected. It is easy to apply the same technique to data which are arranged in a larger number of categories on two dimensions. For illustration, we present a problem in which four groups of subjects have been dichotomized. (The method is applicable to R groups each sorted into C classes, where R and C may be any values greater than 1.)

The 300 subjects of this study were all asked to "write a story about a Tree, a House, and a Person." We shall consider only data on whether the Person fantasied under these conditions is of the same sex as the author of the story or of the opposite sex. These data are shown in Table 9.4.

TABLE 9.4

Incidence of Same-Sexed and Opposite-Sexed Persons Appearing in Fantasy Material*

	Sex of "Person"		
Subjects	Same	Opposite	Row sum
Men	90	6	96
Women	35	46	81
Boys	63	3	66
Girls	29	28	57
All	217	83	300

$$\chi^2 = 87.0; \quad df = 3; \quad P < .001$$

* Based on Diamond.[3]

The null hypothesis states that each group of subjects is a random sample of a universe which is homogeneous with respect to the likelihood of using a same-sexed person as the central figure of a fantasy. The experiment provides many separate tests of this hypothesis, but no more than three of these tests are mutually independent. One set of three independent tests (but not the only possible such set) includes the following comparisons. We test the hypothesis once by comparing

Men	vs.	Women
90		35
6		46

$$\chi^2 = 54.1$$

We test it a second time by comparing

Boys	vs.	Girls	
63		29	
3		28	$\chi^2 = 32.3$

We test it a third time by comparing

Adults	vs.	Children	
125		92	
52		31	$\chi^2 = 0.6$

However, we might also use Formulas 40 and 41 to find a χ^2 value for the entire table, considered as a whole. Using Formula 40, we fix an expected value for each cell on the hypothesis that we are dealing with four random samples of a universe in which $p = 217/300$. Then using Formula 41, we will find that $\chi^2 = 87.0$. But this is precisely the sum of the values found for the three independent tests based on fourfold tables. (This would be true, as the reader may verify in one of the problems at the end of this chapter, for any other set of three independent hypotheses applied to these data. In order not to disturb this agreement, it was necessary to compute χ^2 values for the independent tests without correction for continuity.) This is a striking demonstration of an important quality of χ^2: it is *additive*. Usually there is no purpose in making the separate tests, which have been shown here only in order to give the reader a concrete demonstration of what is meant by the statement that χ^2 is additive.

Since the 2 × 4 contingency table includes three independent tests of one hypothesis, it has three degrees of freedom. We might have come to this conclusion by noticing that in constructing the table of expected frequencies, it is only necessary to compute by formula the values for three cells, since the remaining values can then be found by subtraction from the marginal sums. For any contingency table:

42] $df = (R - 1)(C - 1)$

The value of P which is associated with a χ^2 which has more than one degree of freedom cannot be found in the normal probability table. There is a probability table for χ^2 (Table IV), which must be entered with the appropriate number of degrees of freedom, much as in the case of the t table. However, it would be possible to get along without that table if necessary, because critical values for χ^2 can be found in the table of F, although they are hidden there in a disguised form.

Recall that the critical values for χ^2, with $df = 1$, are found in the first cell of the last row of the table of F. Let us follow this clue. Any value of χ^2 with $df = 2$ is a sum of two components. Divide it by 2, and it becomes a variance ratio with 2 degrees of freedom for its numerator, but one which still assumes completely adequate information for its denominator. The critical values for such a ratio are found in the second cell of the bottom row of the table of F. With 3 degrees of freedom, as in the problem we have been working, χ^2 is a sum of three separately determinable χ^2's. Divide this sum by 3, and it becomes a variance ratio with 3 degrees of freedom for its numerator; its critical values are found in the third cell of the bottom row of the table of F. In general, if we divide any value of χ^2 by the number of degrees of freedom associated with it, the result is a variance ratio which has the specified number of degrees of freedom in its numerator, and unlimited degrees of freedom (assumed, if not actual) in its denominator.

The relationships among the normal, t, χ^2, and F distributions can be studied in the abbreviated composite table, Table VI.

THE CHI-SQUARE DISTRIBUTION

Some formidable mathematical reasoning goes into the calculation of the probability distribution for χ^2 with $df > 1$. We shall not attempt that, but we shall find it interesting and perhaps even entertaining to consider some characteristics of this distribution.

Take a normal distribution, and represent each of its elements as z^2, that is, as the square of its standardized value. This means that there will be a great many very small values, and relatively few large values. For example, since about 38 per cent of the elements in a normal distribution have z scores between $-.5$ and $+.5$, this same percentage of the new distribution have values less than .25. And since about 2 per cent of z scores lie between $-.05$ and $+.05$, this percentage in the new distribution lie between 0 and .0025. This means that if we go on using the same markings on the abscissa, the area representing this 2 per cent of the distribution is compressed into a width which is only one-fortieth of what it occupied in the normal distribution. For the frequency curve, under these conditions, there is no place to go but up, and so it rises indefinitely higher and higher as z^2 becomes smaller and smaller (see Figure 9.2). At the other end of this distribution we witness an opposite phenomenon. Four per cent of all cases have z scores, disregarding sign, between 1.96 and 2.58. Now this 4 per cent of the probability surface spreads itself along the abscissa from 3.84 to 6.64. And so here the frequency curve settles closer to the abscissa, although it must still stretch interminably to the right, never quite descending to zero. The net effect is as if the normal probability surface had been modeled in soft wax, folded over on its median

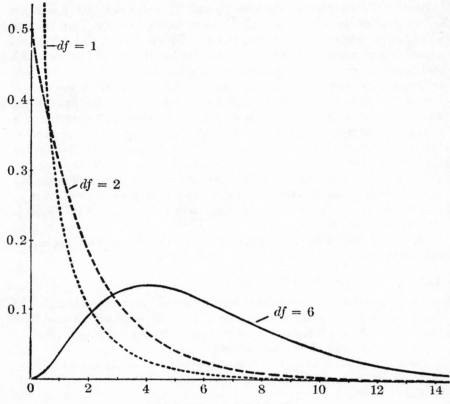

FIG. 9.2. Some χ^2 distributions.

line (since the negative values are eliminated by the squaring), and then squeezed down into the angle formed by the two limiting axes, so that part of it is pushed upward along the ordinate which represents the zero value of z^2, and part of it flows off toward the right along the abscissa.

The curve which we have described is the probability distribution for χ^2 with $df = 1$. The mean of this distribution equals 1, because that is the mean square of any standardized distribution.

Now consider the sum of n elements taken at random from such a distribution. Obviously, as the number of elements entering into the sum increases, very small values grow less common, and large values grow more common. Therefore, as n increases, the mean moves steadily to the right, and it is not difficult to see that for a universe of such sums, for samples of a given n, the mean equals n. The behavior of the mode, or the point of highest relative frequency, is very interesting. When $n = 2$, it is still true that the relative frequency of χ^2 steadily declines as the value of χ^2 increases. Therefore the mode is at zero, but it is no longer asymptotic to that value. When $n = 3$, very small values become relatively less common, and the modal value of χ^2 is unity. From this point forward, as n increases unit by unit, the mean and the mode both advance at the same pace, keeping step precisely, so that henceforth the mode is always equal to $n - 2$. This means that the skew which is such a prominent feature of the χ^2 distribution, for small values of n, becomes less and less pronounced as n increases. That is as we should expect, since we know that the sampling distribution of the mean (or of the sum) approaches normality more and more closely as the sample size increases, even when the parent distribution is quite un-normal in form.

Critical values for these distributions are given in Table IV. In order to use the table it is necessary first to select the appropriate row, that is, to decide how many degrees of freedom are present in the problem. For this we follow the simple rule that $df = (R - 1)(C - 1)$. After that, we select the P value which is associated with the obtained χ^2, just as we select P in the table of t.

The critical values of χ^2 are selected to cut off the stated proportion of the probability surface in a single tail, that is, in the long tail of high values which stretches to the right. However, the squares of both positive and negative deviations have gone into this tail, and therefore the indicated probabilities are those for a two-tailed test of the null hypothesis. Whenever a one-tailed test is appropriate, the P value read from the table may be halved.

COMBINING RESULTS*

The fact that any value of χ^2, with $df > 1$, is an aggregate of other χ^2 values, makes it possible to pool the results of two or more separate investigations of the same problem in order to arrive at a single judgment of their overall significance. Taking each investigation separately, no matter what method of statistical analysis has been used, the P value which has been reached can be converted into a χ^2, and these may then be added together to form a new χ^2 sum, which has as many degrees of freedom as it has independent components. After all, this is essentially what takes place whenever we compute χ^2 from a contingency table which has more than one degree of freedom, as we have already seen in the "case of the loving sons." This method permits us to deal effectively with a problem which we mentioned earlier, namely, how to interpret the results of an investigation which has included several tests of the same hypothesis,

---

* This section presents a deceptively simple approach to an often perplexing problem. The reader who wants to look into the matter more thoroughly might begin with Mosteller and Bush,[4] who describe several more sophisticated techniques, and show that they may still lead to differing conclusions.

some of which yielded results which appear to be significant (see page 117). If the probability of each separate outcome is converted into a χ^2, the sum may be used to judge the joint significance of all the outcomes. For example, if three independent tests of one hypothesis yield χ^2 values of 1.74, 2.80, and 3.52, none of which is significant by itself, their joint significance, if they are consistent in trend, is that of $\chi^2 = 8.06$ with $df = 3$, whence $P < .05$. If, on the other hand, the χ^2 values for the independent tests had been 1.07, 0.56, and 3.92, one would not be justified in basing a conclusion on the last of these values alone. Since their sum, which has $df = 3$, equals 5.55, it is necessary to conclude that $P > .05$. We cannot rely on the single significant-seeming result, in the light of the others. This is an application of the general principle that the amount of allowance which we make for error depends on the degree of consistency in our experience.

This also has implications for the interpretation of the separate discrepancies which exist in a large contingency table. It will sometimes happen that the discrepancy between the obtained and expected frequency for a single cell may seem significant by itself, although the value for the table as a whole is not significant. In such a case, we must remember that by incorporating n tests of a single hypothesis in a large experimental plan, we have multiplied n-fold the chance of obtaining a result which, viewed by itself alone, would appear significant. If χ^2 for the table as a whole is not significant, we must assume that all discrepancies within the table are chance. However, if χ^2 for the entire table meets the test of significance, then we should look at the contribution of each row and column, regarding each as having df equal to the number of cells in the row or column, less one. Such interpretations will err slightly on the side of conservatism. Wherever we have a significant row or column figure, we should look at the contributions of the individual cells. In this way we can form a fairly good picture of the source of the effects which have been observed in the experiment.

GOODNESS OF FIT

In tests of independence or homogeneity (two names for the same method), the empirical data are used to construct the null hypothesis. Another way to state this is that the column sums, in the table of expected frequencies, constitute the null hypothesis, for they give rise to the estimate of proportions for the hypothetical parent universe. The χ^2 method also permits us to free ourselves from this empiricism. It is often possible to set up a series of expectations, or predictions, which are based on some theory that is independent of the empirical observations, and then to test whether theory and experience are in reasonable agreement. This method is called testing *goodness of fit*.

We can illustrate this by fulfilling a promise made in Chapter 6. There, we presented the results of a small experiment of the Monte Carlo type, in which odd and even digits taken from a random table were regarded as representing "heads" and "tails" resulting from imaginary coin-tossing. We said then that later we would test whether the results conformed to the expectation fixed by the binomial expansion. Table **9**.5 presents the

TABLE **9**.5

Goodness of Fit in a Monte Carlo Experiment, Where Each Observation Records the Number of "Heads" in a Group of Five

"Heads"	f_o	f_e	$(f_o - f_e)^2/f_e$
5	9	10	.10
4	47	50	.18
3	95	100	.25
2	115	100	2.25
1	47	50	.18
0	7	10	.90
	320	320	3.86

$$\chi^2 = 3.86; \quad df = 5; \quad .50 < P < .70$$

obtained and expected frequencies. Each unit in the f_o column represents the result of five symbolic "tosses." The proportions for the f_e column are taken from the Pascal triangle (Table I), since the hypothesis implies that $p = q$, that heads will be as likely as tails. The last column of the table gives the cell contribution to χ^2. This value has 5 degrees of freedom, because there is only one way in which the obtained frequencies have been constrained to agree with the expected frequencies, namely, in their total number. It is therefore very much a chance result, and we cannot reject the null hypothesis that the "coins" have behaved as predicted. This is an example of exceptionally good fit of experience to theory. If we were to make a large number of tests of this sort, in order to test the randomness of the table of digits which was used in the experiment, we would not be satisfied with the results unless a proper proportion of the results yielded lower probability figures. For, if the table of random numbers is to be an adequate model of chance, it must include the rare chance as well as the common chance, each in its proper frequency.

The test for "good fit" is often used to determine whether a given set of data may be regarded as a sample from a normal universe. For example, we might ask whether the distribution of IQ's among the school-age children in a certain rural district "fits" a normal distribution. In making the test, we must be careful in the definition of our theoretical assumptions. If we wish to test *only* whether the data may be regarded as a sample from a normal universe, without making any assumptions as to the parameters of that universe, then for the calculation of the f_e values we would use the mean, the variance, and the n of the sample. This means that there would be three ways in which the two series of frequencies would be constrained to agree, and the resulting value of χ^2 would have $df = k - 3$, where k is the number of categories in which the obtained and expected frequencies are compared. (To set up the expected frequencies, we first define convenient IQ classes; we then transform the theoretical limits of those classes into z scores; the normal table tells us what proportion of the distribution to expect within each class so defined; multiplying these proportions by the sample n gives the expected frequencies.)

Suppose, however, that we wish to know whether the sample may be regarded as coming from a normal universe in which $\bar{X} = 100$. In this case we would use both the n of the sample and its variance to determine the expected frequencies, but we would not constrain the two series of frequencies to agree with respect to their mean values. Therefore, $df = k - 2$.

Finally, if we wish to know whether the sample may be regarded as coming from a normal universe in which $\bar{X} = 100$ and $\sigma = 16$, we would use these values together with the n of the sample to determine the expected frequencies. The two series of frequencies would be constrained to agree in only one way, and $df = k - 1$.

Every statistical test of significance is, in one sense, a test of fit. We select an appropriate pattern which has been designed by the mathematical statistician, and we make it up in a size which has been determined by some of the measurements in our own experience. This becomes the error estimate of variance. We try this on for fit, by matching it against the information estimate of variance. When "goodness of fit" is what we are interested in, we look closely at the tails and shoulders, and insist on fairly close limits of tolerance throughout. But in the usual test of significance we are no more critical than a five-year-old who tries on his father's jacket. The bigger the tails, the happier we are, for we only want to insure ourselves that the garment is big enough. If it is outsize, or just a little skimpy, we accept it nonetheless. We reject it only when it is hopelessly too small to provide decent coverage.

PROBLEMS

1. *Bernstein*[5] *studied the relationship between coercive bowel training in infancy and certain behavior in children 4 to 5 years old. Some of the*

data which he reports are summarized in Table **9.6.** *Which of these relationships is significant?*

TABLE **9.**6

Frequency of Certain Behavioral Characteristics in Children Who Had
Received Coercive or Noncoercive Bowel Training in Infancy*

| | Bowel Training | |
	Coercive	*Noncoercive*
Collector	22	12
Noncollector	9	4
Negativistic	13	2
Cooperative	18	14
Uncommunicative	17	4
Verbal	13	12
Constipated	16	6
Nonconstipated	15	10

*Based on Bernstein.[5]

2. *Requests for renewal of membership in a university alumni association were printed on colored mailing cards. Returns were received from 88 of 147 who received white cards, from 105 of 144 who received yellow cards, from 92 of 141 who received blue cards, and from 74 of 140 who received cherry cards. Does color influence the returns? (Based on Dunlap[6].)*

3. *"What kind of work would you like to do as an adult?" Douvan and Adelson[7] put this question to boys, aged 14 to 16, whose fathers were in skilled or semi-skilled manual jobs, sales or clerical jobs, or small business enterprises. The answers were classified as indicating a tendency to upward or downward social mobility, or stability in this regard, relative to the father's occupation. The boys were also classified as to many other characteristics of behavior or background. Table* **9.**7 *reports several of the resulting comparisons. In each case, determine whether the background characteristic is significantly related to social mobility.*

4. *The 1958 Directory of the American Psychological Association lists 1284 members who are diplomates of the American Board of Examiners in Professional Psychology. Of these, 872 hold the diploma in clinical psychology, 249 in counseling psychology, and 163 in industrial psychology. Table* **9.**8 *reports the distribution of diplomates in these specialty areas, for each state in which at least 35 diplomates reside. Are there significant differences in the distribution from state to state? Pinpoint the differences as well as you can. Do these states, taken as a group, differ significantly from those having less than 35 diplomates?*

TABLE 9.7

Per Cent of Boys Showing Various Kinds of Social Mobility in Their Job
Aspirations, Relative to Certain Other Characteristics*

| | Social Mobility | | |
	Upward $n = 277$	Stable $n = 168$	Downward $n = 73$
Dating			
Do date	66	59	52
Do not date	34	41	48
Humor			
Present	74	67	58
Absent	26	33	42
Punishment			
Physical	2	8	15
Deprivational	66	69	65
Psychological	32	23	20

* Based on Douvan and Adelson.[7]

TABLE 9.8

Number of ABEPP Diplomates, by Specialty Areas, in Each of Nine States
and the District of Columbia.

| State | Specialty Area | | |
	Clinical	Counseling	Industrial
California	114	30	13
Connecticut	19	7	10
Illinois	67	15	9
Massachusetts	33	7	2
Michigan	32	5	10
New Jersey	34	7	4
New York	165	49	33
Ohio	36	11	11
Pennsylvania	41	5	10
Dist. of Columbia	23	11	8
	564	147	110

5. *The following question is put to 30 10-year-old boys: "Would you
rather be a doctor or an engineer when you grow up?" How many choices
must be made for one of these professions in order to conclude that there is
evidence of a real preference in the population being sampled? (Hint: Let
$f_o = f_e \pm d$, and solve for the smallest integral value of d needed to produce
a significant χ^2.)*

6. *State and test a goodness-of-fit hypothesis with respect to the class experiment on the sampling variance of means.*

7. *Hartshorne and May*[8] *compared the incidence of cheating among elementary school children from families of good socio-economic status and from those of poor socio-economic status. They detected cheating in the experimental situation by 144 of 348 children in the former category, and 133 of 215 children in the latter category. Test whether this might be regarded as a chance difference, using both (a) the method of difference in proportions and (b) the chi-square technique.*

8. *Devise and test a new series of three independent null hypotheses regarding the data in Table* 9.4, *and verify that the sum of* χ^2 *values is still the same. (Do not use correction for continuity.)*

REFERENCES

1. MacKinnon, D. W. Violation of prohibitions. *In* H. A. Murray, *Explorations in personality*, 1938, New York: Oxford Univ. Press., *pp.* 491–501.

2. Armsen, P. Tables for significance tests of 2 x 2 contingency tables. *Biometrika*, 1957, 13:113–115.

3. Diamond, S. The house and tree in verbal fantasy: I. Age and sex differences in themes and content. *J. proj. Tech.*, 1954, **18**:316–325.

4. Mosteller, F., and Bush, R. R. Selected quantitative techniques. In *Handbook of social psychology*, vol. 1. Ed. by G. Lindzey. Cambridge, Mass.: Addison-Wesley, 1954.

5. Bernstein, A. Some relations between techniques of feeding and training during infancy and certain behavior in childhood. *Genet. Psychol. Monogr.*, 1955, **51**:3–44.

6. Dunlap, J. W. The effect of color in direct mail advertising. *J. appl. Psychol.*, 1950, **34**:280–281.

7. Douvan, Eliz., and Adelson, J. The psychodynamics of social mobility in adolescent boys. *J. abn. soc. Psychol.*, 1958, **56**:31–44.

8. Hartshorne, H., and May, M. A. *Studies in deceit*, 1928, New York: Macmillan.

10

PRODUCT MOMENT CORRELATION

When boy meets girl, what happens depends on how much they have in common. So it is when X meets Y, that is, when two variables are joined in our deliberations. It is the sound evaluation of that "something in common" which permits us to make an informed surmise about the behavior of Y when we know something about the behavior of X. What they have in common can be measured as common variance.

BIVARIATE DISTRIBUTION

Preceding chapters have studied the vicissitudes of a single variable, X, under changing circumstances. In each problem, these different circumstances have constituted the independent variable, but they have been defined only as categories (such as sex or national origin) and not as measured steps on a continuum. A statistic which we have found useful under these conditions is the differentiation ratio. Neither the order of the categories nor the logic of their relationship enters into the computation of this ratio. We need the categories only in order to sort the scores on the dependent variable into convenient groupings. The magnitude of the ratio, and its significance, tell us whether the method of classification is a useful one.

It often happens that the independent variable is just as amenable to measurement as the dependent variable, and that the categories are simply convenient classes of scores on this second dimension. The fact that each observation on the Y dimension has also been classified on the X dimension means that the scores are paired, like the animals marching

166

into Noah's ark. It is possible then to regard one set of scores as a function of the other set, as grades are a function of time spent in studying, or as glamor is a function of money spent on the wardrobe. As one can see from these examples, we are not supposing that one variable is completely dependent on the second, to the exclusion of other influences, for who would deny, for example, that intelligence heightens glamor, or that beauty influences grades?

In any such case of *bivariate distribution* it is possible to compute two quite distinct differentiation ratios, for it is only in our own point of view that one of the variables is identified as dependent, and the other as independent. Ordinarily, these two ratios have different values. For illustration, let us take up the question of what happens when boy meets girl. This would be a less frustrating world if love were always requited in equal measure. In that case, we would always know how much Tom loves Mary, from knowing how much affection Mary has for Tom. But alas! the love we receive is not always equivalent to the love we give. Surely, this is a matter which deserves scientific investigation. Table **10.**1

TABLE **10.**1

Ratings of Intensity of Love Felt by Each Member of a "Steady" Pair
toward the Other Member (Fictional Data)

Pair	His Love (B)	Her Love (G)
Arthur-Alice	2	5
Ben-Betty	8	6
Charles-Claire	7	5
David-Doris	5	5
Edward-Edith	4	6
Fred-Frances	4	3
George-Gladys	3	4
Henry-Harriet	2	3
Irving-Isabel	5	3
Joseph-Janet	6	6
Kenneth-Kay	7	7
Lawrence-Louise	3	2

presents data on the reciprocity of affection in 12 pairs of young people, all of whom had been "going steady" for six months or more. The scores given in the table are ratings on the Timeless Scale of Love, for which, unfortunately, no convenient reference is available. However, this scale assigns a rating of zero to humane indifference and a rating of 10 to the passion of Tristan for Isolde.

TABLE **10**.2

Scatter Diagram of Scores Given in Table **10**.1, with Computations for
the Differentiation Ratios

				His Love (B)					Summary for grouped rows
	2	3	4	5	6	7	8		
7						o			$m = 4$ $\Sigma B = 25$ $\Sigma B^2 = 165$
6			o		o		o		
5	o			o		o			$m = 4$ $\Sigma B = 17$ $\Sigma B^2 = 87$
4		o							
3	o		o	o					$m = 4$ $\Sigma B = 14$ $\Sigma B^2 = 54$
2		o							

Her Love (G) — (row label on left axis)

Grand Sums

Summary for grouped columns

$m = 4$	$m = 4$	$m = 4$		$n = 12$
$\Sigma G = 14$	$\Sigma G = 17$	$\Sigma G = 24$		$\Sigma\Sigma B = 56$
$\Sigma G^2 = 54$	$\Sigma G^2 = 79$	$\Sigma G^2 = 146$		$\Sigma\Sigma B^2 = 306$
				$\Sigma\Sigma G = 55$
				$\Sigma\Sigma G^2 = 279$

Table **10**.2 shows the distribution of these 12 pairs of scores in a two-dimensional space which is defined by the scales for B and G. Each *pair* of scores is represented by a single point in this space. Since each point is fixed by two scores, the distribution of points is called bivariate. Looking at this *scatter diagram*, we perceive that there is a tendency for each lover to receive a fair return on his or her investment of affection. However, this equity is far from absolute. At least one young man gets a good though not spectacular return on a fairly low investment; the young lady in this pair is receiving less than "measure for measure."

The broken lines in the table show how the scores on each dimension have been used to assort the scores *on the other dimension* into categories, and a summary of the basic data for each of the categories is given in the margin of the table. Using Formula 10 (see page 55), let us first compute the differentiation ratio* based on the scores of boys, when they are classified according to the scores of their girl friends:

$$\eta^2_{b.g} = 1 - \frac{306 - (25^2 + 17^2 + 14^2)/4}{306 - 56^2/12} = .36$$

We read "eta-square of b on g," understanding this to mean "the differentiation ratio for scores of boys as dependent on the scores of girls." The other differentiation ratio is based on the scores of girls, classified according to the scores of their boy friends:

$$\eta^2_{g.b} = 1 - \frac{279 - (24^2 + 17^2 + 14^2)/4}{279 - 55^2/12} = .49$$

It may at first puzzle the reader that these two values are not the same. Yet, after all, do we not commonly assume that the human female is more responsive to attentions, and hence less "independent" in the formation of attachments, than the human male? It is just this difference in the degree of dependency which is expressed in the inequality

$$\eta^2_{g.b} > \eta^2_{b.g}$$

Furthermore, the inequality of the differentiation ratios is in keeping with the fact that, if the data were subjected to a two-dimensional analysis of variance, we would hardly expect that the row-estimate and the column estimate of variance should be identical.

To make the matter clearer, let us look at a more extreme illustration of the fact that the influence of X on Y may often be quite different from the influence of Y on X. There is experimental evidence to show an interactive effect between anxiety and rote learning, in the sense that low-anxiety subjects do relatively better on difficult tasks, and high-anxiety subjects do relatively better on easy tasks. This suggests an hypothesis that the optimal level of anxiety for top efficiency varies from one task to another, and that for some tasks a medium level of anxiety would lead to better performance than that of either nonanxious or highly anxious subjects. Assuming this to be true, a distribution of scores for anxiety level and for performance on such a task would take a ∪-shaped form, which has been shown schematically in Table 10.3. (Such a distribution is called ∪-shaped even when, as in this case, it looks like a ∨ turned upside down.) Possibly the learning of elementary statistics would provide such a case, in which moderate anxiety would provide needed motivation without leading to the disabling effects of high anxiety. In a case of this

* We ask the reader to be tolerant of the small number of cases involved in this fictional problem. However, the trustworthiness of the result is not at issue here, and we trust no one will be persuaded by this example to use the differentiation ratio on such scant data.

TABLE 10.3

Per Cent of Subjects, at Each of Five Anxiety Levels, Scoring at Various Performance Levels on a Task for Which Medium Anxiety is Optimal (hypothetical)

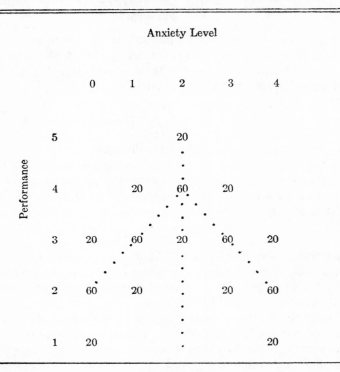

	Anxiety Level				
Performance	0	1	2	3	4
5			20		
4		20	60	20	
3	20	60	20	60	20
2	60	20		20	60
1	20				20

sort, the differentiation ratio for learning as dependent on anxiety could attain a significant level, although the differentiation ratio in which anxiety is the dependent variable would be essentially zero. This reflects the fact that knowledge of an individual's anxiety level permits us to conclude that his performance will probably be average, better than average, or worse than average, but a knowledge of his performance does not provide the basis for a similar conclusion regarding anxiety.

The dotted lines in Table 10.3, which connect the mean values of categories, are called *regression lines*. (This may seem like an odd name; the reason for it will appear later.) Notice that the line which connects the means of horizontal arrays is not only straight, but is also perpendicular to the horizontal axis. These means are not differentiated, and hence the differentiation ratio in which this axis represents the dependent variable equals zero. The line which connects the means of vertical arrays changes direction, and it is therefore described as *nonlinear*. This indicates that the influence in question is not exerted uniformly throughout the range of categories represented. That is, anxiety does not always have the same effect on performance in this task, so that successive increments of anxiety do not lead to successive increments in performance. As anxiety builds up, one reaches a turning-point in anxiety tolerance, and at this point the regression line also takes a turn.

REGRESSION AND PREDICTION

The concept of regression was developed by Francis Galton in the course of his studies of heredity. One of the problems to which Galton devoted much careful thought was the influence of a father's physical stature on that of his son. He organized his data into a two-dimensional scatter diagram, and as he pored over it he was struck by the fact that the sons of tall men are, on the average, not so tall as their fathers, and the sons of short men are, on the average, not so short as their fathers. To guess a man's height, knowing the height of his father, it is best to pick a value somewhere between the general mean of the population and his father's height. (The same kind of generalization would apply if we wanted to guess a father's height from a measurement on his son.)

For someone less firmly convinced than Galton about the central importance of heredity, it might have seemed natural to sum this up by saying that the son's height can be represented as the population average modified by the influence of paternal heredity. From Galton's point of view, however, it seemed better to describe the son's height as the father's height modified by other factors. As he phrased it, there is a tendency to "regress to mediocrity," to return toward the general average, as an expression of the hereditary influence of all earlier generations. This formulation of the problem survives in our terminology. Whenever we speak of the possibility of forecasting one score from another, we speak of *regression* in the sense of *prediction*.

The story has a moral which every psychologist must bear in mind whenever he interprets a test score. When we attempt to forecast scholastic grades from a test of academic aptitude, or job success from a vocational aptitude test, or therapeutic outcomes from a clinical test—or "her love" from what we know of "his love"—we must always bear in mind that other factors are active in determining the outcome besides those about which we have information. We must therefore anticipate "regression to mediocrity"—that is, an outcome which will probably be less extreme than the individual's standing on the prognostic instrument.

When an individual has been classified according to his score on the independent variable, it is possible to forecast his "most probable" score on the dependent variable. The forecast should be our best estimate of the representative score for all the individuals classified in the same category. If we had abundant data in every class, this would imply that when an individual has been classified according to his score on X, the best guess for his score on Y is $\bar{Y}_k$, that is, the mean Y score of all persons in the same class. However, the obtained mean is not necessarily the best estimate of the representative score for a class in which we have limited information. When we look at the general trend of all the class means, it may be quite evident that some are "out of line." Thus, if a sample of 10-year-olds makes higher vocabulary scores than an otherwise comparable sample of 12-year-olds, we feel sure that the result is due to sampling error, and we feel justified in adjusting the estimates for both classes, if need be, in order to arrive at a more consistent picture. When we do this we are acknowledging that the scores of 8-year-olds and 12-year-olds, and those of other children younger and older, all give us some information about 10-year-olds. We cannot doubt this, because if we had information *only* about 8-year-olds and 12-year-olds we would still be able to form a reasonable hypothesis about the probable scores of 10-year-olds. The most reasonable hypothesis would be to assume a linear regression—that is, to place the mean for 10-year-olds midway between the means for 8-year-olds and for 12-year-olds.

When we have data in many classes, we face a similar but more complex problem of adjustment by give-and-take, for we are aware that every one of the class means includes some sampling error. It is natural, therefore, to entertain the hypothesis that the true class means should all fall on a straight line, and that any departure from such linearity is due to sampling error. This is a simplifying or *parsimonious* hypothesis, and it is customary to make this assumption unless there is compelling evidence to the contrary. It amounts to stating that whatever influence X may have on Y, or Y on X, or some third factor on both, is exercised "measure for measure" throughout the range of scores being studied on both variables. We assume that if a one-unit increment in X leads to a certain amount of increment in Y in one part of the range, then a one-unit increment in X will lead to the same increment in Y in any other part of the range. Following the basic logic of the null hypothesis, we assume that any departure from this kind of regularity is due to sampling error, unless it is big enough to make this explanation seem implausible. A visual inspection of the scatter diagram often suffices to convince us that the hypothesis of linear regression cannot be safely rejected. (A later section will describe a formal test for the significance of the departure from linearity.)

The Line of Best Fit

Thus, we formulate the hypothesis of linear regression because we recognize the need for some method of adjusting the class means, in order to arrive at a more valid series of representative scores. Necessarily, the within-sum of squares—that is, the sum of squares of all obtained scores from the class means—will be increased when the deviations are taken with respect to these adjusted means or *regressed scores* rather than with respect to the obtained class means. That is,

$$\Sigma(Y - Y')^2 > \Sigma(Y - \bar{Y}_k)^2$$

where Y' stands for a regressed score, and the difference $(Y - Y')$ is called an *error of prediction*. The amount of this increase will depend on just how the regressed scores are selected. According to the *least squares principle* (in which we should now have considerable confidence) the most satisfactory set of regressed scores will be that which leads to the smallest sum of squared errors of prediction. The line which connects these regressed scores is called the *line of best fit*. How shall we find it?

Let us experiment with this problem. Look at Table **10**.2 and, using a string or a transparent straight-edge, indicate how you would draw a line to express the trend of the data. Very likely the line which you contemplate is one which runs from lower left to upper right. Perhaps you have made a conscious though hasty effort to apply the least squares principle, that the line must be so placed that the sum of the squared distances of score-points from the line is at a minimum. However, you have probably perceived the distance of each point from the line as measured by a perpendicular to the line. Handling the problem in this way, if you were given the same task with respect to Figures **10**.1 and **10**.2, you would in each

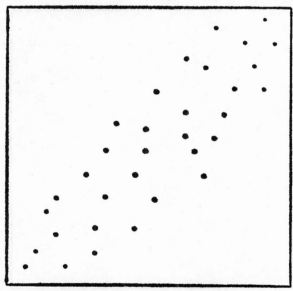

Fig. **10**.1. A case of high positive correlation.

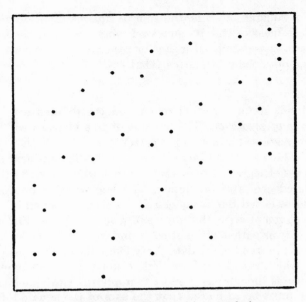

FIG. **10.**2. A case of low positive correlation.

case draw the principal axis of an ellipse which might be drawn to enclose all the points. Then, coming to Figure **10.**3, you would be perplexed. If

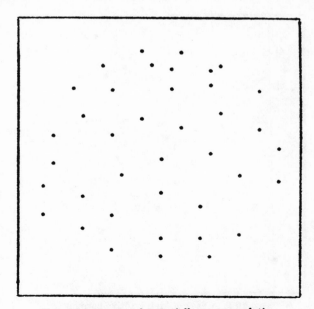

FIG. **10.**3. A case of essentially zero correlation.

this is what you have done, you must now be aware that it cannot be a satisfactory solution, since it leads to similar results in different cases, and sometimes to an indeterminate result.

What has been overlooked is that just as there are two differentiation ratios, so there are two regression lines. Since the Y regression must select values of Y' for *given* values of X, the residual errors must be measured perpendicular to the X axis. This changes the problem from the form in which we first tend to perceive it. Now we see that the line which seemed plausible at first must be shifted, by pushing the left end up just a little above the diagonal position, and pulling the right end down. We shall call this line (or rather, the line which it approximates, which really reduces $[\Sigma (Y - Y')^2/n]$ to a minimum), the Y regression, or the regression of Y on X. Now draw the regression of X on Y, that is, the line which reduces $[\Sigma (X - X')^2/n]$ to a minimum, when the residuals are measured perpendicular to the Y axis. Try the same thing for Figures **10.1**, **10.2**, and **10.3**. In Figure **10.1**, the angular separation of the two lines should be about 5 degrees; in Figure **10.2**, it should be about 30 degrees; while in Figure **10.3**, the two best fit lines are approximately parallel to the axes and hence virtually perpendicular to each other. (The reader should satisfy himself about the necessity of these results.) This approach to our problem gives some promise of useful meaning, for the position of the regression lines, and the angle of their separation, seem to be related to the strength of association of the scores on the two variables. However, we need a better way to find these lines than just guessing at their position.

THE LINE OF BEST FIT: INTUITIVE DEMONSTRATION

Every schoolboy learns that the position of a straight line can be fixed by two points. For our problem, it will be more convenient to use the relatively sophisticated technique of the surveyor: to define the line by fixing one point and the line's direction. We shall do this first in intuitive terms, which are intended only to arrive at a plausible hypothesis. The following section will offer an algebraic proof that the hypothesis so formulated is correct.

Let us begin by considering a bivariate distribution in which X and Y are quite independent. This might be the case, for example, if we were to study the relationship between hair pigmentation (X) and villainy (Y). Let us suppose that the data have been summarized in a scatter diagram (Figure **10.4**) in which the four quadrants are defined by the lines $x = 0$ and $y = 0$. The points which represent dark villains fall in the upper-right quadrant, while those representing fair and honest men fall in the lower-left. These are called *positive quadrants*, since the value of the xy product for any point within them is positive. Fair villains, and dark but honest men, inhabit the two *negative quadrants*. If we find

Hair Pigmentation (X)

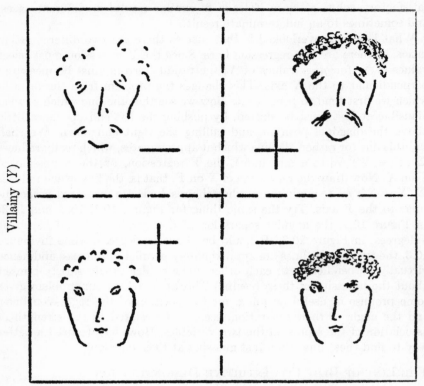

FIG. **10**.4. The quadrants of a bivariate distribution.

that the positive quadrants and the negative quadrants are about equally populated, it would be rash to use the pigment in a man's hair to blacken his reputation. Be he black or be he blond, in the absence of other information our best estimate of his character must be that he is middling-honest. That is, under these conditions the regressed score for Villainy is always $\bar{Y}$. The regression line coincides with the line $y = 0$, which runs parallel to the X axis.

But suppose that it were really true that dark men tend to be more villainous, and fair men more honest? In that case, the positive quadrants would be relatively more populated, reflecting the increased probability that the fair are honest, and the dark are villains. Following this evidence, we must suppose that whenever a man is darker than his fellows, he is likely also to be a greater villain, and he who is fairer is likely to be the more honest. The regression line to represent this trend must tip upward at the right, and downward at the left. If, contrary to expectation, we find that more of the fair are villains, and more of the dark are honest, the regression line will rise to the left and decline to the right. In all cases, there remains one constant point, on which the line pivots: as long as the regression remains linear, no matter what the strength or manner of the relationship between the two variables, the mean score on X must always have the mean score on Y as its most probable associate. Therefore, at the point where $x = 0$, the line of best fit must cross the line $y = 0$. This point is called the *origin*.

Having fixed one point through which the line of best fit must pass, let us see what we can infer about its direction. This task will be simplified if we assume that each set of scores has been standardized, so that

$$\frac{\Sigma x^2}{n} = \frac{\Sigma y^2}{n} = 1$$

(To avoid the cumbersome notation of z scores, we shall use small boldface letters to represent standard scores.)

This time let us consider the case of total linear dependence of Y on X, so that every increment in x is associated with an exactly equal increment in y. Since the two scores in each pair match exactly, the sum of products is equal to the sum of squares for either set of scores:

$$\Sigma xy = \Sigma x^2 = \Sigma y^2$$

Hence the mean product, $\Sigma xy/n$, is equal to the mean square of either distribution, which is 1.

In a scatter diagram, all of the points fixed by these perfectly matched pairs of scores lie on a straight line through the origin, which is the diagonal of the positive quadrants. The direction of this line can be defined by its *slope*, or rate of rise relative to one of the axes, in the same way that we speak of the slope or grade of a mountain road. A road with a 6 per cent grade is one which rises 60 feet in very 1000. When we are dealing with the Y regression, it is the line for $y = 0$ which represents the "water level" against which we measure its rise or fall, and along which we measure the length of x, the horizontal component. If we let r stand for the *rate of rise* or the *slope* of the Y regression—a meaning which is compatible with other meanings which we shall associate with this symbol as the discussion continues—then

$$r = \frac{y'}{x}$$

Where there is complete linear dependence, $y' = x$, and hence $r = 1$, which is also the value of the mean product.

It is possible to have an equally complete dependence of Y on X, in which the smallest X is paired with the largest Y, and largest X is paired with the smallest Y. In that case, each standard score is paired with one which is exactly equal in magnitude, but opposite in sign. Hence, $\Sigma xy = -\Sigma x^2$. The mean product is -1, and the points which represent the bivariate distribution fall on a line through the origin which is the diagonal of the negative quadrants, and which drops one unit for every unit of horizontal advance.

The two cases which we have just described are limiting cases, which show that the mean product of standardized scores cannot have a value greater than $+1$ nor less than -1. Notice that in each case the mean product is also equal to the slope of the regression line.

As a third case, we may take up again the situation in which there is a complete lack of dependence between the two variables, so that $\mathbf{y} = 0$ constitutes the regression line. Under this condition, the negative values of within-pair products are about as large, and about as frequent, as positive values, and the sum of products will differ from zero only by chance. The slope of the best-fit line is zero, and that is also the mean product.

In each of the cases which we have considered, the mean product has been equal to the slope of the regression line. If this should be true in all cases, it would be a most convenient solution to the problem of locating that line.

The Line of Best Fit: Algebraic Proof

The complete hypothesis which we developed in the preceding section is that the line of best fit, in any case of linear regression, passes through the point $x = 0$, $y = 0$, and that it has a slope which is equal to the mean product of standardized scores. In mathematical treatises on statistics, these facts are ordinarily established by the solution of two differential equations. Though less elegant, a proof which does not resort to calculus will be more useful to us, particularly in developing insight into certain important relationships among the distributions of obtained and regressed scores. (Readers who are highly allergic to mathematical proofs may prefer to skip this section.)

Figure **10**.5 represents a two-dimensional space in which we have drawn the lines for $x = 0$ and $y = 0$. Through their intersection we have drawn a trial best-fit line. For any value of $\mathbf{x}$, the corresponding regressed score, $\mathbf{y'}$, is the height of this line. Therefore the slope of the line at any point is

$$r = \mathbf{y'}/\mathbf{x}$$

Hence, $\mathbf{y'} = r\mathbf{x}$. To obtain a general expression for the mean squared residual, we . . .

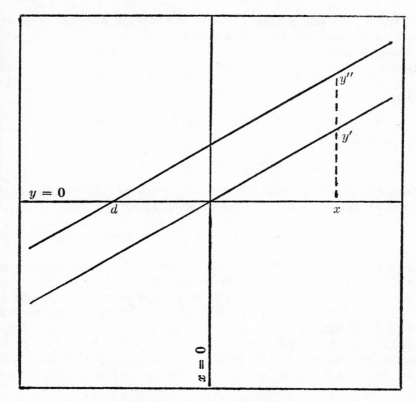

FIG. **10.5.** Comparison of trial best-fit lines.

make that substitution:

$$\mathbf{y} - \mathbf{y}' = \mathbf{y} - r\mathbf{x}$$

then square:

$$(\mathbf{y} - \mathbf{y}')^2 = \mathbf{y}^2 - 2r\mathbf{x}\mathbf{y} + r^2\mathbf{x}^2$$

then sum:

$$\Sigma(\mathbf{y} - \mathbf{y}')^2 = \Sigma\mathbf{y}^2 - 2r\,\Sigma\mathbf{x}\mathbf{y} + r^2\,\Sigma\mathbf{x}^2$$

and then divide by n:

$$\frac{\Sigma(\mathbf{y} - \mathbf{y}')^2}{n} = 1 - 2r\frac{\Sigma\mathbf{x}\mathbf{y}}{n} + r^2$$

Now imagine that the trial line is shifted to the left by a distance d, without changing its slope, as in the figure. As a result, the value of the regressed score which is associated with any value of x is equal to $y'' = r(x + d)$. We now repeat the same steps as above:

Make the substitution:

$$y - y'' = y - r(x + d) = y - rx - rd \,,$$

and square:

$$(y - y'')^2 = y^2 - 2rxy - 2rdy + r^2x^2 + 2r^2dx + r^2d^2$$

and sum:

$$\Sigma(y - y'')^2 = \Sigma y^2 - 2r\,\Sigma xy - 2rd\,\Sigma y + r^2\,\Sigma x^2 + 2r^2d\,\Sigma x + nr^2d^2$$

Here the third and the fifth terms on the righthand side drop out, since Σx and Σy equal zero. Now, taking the mean square:

$$\frac{\Sigma(y - y'')^2}{n} = 1 - 2r\,\frac{\Sigma xy}{n} + r^2 + r^2d^2$$

The last term represents an "excess" which resulted from shifting the line without changing its slope. If we had made the shift in the other direction, then $y'' = r(x - d)$. The same steps would have brought us to the same final result. We conclude that the mean squared residual from a linear regression, with any given slope, is smallest when the line passes through the origin. Therefore, when we seek the line of best fit, we need to consider only the bundle of lines which pass through that point. From among these lines we must select one which has the optimal slope.

We now turn to the second part of the hypothesis which arose from the intuitive discussion in the preceding section: that the slope of the best-fit line is equal to the mean product of standard scores. We return to the general expression for the mean squared residual from any line which passes through the origin:

$$\frac{\Sigma(y - y')^2}{n} = 1 - 2r\,\frac{\Sigma xy}{n} + r^2$$

Letting $r = \Sigma xy/n$, in accordance with the hypothesis, this becomes:

$$\frac{\Sigma(y - y')^2}{n} = 1 - 2\left(\frac{\Sigma xy}{n}\right)^2 + \left(\frac{\Sigma xy}{n}\right)^2 = 1 - \left(\frac{\Sigma xy}{n}\right)^2$$

Now, for comparison, we will let $r = \left(\dfrac{\Sigma xy}{n} - d\right)$, where d may have any value whatever. Substituting as above,

$$\frac{\Sigma(y - y')^2}{n} = 1 - 2\left(\frac{\Sigma xy}{n} - d\right)\left(\frac{\Sigma xy}{n}\right) + \left(\frac{\Sigma xy}{n} - d\right)^2$$

$$= 1 - 2\left(\frac{\Sigma xy}{n}\right)^2 + 2d\left(\frac{\Sigma xy}{n}\right) + \left(\frac{\Sigma xy}{n}\right)^2 - 2d\left(\frac{\Sigma xy}{n}\right) + d^2$$

$$= 1 - \frac{\Sigma xy^2}{n} + d^2$$

Again, the last term represents an excess over the sum of squares obtained when $r = \Sigma xy/n$. If we had let $r = \left(\frac{\Sigma xy}{n} + d\right)$ we would have reached the same result. Our hunch is confirmed: the slope of the best fit line is the mean product of the standard scores, for a line of any other slope will yield a larger sum of squares.

Notice this interesting corollary: since the slope depends only on the mean product of standard scores, it is the same for both regression lines. Here, at last, we have found something which both variables do truly "have in common"!

THE PRODUCT MOMENT CORRELATION

The usual symbol for the mean product of standard scores in a bivariate distribution is r. This symbol, to use a Freudian term, is "overdetermined." It originated in Galton's conception of *r*egression, but it may also be regarded as standing for a measure of *r*elationship, or as the *r*ate of change in one variable expressed as a proportion of the change taking place in the other. In any event, it is the accepted symbol for the statistic which Karl Pearson devised to meet the problem set by his fellow-Londoner, Galton. It is called the product moment correlation, or Pearson's coefficient of correlation. He defined it thus:

43] $$r_{xy} = \frac{\Sigma xy}{n\sigma_X\sigma_Y}$$

Since $\Sigma xy/n$ is called *covariance*, r may be called the *standardized covariance*. But these are confusing terms, for later we shall find occasion to speak of r^2, rather than r, as the measure of *common variance*.

We need a convenient computational substitute for Formula 43. To develop this, we shall handle the numerator and the denominator separately, so that the steps can be more easily followed by the reader. The numerator is developed in this manner:

$$\Sigma xy = \Sigma[(X - \bar{X})(Y - \bar{Y})]$$

$$= \Sigma[XY - \bar{X}Y - X\bar{Y} + \bar{X}\bar{Y}]$$

$$= \Sigma\left[XY - \frac{\Sigma X}{n}Y - X\frac{\Sigma Y}{n} + \left(\frac{\Sigma X}{n}\right)\left(\frac{\Sigma Y}{n}\right)\right]$$

$$= \Sigma XY - \frac{(\Sigma X)(\Sigma Y)}{n} - \frac{(\Sigma X)(\Sigma Y)}{n} + n\left(\frac{\Sigma X}{n}\right)\left(\frac{\Sigma Y}{n}\right)$$

$$= \Sigma XY - 2\frac{(\Sigma X)(\Sigma Y)}{n} + \frac{(\Sigma X)(\Sigma Y)}{n}$$

$$= \Sigma XY - \frac{(\Sigma X)(\Sigma Y)}{n}$$

The denominator is developed in this fashion:

$$n\sigma_X\sigma_Y = \sqrt{n^2\sigma^2{}_X\sigma^2{}_Y}$$

$$= \sqrt{n\sigma^2{}_X}\ \sqrt{n\sigma^2{}_Y}$$

$$= \sqrt{\Sigma X^2 - (\Sigma X)^2/n}\ \sqrt{\Sigma Y^2 - (\Sigma Y)^2/n}$$

Putting the parts together again:

43a] $$r = \frac{\Sigma XY - (\Sigma X)(\Sigma Y)/n}{\sqrt{\Sigma X^2 - (\Sigma X)^2/n}\ \sqrt{\Sigma Y^2 - (\Sigma Y)^2/n}}$$

This is only one of many computational formulas for r, each of which has advantages for some special situation. We have selected this one because it lends itself easily to paper-and-pencil computation, and to the use of a slide-rule as an aid. A different formula would be preferred if a calculating machine were to be used.* And, although the formula is stated here in raw score terms, the same form is applicable to transformed scores, as we shall soon see in an example.

When n is small, one may list the two series of scores side by side and find the necessary sums directly, as shown in Table 10.4. This computation is based on the fictitious data of Table 10.1, dealing with the reciprocity of affection in 12 young couples. Here we have chosen to solve for r^2, rather than r, and accordingly we have modified the formula in this obvious way:

43b] $$r^2 = \frac{[\Sigma XY - (\Sigma X)(\Sigma Y)/n]^2}{[\Sigma X^2 - (\Sigma X)^2/n][\Sigma Y^2 - (\Sigma Y)^2/n]}$$

However, a drawback of this method is that it does not provide the easy visual check on linearity of regression which the scatter diagram offers.

* If r is to be computed with the help of a calculating machine, the transformed scores should not include negative values, and the formula should be restated thus:

$$r = \frac{n\,\Sigma x'y' - \Sigma x'\,\Sigma y'}{\sqrt{[n\,\Sigma x'^2 - (\Sigma x')^2][n\,\Sigma y'^2 - (\Sigma y')^2]}}$$

This leads to bigger numbers, but fewer operations.

There is an efficient procedure for obtaining all of the sums simultaneously on any modern calculator. The manufacturer's representative will provide a manual of instructions.

TABLE 10.4

Computation of r^2 Without the Use of a Scatter Diagram, Using the Data
of Table 10.2, and Formula 43b

Pair	(B) His Love	(G) Her Love	B^2	G^2	BG
1	2	5	4	25	10
2	8	6	64	36	48
3	7	5	49	25	35
4	5	5	25	25	25
5	4	6	16	36	24
6	4	3	16	9	12
7	3	4	9	16	12
8	2	3	4	9	6
9	5	3	25	9	15
10	6	6	36	36	36
11	7	7	49	49	49
12	3	2	9	4	6
	56	55	306	279	278

$$r^2 = \frac{[278 - (55)(56)/12]^2}{[306 - (56)^2/12][279 - (55)^2/12]}$$

$$= 21^2/(45)(27) = .36.*$$

* Although r^2 in this computation is greater than η^2 in Table 10.2, based on the same data, this does not disprove the rule that η^2 must always exceed r^2. If scores for "her love" were grouped, with $i = 2$, corresponding to the coarser grouping used in the computation of η^2, the value of r^2 would be reduced.

FINDING r FROM A SCATTER DIAGRAM

A convenient method for computing the value of a product moment correlation is to prepare a scatter diagram, and do the work with transformed scores. Besides being a fairly economical procedure, it provides a visual check on linearity of regression and calls attention to any peculiarity in either of the distributions. The following procedure is recommended as relatively foolproof. The instructions should be read with constant reference to Table 10.5, where they are illustrated.

1. Decide on a convenient value of i for each dimension independently.

2. Prepare a roomy two-dimensional chart for the scatter diagram, and fill in the working limits of the classes on each dimension. Be sure that the values of X increase from left to right, and that those of Y increase from bottom to top.

3. Enter each *pair* of scores as *one* tally in the appropriate cell, making all tally marks in the upper half of the cell.

TABLE 10.5

Computation of r from a Scatter Diagram, for the Scores of 69 Upperclass College Men on Two Parts of the Michigan Vocabulary Profile

Y \ X	Biological Science Vocabulary Score								f_y	y'	fy'	fy'^2	$\Sigma_r x'y'$
	6–8	9–11	12–14	15–17	18–20	21–23	24–26	27–29					
27–29						/ 4 4			1	4	4	16	4
24–26			// −6 −12	/ −3 −3	//	/ 3 3	/// 6 18	/ 9 9	10	3	30	90	15
21–23			/// −4 −12	/ −2 −2	⊮ /	/ 2 2	/ 4 4		12	2	24	48	−8
18–20		/ −3 −3	/ −2 −2	/ −1 −1	//	// 1 2			7	1	7	7	−4
15–17			/	⊮ //	////	//			14	0	0	0	0
12–14	/ 4 4	3	/// 2 6	⊮ 1 5	⊮ /	// −1 −2	/ −2 −2		18	−1	−18	18	11
9–11		/ 6 6	4	/// 2 6	/				5	−2	−10	20	12
6–8		/ 9 9	6	/ 3 3					2	−3	−6	18	12
f_x 69	1	3	10	19	21	6	5	1			31	217	42
x'	−4	−3	−2	−1	0	1	2	3					
fx' −30	−4	−9	−20	−19	0	6	10	3					
fx'^2 140	16	27	40	19	0	6	20	9					
$\Sigma_c x'y'$ 42	4	12	−20	8	0	6	20	9					

$n = 69$
$\Sigma x' = -30$
$\Sigma x'^2 = 140$
$\Sigma y' = 31$
$\Sigma y'^2 = 217$
$\Sigma x'y' = 42$
$r = .345$

$$r = \frac{42 - [31(-30)/69]}{\sqrt{140 - 30^2/69}\ \sqrt{217 - 31^2/69}} = \frac{55.5}{\sqrt{126.9}\ \sqrt{203.1}} = 0.345$$

---

4. Rule and label columns headed f_y, y', fy', fy'^2, and $\Sigma_r x'y'$. Then turn the sheet 90 degrees counterclockwise, and prepare a similar set of columns for the X dimension.

5. Count the tallies in each row of the diagram, and enter their number into the f_y column. Do likewise for the columns of the diagram, entering the numbers under f_x. The sums must agree.

6. Decide on an assumed mean for each dimension, choosing a fairly central position, and enter the transformed scores into the y' and x' columns. Take care to see that the smaller or negative values of the transformed scores for the X dimension are really at the lower end of that scale.

7. Find $\Sigma y'$, $\Sigma y'^2$, $\Sigma x'$, and $\Sigma x'^2$ by the procedures with which you are already familiar.

8. Now mark off with heavy or colored lines the row and the column of the scatter diagram to which you assigned zero transformed score values. Notice that the $x'y'$ product for every cell in this row and column is zero, and therefore observations falling in these cells will contribute nothing to the sum of products. The positive and negative quadrants, with respect to the transformed scores, stand out clearly, as insurance against errors in the following steps.

9. In the lower left corner of each cell which lies outside the zero-row and zero-column, write the product of the x' value for its column and the y' value for its row. These numbers may be written inconspicuously, for they are merely memoranda. In the table, they are in italics. Notice that all of these values are positive in two of the quadrants, and negative in the other two. Notice also that the entries on each row (and likewise in each column) form an arithmetical progression, a circumstance which makes this a swift and troublefree routine.

10. Using a differently colored pencil, write into each cell the value of $fx'y'$ for that cell. To insure against oversights in the next step, write these numbers boldly. They are in boldface type in the table.

11. Add the $fx'y'$ values across each row, entering the row sums into the column headed $\Sigma_r x'y'$. As a check, add the same values by columns, entering the sums under $\Sigma_c x'y'$.

12. Add these columns to obtain, from either, the uncorrected sum of products, $\Sigma x'y'$.

13. Substitute the various sums into the formula, which now takes the form:

43c]
$$r = \frac{\Sigma x'y' - \Sigma x'\,\Sigma y'/n}{\sqrt{\Sigma x'^2 - (\Sigma x')^2/n}\ \sqrt{\Sigma y'^2 - (\Sigma y')^2/n}}$$

14. Solve the three correction terms first, reducing the entire expression to the form $r = a/\sqrt{b}\,\sqrt{c}$. Then solve for r. (See slide-rule hint on page 60.)

Tests of Significance

Each set of bivariate data yields one value of r and two values of η. These three ratios are subject to separate tests of significance. In addition, it may be necessary to decide whether r^2 or η^2 is the more valid measure of the extent to which one of the variables is dependent on the other. For each test, a different portion of the sum of squares is isolated as representing "information" which bears on the particular null hypothesis, and another portion (usually all the remainder) is used to construct the error standard. Dividing each portion by the appropriate number of degrees of freedom, we obtain a variance ratio.

We are already familiar with the variance ratio for testing the significance of η^2, for this is the same F which is used to test whether the class means differ significantly. In a one-dimensional analysis of variance, the between-sum of squares equals $\eta^2 \Sigma x^2$ and the within-sum equals $(1 - \eta^2) \Sigma x^2$. The ratio of the corresponding mean squares determines whether the between-sum is significantly greater than chance, and hence also whether η^2 is significant. Without referring to sums of squares, we can formulate this test in the following manner:

$$44] \qquad F = \frac{(n - k)\eta^2}{(k - 1)(1 - \eta^2)} \; ; \qquad df = (k - 1)/(n - k)$$

(Instead of dividing by the degrees of freedom, we are multiplying by their reciprocal, for computational convenience.) In this variance ratio the numerator, or information estimate, is based on the variance of the obtained class means, and the denominator, or error estimate, is based on variance within the classes. The ratio tests the null hypothesis that the dispersion of class means is a chance phenomenon. When we reject this hypothesis, the implication is that the use of the obtained class means as estimates of the corresponding "true" values represents an improvement over the use of the grand mean for all groups, indifferently.

A similar test can be made to determine whether the use of adjusted means (or regressed scores) fixed by the best-fit line leads to better-than-chance improvement over the use of the grand mean for all the groups. For this test,

$$45] \qquad F = \frac{(n - 2)r^2}{(1 - r^2)} \; ; \qquad df = 1/(n - 2)$$

Here r^2 has replaced η^2 in the information estimate, and there is but one degree of freedom associated with this estimate, because all the regressed scores are constrained to fit a one-dimensional strait jacket, the best-fitting straight line. The sum of squares for the error estimate has been increased by that proportion of the sum of squares which is excluded from the numerator, and the number of degrees associated with it has been increased accordingly, by the $k - 2$ degrees which have been sacrificed in the numerator.

When both η^2 and r^2 are significant, we must select one as the more appropriate measure of relationship. Since r^2 will always be less than η^2, it represents the more conservative statistic, and we are justified in using η^2 only if there is evidence that the difference between the two statistics is not a matter of chance. When we use the differentiation ratio to express the strength of the relationship between two variables, we are stating in effect that the obtained class means constitute a better set of estimates of the "true" class means, than those fixed by the linear regression. To test this proposition, we state a null hypothesis that the departure of the obtained class means from the best-fit line can be dismissed as chance. The test of this hypothesis is a *test of linearity*, and it is the criterion by which we decide whether η^2 or r^2 is a better estimate of the proportion of the total sum of squares which arises from the influence of the independent variable. For this test,

$$46] \qquad F = \frac{(n - k)(\eta^2 - r^2)}{(k - 2)(1 - \eta^2)} \; ; \qquad df = (k - 2)/(n - k)$$

Here, the sum of squares used for the information estimate consists of that which is associated with the dispersion of the obtained group means, reduced by as much as is associated with the dispersion of the adjusted means or regressed scores. The degrees of freedom have been reduced accordingly, from $k - 1$ to $k - 2$. The error estimate is the same which was used to test the differentiation ratio. We refrain from merging into this estimate the sum of squares associated with the regressed scores, even though that is no longer included in the information estimate, because we would not be making this test at all unless it had already been shown that the regressed scores have greater than chance variance, and therefore it does not seem proper to include their contribution in an error estimate.

We shall illustrate the use of these formulas by applying them to results already obtained in the fictitious problem of the dependence of affection displayed by girls on that displayed by their boy friends. (If we were interested in both differentiation ratios, it would be necessary to make separate tests for each.) On page 169, we found $\eta^2_{g.b} = .49$, whereas in Table **10.**4 we found $r^2 = .36$ for the same data. We calculate the following ratios, by Formulas 44, 45, and 46:

(a) To test η^2:

$$F = \frac{9\,(.49)}{2\,(.51)} = 4.32; \qquad df = 2/9; \qquad P < .05.$$

(b) To test r^2:

$$F = \frac{10\,(.36)}{.64} = 5.63; \qquad df = 1/10; \qquad P < .05.$$

(c) To test $\eta^2 - r^2$:

$$F = \frac{9\,(.13)}{.51} = 2.29; \qquad df = 1/9; \qquad P > .05.$$

Consulting the table of F, which we must enter in each case with the indicated degrees of freedom, we find that the first two values surpass the critical value for the 5 per cent level of significance, but the third does not. We conclude that there is a significant relationship between the two variables, but there is not sufficient evidence to reject the null hypothesis regarding linearity. Therefore the product moment correlation, rather than the differentiation ratio, should be used to express the strength of relationship.

THE SAMPLING DISTRIBUTION OF r

The obtained value of r is, of course, only an estimate of the true value, r_∞, which would be found by exhaustive sampling of the universe. The study of the sampling distribution of r is a complex problem, which we can treat only in a superficial manner. We distinguish three problems: (a) to test the null hypothesis that the variables are unrelated; (b) to establish confidence limits for r_∞ in the universe; and (c) to judge whether two obtained values of r differ significantly. Everything that follows in this section rests on the assumption that both variables are normally distributed.

(a) We have already shown, in Formula 45, how one-dimensional analysis of variance can be used to test the null hypothesis that the variables are uncorrelated. It is often convenient to determine the critical value of r for a given number of observations and at a given level of significance, rather than to test the significance of each obtained r. For this purpose, Formula 45 can be altered into the following form:

$$47] \qquad \frac{t^2}{t^2 + n - 2} = r^2$$

To find the critical value of r^2, when n is the number of pairs of scores, enter into this formula the critical value of t^2 for $n - 2$ degrees of freedom. For example, when $n = 12$, $df = 10$, and t^2 at the 5 per cent level is 4.96. The value $4.96/14.96 = .332$ is the critical value of r^2. It appears in one of the columns of Table VI.

An approximation formula which is commonly used to test the null hypothesis is this:

$$48] \qquad s_r = \frac{1}{\sqrt{n - 1}}$$

This formula must never be used to establish confidence limits for an obtained r, since it is intended only as a description of the sampling distribution of r when $r_\infty = 0$. When r_∞ departs substantially from zero, the sampling distribution is extremely skewed. The formula is fairly satisfactory for its intended purpose at the 5 per cent level, when $n > 30$, but it is much less satisfactory at the 1 per cent level, and for smaller samples. Much more satisfactory approximations can be reached by the following empirical formulas:

48a] $$r_{.05} = \frac{1.96}{\sqrt{n - .5}}$$

and

48b] $$r_{.01} = \frac{2.576}{\sqrt{n + 1}}$$

With $n > 20$, these formulas have negligible error. At the 5 per cent level, Formula 48a makes the same error (.003) at $n = 10$ that Formula 48 makes at $n = 30$; at the 1 per cent level, Formula 48b makes the same error (.007) at $n = 12$ that Formula 48 makes at $n = 50$.

(b) The computation of confidence limits for r is complicated by the fact that whenever r_∞ is moderately large, the sampling distribution of r is markedly skewed. However, Fisher has shown that even under these conditions the following transformation gives rise to a distribution which is very nearly normal:

49] $$z = \tfrac{1}{2} [\log_e (1 + r) - \log_e (1 - r)]$$

As an approximation, using common logarithms,

49a] $$z = 1.15 \log \frac{1 + r}{1 - r}$$

Since the distribution of z is virtually normal, it is relatively easy to establish confidence intervals for z, and thus indirectly for r. The calculation of the confidence interval is based on the fact that

50] $$\sigma_z = \frac{1}{\sqrt{n - 3}}$$

To illustrate: the obtained r for Table **10.5** is .345, with $n = 69$. Using the appropriate part of Table XI, we find that the equivalent z is .360. By Formula 50, the standard error of this value is $1/\sqrt{66} = .123$. Therefore the 5 per cent confidence limits of z are .360 $\pm$ 1.96 (.123), whence: .119 $< z_\infty <$ .601. Again referring to Table XI, we find that the equivalent r's are .119 and .537. These are the limits of the 5 per cent confidence interval for r_∞.

(c) The z function can also be utilized in order to test the significance of a difference between two r's based on independent samples. Each is transformed into a z, and the difference between those statistics is tested by their standard error, which is:

$$51] \qquad s_{z_1 - z_2} = \sqrt{\frac{1}{n_1 - 3} + \frac{1}{n_2 - 3}}$$

This method does not apply to two r's based on the same sample of subjects. In that case, one has a situation which is somewhat analogous to the testing of a difference observed between matched pairs of scores, so that a somewhat smaller difference will satisfy a valid test of significance. However, the valid test in that case is a more complicated matter, which we shall not discuss.

As an aside, we may mention another use of the z function. When it is desired to determine an average value for a series of r's, this can be done by transforming each r into a z, finding the mean z, and transforming this into an r. Approximately the same result can be obtained by averaging the r^2 values, which is another method of giving more meaningful weights to the different correlations entering into the average.

PROBLEMS

1. Refer to the data of Table 2.4, *which reported the average ratings that students gave to their instructors on three rating scales: sense of humor, consistent planning for class meetings, and the appearance of being proud of the class. Find r, and test it for significance, for ratings on* (a) *Humor and Plan,* (b) *Humor and Pride, and* (c) *Plan and Pride.*

2. Cushing[1] studied perseverative tendency in nursery school children by observing each child in six different solitary play situations. Table 10.6 *records the time which each child spent in each of four situations before discontinuing his activity with the play materials which had been provided. Find r for any pair of these situations, and test it for significance.*

3. Dunlap[2] studied relationships between various measures of aptitude and personality, for senior students in Los Angeles high schools. Table 10.7 *is based on his data. The two variables are: A, an adjustment score, which is the sum of scores on four scales of the Guilford-Zimmerman Temperament Analysis (Scales E, O, F, P), and V, the Verbal Meaning score of PMA (Primary Mental Aptitudes, published by Science Research Associates). Find both r and $\eta_{V.A}$, and test for linearity. If the departure from linearity is significant, interpret it in words. (Note: In computing η, merge classes at the ends of the distribution for the independent variable, to avoid having any class with a very small m.)*

4. Repeat the computation of r^2 for the data in Table 10.4, *using a linear transformation of scores to reduce the sums entering into the computation.*

TABLE 10.6

Time, in Whole Minutes, of Continuous Activity with Four Different Kinds of Play Materials*

Sj	A**	B	C	D	Sj	A	B	C	D
1	22	11	21	10	26	28	8	11	5
2	9	28	9	16	27†	27	20	30	21
3†	18	7	9	15	28	8	35	14	37
4†	8	6	7	15	29	19	5	11	12
5†	18	11	22	11	30	7	17	16	28
6†	6	16	24	40	31†	48	33	28	36
7	10	16	13	27	32	19	29	19	60
8†	16	16	16	20	33	20	24	17	24
9	5	11	11	16	34†	8	10	7	12
10†	12	8	13	7	35	20	15	3	21
11†	15	12	18	19	36†	44	30	36	34
12†	23	14	34	22	37†	9	17	18	11
13	7	10	21	32	38†	50	15	32	39
14†	42	13	19	18	39	8	10	5	12
15†	39	19	17	25	40†	60	21	46	47
16†	13	12	11	20	41	8	28	12	15
17	15	9	20	20	42†	3	10	18	5
18	19	25	25	23	43	21	12	23	19
19†	28	24	36	37	44†	10	4	8	20
20	10	11	7	30	45†	25	7	33	17
21	11	7	8	7	46	36	32	13	30
22	29	3	6	23	47	26	7	11	18
23†	21	12	14	24	48†	12	9	6	14
24†	8	11	10	9	49†	31	22	7	22
25†	4	8	31	8					

* Based on Cushing.[1]
** A, dropping marbles through a hole; B, sounding bells, etc.; C, playing with nest of boxes; D, playing with motor toys. Subjects are nursery school children.
† Female subjects.

5. *Table* **10**.8 *presents data on the accident records and "interpersonal desirability" of workers in a steel mill, on the "hot strip." The sociometric score for each man is based on the answers of about half the other men to questions as to whom they would "most like to work with" and whom they would "least like to work with." The men studied worked in teams of 4 to 6 men, and were paid on a group-incentive plan. Data from Speroff and Kerr.*[3]

Find the product moment correlation and the relevant differentiation ratio, and determine which is the more appropriate measure of strength of association between the sociometric scores and proneness to accident.

TABLE 10.7

Relationships Between Measures of Adjustment and Verbal Intelligence*

V \ A	16–23	24–31	32–39	40–47	48–55	56–63	64–71	72–79	80–87	88–95	96–103	104–111	f_V
48–51			1		1	3	5	4	1	2		1	18
44–47	1	2		1	6		6	2	4	3			25
40–43	1	1	3	2	7	5	5	6	2	3	2	1	38
36–39		1	4	4	9	6	10	3	5	2	1		45
32–35		1	3	1	6	8	7	16	6	3	2		53
28–31		2	1	5	13	13	11	5	6				56
24–27		1	3	6	8	9	10	7	6		1	1	52
20–23				4	6	8	5	4					27
16–19			1		3	3	3	1	1				12
12–15				2	1		2				1		6
8–11				1				1					2
f_A	2	8	16	26	60	55	64	49	31	13	7	3	334

* See Problem 3 for fuller description.

TABLE 10.8

Accidents and "Interpersonal Desirability" Among 88 Hot-strip Steel Mill Workers*

		\multicolumn{5}{c}{Number of Accidents in Three Years}
		0	1	2	3	4
Sociometric Score	4	6	6	2		
	3	3	11	7	1	2
	2	3	15	9	2	
	1		2	4	2	
	0	2		1	5	5

* From Speroff and Kerr.[3]

REFERENCES

1. Cushing, Hazel M. A perseverative tendency in pre-school children. *Arch. of Psychology*, No. 108, 1929.

2. Dunlap, D. N. *Psychological test score differences and predictions.* Unpublished doctoral dissertation, Claremont Graduate School, 1958.

3. Speroff, B., and Kerr, W. Steel mill "hot strip" accidents and interpersonal desirability values. *J. clin. Psychol.*, 1952, **8**:89–91.

11

SOME USES OF CORRELATION

Regression Formulas

Once we know the value of r, it is a simple matter to determine the regressed score on one dimension which is associated with a given obtained score on the other dimension. If both scores are stated in standard units of the respective distributions, we have this relationship:

52] $$z_{Y'} = r z_X$$

where $z_{Y'}$ represents $(Y' - \bar{Y})/\sigma_Y$. That is, *a regressed standard score is the product of the correlation coefficient and the standard score on the correlated dimension*. For example, if two sets of scores have a linear relationship with $r = 0.5$, then a score 1σ above the mean on one dimension has as its most probable associate on the other dimension a score which is only $.5\sigma$ above the mean. To express this same example in terms of centile scores, if an individual scores at the eighty-fourth centile on one of these dimensions, his most likely score on the other dimension is at the sixty-ninth centile.

Formula 52 can be readily converted into a computational formula in raw score terms. We begin with an expanded statement of Formula 52:

$$\frac{(Y' - \bar{Y})}{\sigma_Y} = r \frac{(X - \bar{X})}{\sigma_X}$$

whence

193

$$Y' - \bar{Y} = r \frac{\sigma_Y}{\sigma_X} (X - \bar{X})$$

and finally

52a]
$$Y' = \bar{Y} + r \frac{\sigma_Y}{\sigma_X} (X - \bar{X})$$

If one has occasion to make many such computations for the same set of data, it is economical to compute the value of $r \frac{\sigma_Y}{\sigma_X}$. This is called the *regression coefficient*, and it is commonly represented by the symbol b. With this understood, the formula becomes

52b]
$$Y' = \bar{Y} + b(X - \bar{X})$$

One may go still another step, letting A represent $(\bar{Y} - b\bar{X})$. Then:

52c]
$$Y' = A + bX$$

Most readers will recognize this as the typical form of the equation for a straight line. When the constants A and b have been given their values, this equation fixes the regression line in the plane defined by the scales for X and Y in original score terms. This is the same line whose slope is defined by r, in the space which is defined by the standard scales for X and Y. In that case the constant A is equal to zero, and the factor σ_Y/σ_X is equal to unity, so that the equation takes the simple form from which we started, in Formula 52.

Now at last we can turn back to the young man whom we met in the first pages of this book, who was concerned about his chances in law school. His score on a legal aptitude test, you may remember, was exceeded by 80 per cent of his competitors, and one-fourth of the entire class is expected to fail to make the grade academically, for the first year. We can now add some further relevant information, and some assumptions. On the information side, let us say that it has been demonstrated in practice that scores on this test correlate 0.62 with grade-point average for the first year. (This is rather generous, for few tests of this kind do so well.) We shall assume in addition that both test scores and grade-point averages are approximately normally distributed. Now to work:

We begin by transforming the young man's centile score into a standard equivalent. In the table of the normal distribution, we find that

$$20\text{th centile} = -.84\sigma$$

Multiplying the standard score by r gives the regressed score, in standard form:

$$z_{Y'} = rz_X = (.62)(-.84) = -.52$$

This can be reconverted into a centile by the normal table, since the distribution of grade-point averages is also assumed to be normal:

$$-.52\sigma = \text{30th centile}$$

Having done this, we find that the young man's probable achievement places him above the failing fourth! "Regression to mediocrity" means that his most probable position as regards grade points is not nearly so low as his position on the prognostic test. Instead of flunking out, he will probably be out-flunked by a number of students who, although they did better on that test, will fall victims to the operation of factors which the test did not adequately assess. Although we can predict (en masse) that one-fourth of all the entrants will fail, we cannot predict failure for one-fourth of the entrants (individually). The first prediction is a probability based on an experienced proportion, whereas the second expresses an observed relationship between two variables. We must not permit our confidence in the first prediction to lead us into overlooking the sources of error in the second.

COMMON VARIANCE

It is clear that if we were to make the same sort of prediction for each entrant who took the aptitude examination, the variance of the regressed scores would be considerably less than the variance of the future grades which they forecast. That is,

$$\sigma^2_{Y'} < \sigma^2_Y$$

The full set of regressed scores is a scale model of the set of test scores, since each X "regresses" in the same proportion in being transformed into a Y'. Therefore, if the X and Y distributions are dissimilar in form, the distribution of regressed scores must resemble in form the distribution of X scores, on which they are based, rather than the distribution of Y scores, which they are intended to forecast. We shall return to this problem later in the chapter. At this point we are interested in learning about the variance of regressed scores, and we can make certain generalizations about this regardless of the forms of the distributions.

Since each $z_{Y'}$ is merely a z_X which has been transformed by the use of a constant multiplier, r, the variance of the new distribution is equal to that of the parent standard distribution (which is unity) multiplied by r^2. That is, $\sigma^2_{z_{Y'}} = r^2$. (If this is not clear, compare Formula 11b, page 63, where the multiplier is i.)

To transform these regressed standard scores into original score units, we again use a constant multiplier, σ_Y. Following the same rule, the variance of the regressed scores, in original scale units, equals $r^2\sigma^2{}_Y$. Stated in another form,

53]
$$r^2 = \frac{\sigma^2{}_{Y'}}{\sigma^2{}_Y}$$

In words: r^2 is *the ratio of the variance of regressed scores to the variance of actual scores.* In still other words, r^2 is that proportion of the variance of the scores on one dimension which is predictable from a knowledge of scores on the other dimension. If there is an understood causal relationship between the variables, it is the ratio of "explained variance" to total variance. In the language with which Chapter 10 opened, it is the measure of "something in common" to both score distributions: *common variance.*

There is still another useful sense in which to interpret the statement that r^2 measures "something in common" between the variables. Variance, we should remember, measures the strength of the factors which produce variation. Every score has multiple determinants, and when two sets of scores correlate, it is because they have some of their determinants in common. Common variance is the measure of the extent to which the scores of two phenomena have common determinants. This "sharing of determinants" is illustrated schematically in Figures **11**.1 and **11**.2. In

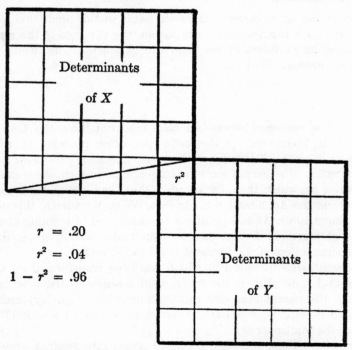

$r = .20$

$r^2 = .04$

$1 - r^2 = .96$

FIG. **11**.1. Overlap of determinants in correlated variables, $r = 0.2$.

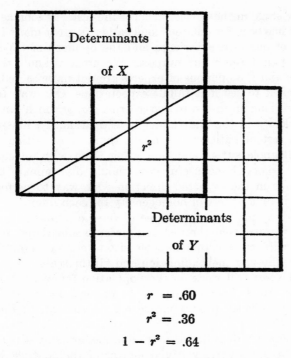

$$r = .60$$
$$r^2 = .36$$
$$1 - r^2 = .64$$

FIG. **11.2.** Overlap of determinants in correlated variables, $r = 0.6$.

these figures, the full set of determinants for each variable is represented by a square of unit area. The area of overlap between the determinants of X and Y is represented by the square on r, the rate of rise of the regression line for standardized scores. If r^2 is designated "explained variance" or "common variance," then the residue, $1 - r^2$, is "unexplained variance" or "alienated variance." Hence, the name *coefficient of alienation* is given to the function

54] $$k = \sqrt{1 - r^2}$$

THE COEFFICIENT OF RELIABILITY: r_{xx}

A good deal of honest toil goes into the development of a psychological test with predictive power. We rarely know how to ask the questions to which nature gives consistent answers, and our subjects are no less contrary. The alchemist's search for a touchstone which would transmute base metals into gold was not more vain than the psychologist's hope for an infallible index to any kind of behavior. Every test, therefore, is an aggregate of a number of separate indicators which, taken together, provide a more or less trustworthy measure of a behavioral trend.

At an early stage in the development of the test—as soon as the general concept for it has been formulated—one gathers a great many items which, on the basis of our own experience and the opinions of experts, look as though they might serve our purpose. We already know the fallibility of experience, and the opinions of experts are not more sacred. Each item must be checked to see if it fulfills expectations. One way to do this is to give this overlong proto-test to two *criterion groups* which can be expected to differ markedly in the trait under investigation. To illustrate: if this were to be a test of patience, we might think of recruiting a sample of professional flagpole sitters and comparing them with an equal number of sideshow barkers. Each useful item should discriminate between the criterion groups in the expected direction. One way to perform such an *item analysis* is by a χ^2 test of homogeneity for each item.

This procedure guarantees a degree of *internal consistency*, and it also gives some assurance that the test can measure something. We now need a new set of subjects—neither flagpole sitters nor sideshow barkers, but ordinary folk who pay their admission and fill the seats. That is, we need to see how the test will work on the population for which it is intended. The scores of this sample will enable us to form a statistical judgment about the test's efficiency as a measuring instrument, in the form of a *coefficient of reliability*.

Nowhere, perhaps, does the revolution in modern statistics appear more clearly than in the relatively trivial matter of the contrast between old and new ways of determining this coefficient. The old way involved an experimental comparison between two series of test scores for the same subjects. Hence the coefficient of reliability is symbolized as a self-correlation, r_{xx}. If two equivalent forms of the test were prepared, the same sample might take both forms, and the correlation between the two sets of scores would be the measure of reliability. If there were but one form, this could be readministered after a suitable interval of time, or a "split-half" correlation might be obtained between separate scores for each subject based on odd-numbered and even-numbered items. This would give a reliability figure for a half-test, and the coefficient for the full test could then be estimated by the Spearman-Brown *prophecy formula*, which estimates the increased effectiveness of a lengthened test. In the special case when one is forecasting the reliability of a test of doubled length (that is, the full test rather than the split-halves used for the preliminary estimate) this becomes:

55]
$$r_{xx} = \frac{2r'}{1 + r'}$$

where r' is the correlation between scores for the half-tests. None of these methods is altogether satisfactory.

The modern method is called the method of rational equivalence, and it is based on the additive qualities of variance. Although the scores for each test item by itself have a very limited range, this distribution nevertheless has a variance. If all scores on the item are either 1 or 0, and the proportion of 1's equals p, then the variance of scores for the item equals pq. (The proof was given in Chapter 9, on page 145.) Hence, by the variance law, the variance of aggregate scores for any number of independent items of this character equals Σpq. It would be a very poor test which would consist of independent items, and since we have already assured ourselves that the items are in some degree consistent we can be quite sure that the variance of aggregate scores will exceed this chance value. If the items are perfectly consistent—an impossibly good and wasteful test, for we could do with just one item of that sort—the variance of n items would be $n\,\Sigma pq$. These considerations lead to the following formula, which is generally referred to as Kuder-Richardson Formula 20:

$$56] \qquad r_{xx} = \frac{n}{n-1} \cdot \frac{\sigma^2 - \Sigma pq}{\sigma^2}$$

in which σ^2 stands for the variance of the set of aggregate scores. If the items are perfectly consistent, $\sigma^2 = n\,\Sigma pq$ and thus $r_{xx} = 1$. If the items have only chance association, $\sigma^2 = \Sigma pq$ and therefore $r_{xx} = 0$.

This formula forecasts the self-correlation which would be found if the test were readministered under identical conditions, and the estimate of reliability is more satisfactory than from an empirical evaluation, for a second testing can never be "identical" with a first testing. However, it must be pointed out that neither this formula nor the split-half method is suitable for a test in which the score is influenced by speed, that is, by the number of items completed. These methods are suited only to tests for which the scores depend only on the manner in which the items are answered, when speed is not a major factor.

In any case, reliability is not a characteristic of the test per se, but of the test-in-a-situation. Study of Formula 56 should make this evident, for we must anticipate that different samples would give very different proportions of pass responses. One of the most important factors affecting determinations of reliability is the range of abilities in the population being sampled. The same test of "quantitative reasoning" which seems highly efficient when it is applied to all entering freshmen will probably be utterly inadequate to discriminate among third-year mathematics majors. The manual of any standard test usually gives reliability coefficients for several different kinds of subjects. One must be very cautious in transferring any of these values to another situation.

THE COEFFICIENT OF VALIDITY

A reasonably high coefficient of reliability tells us that the test is measuring something, but it gives no assurance that the score is useful for the purpose which we have in mind. To investigate this question we must study the relationship of the scores to some independent indicator, or *criterion*. The records of the original criterion groups (cf. page 198), which consisted of such utterly different kinds of people, are of no value for this purpose. Validity, like reliability, is a function of the test-in-a-situation. After all, an item which successfully differentiates flagpole sitters from sideshow barkers (e.g., "Do you frequently spend an hour or more quietly rocking in a chair?") does not necessarily differentiate between patient and impatient grandmothers. Good criteria are very difficult to find, and it is at this point that most test-development programs stumble. Since we are fortunately not committed to developing a test of patience, let us turn back to the test of legal aptitude. The criterion in this case is obvious: grades actually earned and recorded. The basis for the prediction which we made for the young man was the *validity coefficient* or correlation obtained, in earlier experience, between test scores for law school entrants and grades earned during the first year. Unless this figure was based on recent experience in the same school, prediction is risky. Hard experience has taught psychologists that it is foolhardy to assume that because a test has high validity in one situation, it will have comparable validity in another "roughly similar" situation. The practical need for constant rechecking of validities is one reason why every psychologist who uses tests must be trained in research methods.

THE ERROR OF ESTIMATE

Suppose that John and Jim take two different tests, both intended to predict academic performance. Past experience shows that Test A has a validity of .30 and Test B has a validity of .70, taking end-of-term grades as the criterion. Suppose that each scores exactly 1σ above the general mean, on the test he takes. The indicated most likely outcome for John, who took Test A, is a grade average $.3\sigma$ above the class mean, while for Jim, who took Test B, we can make the bolder prediction of a grade average $.7\sigma$ above the general expectation! How can we reconcile these two different predictions based on similar performance?

The act of prediction is a conceptual transport, by which we lift the student out of the class of "students in general" into a more restricted class which not only has a different mean from the general mean, but also a different and smaller variance. The good test gives us sufficient information so that we can place the student into a class which has a relatively restricted variance; the poor test gives us less information, and therefore a good deal more error variance remains in the judgment. Whenever we make a prediction which is based on a test score, we should have clearly in mind the risk of error which attaches to the prediction.

Figure **11**.3 illustrates an ideal situation in which the calculation of

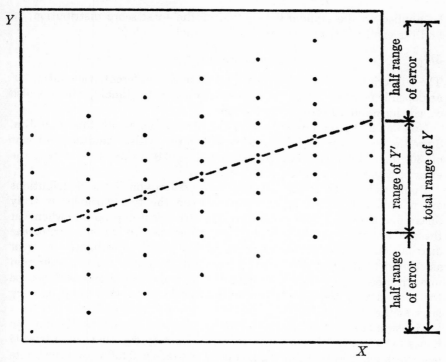

Fig. **11**.3. Error of prediction as a function of correlation, when the score to be predicted is homoscedastic.

this risk offers no difficulty. The distribution of Y is *homoscedastic*, that is, it has the same amount of scatter in every part of the X range. As a result, there is a single error term which applies to every regressed score. From a study of this figure, one can see that the total range of Y is equal to the range of regressed scores plus the range of Y scores within any vertical array. The *standard error of estimate*, the value of which we wish to learn, is the standard deviation of any one of these vertical arrays, which constitute the restricted classes into which individuals are classified for purposes of prediction. The determinants of variation in Y can be reduced to two kinds: those which produce the dispersion of regressed scores, and those which produce dispersion within the arrays. If all the scores have been standardized, then the variance of regressed scores equals r^2, and the within-class variance equals $1 - r^2$. The standard deviation of any one of the arrays is therefore

$$k = \sqrt{1 - r^2}$$

which we have already defined, on page 197, as the *coefficient of alienation*. When scores have not been standardized, this is a multiplier which must be applied to the standard deviation of the total score distribution, to find the error of estimate in units of the original scale:

$$57]\qquad \sigma_{Y.X} = \sigma_Y \sqrt{1 - r^2}$$

The subscript "Y dot X" means, just as in the differentiation ratio, "Y as dependent on X". This is the standard error of estimate, which is also called the standard error of prediction.

Now let us take another look at the predictions about John and Jim. Since the prediction for John was based on a test with a validity coefficient of .30, the error of estimate equals $\sigma_Y \sqrt{1 - .30^2} = .95\sigma_Y$. For Jim, the error of estimate is $\sigma_Y \sqrt{1 - .70^2} = .71\sigma_Y$.

Homoscedasticity is a reasonably safe assumption if the distributions are normal and if the relationship between the two variables is truly linear, and therefore the standard error of estimate is appropriate whenever these conditions seem to prevail. When a relationship is nonlinear, or the distributions not normal, it is much more difficult to estimate the error associated with a regressed score. In general, the errors which result from unwarranted assumption of normality and homoscedasticity will not be too serious near the middle of the distribution, but they may be very large at the extremes.

The standard error of estimate can also be used to establish confidence limits for a regressed score. For example, we may say that there is a 95 per cent likelihood that Jim's grade-point average will fall within the limits $.7\sigma \pm 1.96 (.71\sigma_Y)$, that is, between $-.69\sigma$ and $+2.09\sigma$. This application assumes that the distribution of grade-point averages is also normal. The form of the distribution does not play any part in arriving at the standard error of estimate, but if the distribution is not reasonably close to normal we cannot use the normal probability table to apply this knowledge for establishing confidence limits.

CORRECTION FOR ATTENUATION

Since the correlation between scores on a fallible test and scores on a fallible criterion is reduced (or *attenuated*) by the chance errors in both series of measurements, it does not give us an accurate statement of the relationship which we are trying to assess. For example, the obtained correlation between scholastic aptitude scores and college grades tends to understate the degree of association which exists between the true academic abilities of students and their true academic achievements. With a poor test and careless grading, the obtained correlation will be quite low; with a good test and careful grading, it will be much higher. But some chance error will always remain in both the test and the criterion, and therefore we can always imagine a situation in which a better test, or a better criterion, will produce a higher coefficient of validity. For theoretical purposes we can even imagine, though we can never achieve in fact, a situation in which we have a perfect test and a perfect criterion, yielding two series of "true" scores, free of all error.

Let us be clear on the meaning of these terms. By a *true score*, we mean a score equal to the mean of a great many comparable measurements, and hence a score in which the influence of random errors has been eliminated. By a perfect test, we only mean a test which yields true scores; it is not necessarily the best possible test for the thing we would like to be measuring. A perfect criterion is simply a perfect test which we have selected to use as a criterion; it is not necessarily the best possible criterion for our purpose.

If we let $r^2_{X_\infty Y_\infty}$ stand for the common variance which exists between two such series of true scores, then

$$r^2_{XY} = r_{XX} r_{YY} r^2_{X_\infty Y_\infty}$$

that is, the common variance between the obtained fallible scores represents a certain proportion of the "true" common variance, which has been attenuated by the imperfection of both measures. This relationship is more often expressed in the following manner:

58] $$r^2_{X_\infty Y_\infty} = \frac{r^2_{XY}}{r_{XX} r_{YY}}$$

This formula estimates the true common variance between the two variables, *corrected for attenuation* due to the unreliability of both instruments of measurement, the test and the criterion. It is useful when we wish to look beyond the practical problem of forecasting, to satisfy a theoretical curiosity about the true common variance of the things we are trying to measure. For example, if the obtained validity coefficient of a test used to predict college grades is $r_{XY} = .60$, it would be wrong to conclude that only 36 per cent of the variance in academic achievement is explained by variance in intellectual capacity for college studies. If the test has a reliability $r_{XX} = .90$, and the criterion—that is, the system of grading as actually practiced at this institution—has a reliability $r_{YY} = .70$, then, by Formula 58,

$$r^2_{X_\infty Y_\infty} = .36/(.90)(.70) = .57$$

This correction for attenuation adds to our understanding, but it does not add to the effectiveness of our forecasts. Whether the student survives depends in the last analysis on his grades, not on his scholarship.

It is also possible to correct a coefficient of validity for the attenuation which results from imperfection of the criterion only, and this partial correction may have a very practical application in a test-development program. Reliable criteria are often difficult to find, and therefore the obtained coefficient of validity may seriously underrate the effectiveness of the test instrument. The possibility of accurate grade forecasting is limited by the fact that the reliability of grades based on class examinations is not impressive, and most students will agree that the clinical hunches of professors do not tend to elevate it. In the same way, the development of job-selection tests is limited by the poor reliability of foremen's ratings, which often constitute the only practical criterion in an industrial situation, and the development of clinical tests is hampered by the known unreliability of psychiatric diagnoses. It does not seem reasonable, therefore, to penalize the test for the shortcomings of the criterion. To avoid this, we correct for the attenuation which is introduced by imperfection of the criterion alone. We can do this by Formula 58, if we replace the figure for the test reliability by unity. That is,

58a] $$r^2_{XY_\infty} = r^2_{XY}/r_{YY}$$

where $r^2_{XY_\infty}$ represents common variance between obtained scores on the test and true scores on the criterion. This formula tells us how good the test already is in predicting what the criterion is measuring imperfectly. Of course, this is not necessarily the thing which we are trying to measure.

Another way to arrive at Formula 58a, intuitively, is to say that $r^2_{XY_\infty} = r_{XX} \, r^2_{X_\infty Y_\infty}$, that is, the common variance of the obtained test scores and true scores on the criterion is that proportion of the common variance of true scores on test and criterion, which is determined by the attenuating effect of the chance errors in the test alone. Then replace $r^2_{X_\infty Y_\infty}$ in this expression by the righthand member of Formula 58 and simplify, and the result will be Formula 58a.

INDEX OF RELIABILITY

We can now quickly develop an answer to this interesting question: what is the highest coefficient of validity which we can possibly attain, so long as we use a given criterion or a given test (on the same population of subjects)? The question can be restated in this form: what is the highest correlation which a given set of fallible scores can have, with any other set of scores?

Let X_1 and X_2 stand for two sets of scores, for the same persons, from the same test. The correlation between these two sets of scores is also the coefficient of reliability. Now, let us correct for the attenuation introduced by chance errors in one set of scores. In that case, by Formula 58a,

$$r^2_{X_1 X_\infty} = r^2_{X_1 X_2}/r_{X_1 X_2} = r_{X_1 X_2}$$

Taking square roots, this becomes $r_{X_1 X_\infty} = \sqrt{r_{X_1 X_2}}$, or, returning to the less complicated notation,

59] $$r_{X_1 X_\infty} = \sqrt{r_{XX}}$$

That is, the correlation between a series of fallible scores and true scores on the same test is equal to the square root of the coefficient of reliability. This value is called the *index of reliability*. It is the highest correlation which the fallible test (or criterion) can attain with any set of scores.

The index of reliability has an interesting implication. It is often stated that the reliability of a test sets a ceiling to its validity, and this is mistakenly interpreted to mean that the test, in a given situation, cannot have a validity higher than its *coefficient* of reliability. Actually, it is the *index* of reliability which constitutes the ceiling. This helps to explain why some clinical tests, which have notoriously low reliabilities, nevertheless seem to make a worthwhile contribution to diagnostic procedures.

PROBLEMS

1. *Using the data of Table* **10**.5, *what is the most likely score on Biological Science Vocabulary for a student whose score on Physical Science Vocabulary is 12? 27?*

2. *If an individual scores at the twentieth centile on a prognostic test, what is his most likely score on the criterion variable, if the validity coefficient is .60? Assume normal distribution on both variables. What if his centile score on the test had been 99?*

3. *For each case in the preceding problem, state a 5 per cent confidence interval, in standard score terms and in centile terms.*

4. *A test of clerical aptitude was found to have a validity of .60 for selection of tabulating machine operators, when the criterion was output. Reliability of the criterion was .90. The same test had a validity of .30 for selection of bookkeeping machine operators, when supervisors' ratings were used as the criterion. Is it possible that the test was just as effective, as an employee selection instrument, in the second situation as in the first? If so, what would be the approximate reliability of the supervisors' ratings?*

5. *On a five-item multiple-choice test, the proportions of correct responses on the separate items are: .40, .40, .50, .60, .80. What would be the variance of the test scores if the items are independent? What is the reliability of the test, if the variance of test scores is 1.90? What is the highest possible validity of such a quiz? What would be the reliability of a test twice as long, consisting of "similar" items?*

6. *Suppose that the reliability of final grades issued in a single class is .70. What is the reliability of the mean of two such grades? What is the reliability of a grade-point average for the freshman year, made up of eight such grades?*

12

FACTOR ANALYSIS

The human mind has an insatiable need to organize reality into simple perceptual configurations. We work at this task "by guess and by golly": with fantasies, with snap judgments, with trial-and-error testing, with faith, and with science. In science, we work at it with theory and with experiment, creating hypotheses about how the parts of reality may fit together and testing these hypotheses in controlled samples of experience. Statistics plays its part primarily in the experimental-testing phase of this process, but in this chapter we shall see that it can also contribute to the development of hypotheses. In factor analysis, the statistical analysis of empirical data blends into the process of theory-building through the construction of mathematical models.

Factor analysis was originated by psychologists, and it has been fruitful in application to many diverse problems of psychological theory. It is a way of getting an overview of a large number of correlation coefficients, to see if the common variance which they express, which has been measured only in pairs of variables taken two-by-two, can be described in broader terms. A successful factor analysis is like the contour map of a whole countryside, which is based upon many separate measurements of the relative altitudes of hilltops and hollows. It gives new perspectives over the domain, and it brings into prominence features which had previously escaped attention. Work such as that by Thurstone on primary mental abilities and by Cattell on the primary source traits of personality and temperament, represent attempts to map the contours of whole continents.

THE COSINE MODEL OF CORRELATION

A good tool often makes the difference between success and failure on a difficult job. We shall use the first part of this chapter to become familiar with a powerful tool: the *cosine model* of correlation. The discussion of correlation in the preceding chapters was based on a geometric representation which can be called the *slope model*. The advantages of this model include the fact that it is intuitively appealing, and that it makes use of rectangular coordinates, with which most readers are familiar. The cosine model is another geometric representation of correlation, which has important advantages as an aid to conceptualizing the relationships among a large number of variables.

Figure **12**.1 shows the slope model, and Figure **12**.2 the cosine model, for a simple bivariate situation in which $r_{XY} = .60$. The slope model follows the convention that each variable is represented by an axis at right angles to the other. A score on either axis has as its locus a line at a given distance from the origin, and parallel to the other axis. The intersection of two such lines is a point in bivariate space, denoted (x, y). Any set of points has two best-fit lines, and if all the scores have been

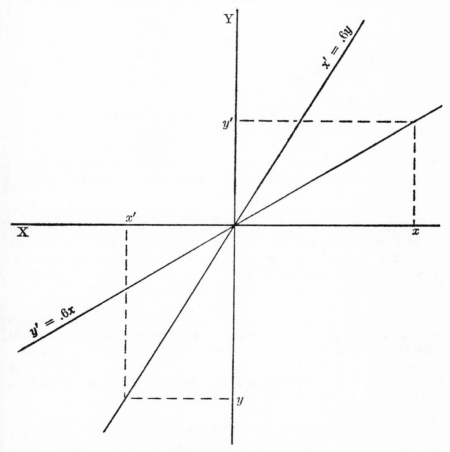

Fig. **12**.1. The slope model ($r = .6$).

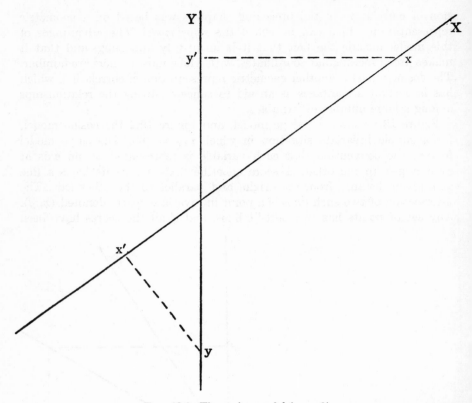

FIG. **12**.2. The cosine model ($r = .6$).

standardized (as we shall henceforth assume) r is equal to the slope of either of these lines with respect to one of the axes. In other words, the equation of one regression line is $\mathbf{y}' = r\mathbf{x}$, and that of the other is $\mathbf{x}' = r\mathbf{y}$. This means that a given deviation on either variable and the corresponding regressed score on the other variable are both projections of the same point on the appropriate regression line.

The cosine model (Figure **12**.2) discards the convention that the axes must be at right angles to each other. Instead, they are placed at an angle such that the projection onto one axis of any point on the other axis satisfies the regression formula. To achieve this, we utilize the relationship that, for either acute angle in a right triangle (and any projection from one axis onto the other forms such a triangle), by definition,

$$\text{cosine} = \frac{\text{side adjacent}}{\text{hypothenuse}}$$

That is, if the two sides which form such an angle are joined by a straight line which is perpendicular to one of them, then the cosine of the angle is one of the lengths which is marked off in this manner, expressed as a proportion of the other. The cosine therefore provides a convenient geometric model for regression. If we choose an angle of separation, θ, such that $r = \cos \theta$, a single projection in the cosine model does the same work for which a regression line and two projections are required in the slope model. (See Table XI for the cosine transformation.)

In the cosine model, two axes are at right angles only if the variables which they represent are not correlated, since the cosine of a right angle is zero. In that case, of course, the projection of any point on one axis falls at the zero point or origin of the other axis. (This circumstance leads to the use of the term *orthogonal* as a synonym for *independent*.) The more there is in common between two variables, the smaller is the angle included between their axes, so that variables with high positive correlation can be said to "point the same way" as a matter of geometric representation as well as in the implications of their scores. If they are in perfect agreement the axes coincide, becoming one line, which is consistent with the fact that the limiting value of the cosine for a very small angle is unity. If they are in perfect negative correlation they also coincide, but in that case they point in opposite directions, and the positive values of one scale have negative projections on the other. Since the cosine of an obtuse angle is found by the rule that

$$\cos \theta = -\cos (180° - \theta)$$

a negative correlation is associated with a negative cosine.

Just as in the slope model, the locus of a score on either axis is a line which lies parallel to the other axis, and the intersection of these lines determines a point in bivariate space, (x, y).

Let us now look at the slope model for a three-variable problem. Figure **12**.3 depicts a three-dimensional space defined by rectangular coordinates. The space is shown as a cube, and the ends of each axis terminate in the centers of opposite sides. A score on one of these axes has as its locus a plane which lies at the given distance from the origin and which is parallel to one of the walls of the cube or, otherwise stated, to the plane fixed by the other two axes. A pair of scores on two axes determine a line which is the intersection of two such planes and which is parallel to one of the edges of the cube, that is, to the remaining axis. A triad of scores on all three axes determine a single point which three such planes have in common. A set of points in trivariate space has three *regression planes*. The criterion for a regression plane is this: the sum of the squared distances of all the score-points from one of these planes, when the distances are measured parallel to the appropriate axis, is smaller than for any other plane what-

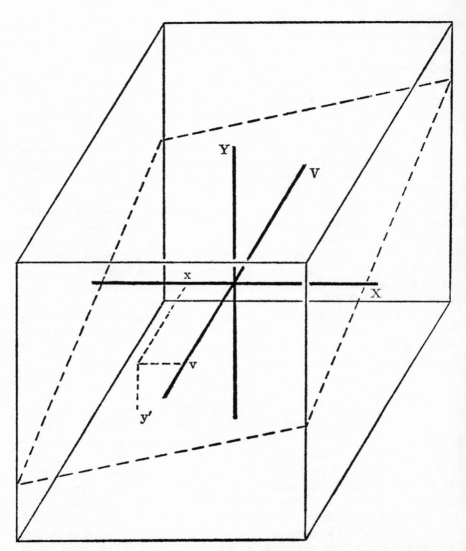

FIG. **12**.3. Regression plane in a three-dimensional space, with orthogonal reference axes. ($r_{XY} = .2$, $r_{VY} = .4$, $r_{VX} = 0.0$).

ever. The diagram shows only one of these planes. It would be difficult to show all three simultaneously in a single drawing, and it would be still more difficult, though not impossible, to present them together in a physical model. (The formula for a regression plane will be given later, on page 212.)

Figure **12**.4 depicts the relationships among three variables in a cosine

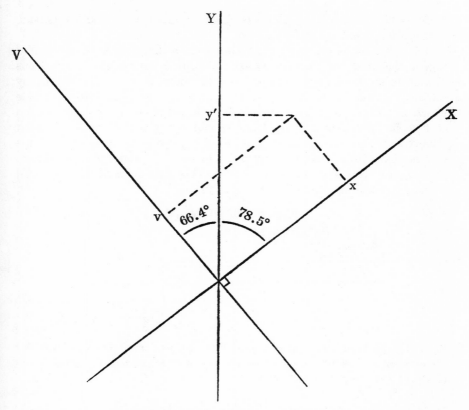

Fɪɢ. **12**.4. Cosine model for the three-dimensional problem shown in Figure **12**.3.

model. Notice that values for the angles are stated in the diagram, but they do not correspond to the angles on the plane of the page. This is because the three-dimensional problem cannot be successfully modeled in two dimensions, by this method, any more than by the slope model. We must interpret the drawing as indicating that the positive extension of the Y axis tips forward over the positive quadrant of the VX plane. However, we need not struggle to envisage the relationships in a flat drawing, for it is an easy matter to construct the cosine model for three dimensions. Draw a circle on a piece of light cardboard and draw radii to mark off adjoining sectors with central angles like those called for in Figure **12**.4. Cut out the three sectors all as one piece, crease sharply on the interior lines, and fold the model so that each sector is contiguous to each of the other sectors along the length of one side. Use a strip of mucilage tape to join it. Enclosed within its walls is that octant of the three-dimensional space which includes all points fixed by positive deviation scores on all three variables. This is called the first octant, and it is enough for our discussion.*

It is with the model in hand, rather than a diagram, that one should review the following relationships. Just as in the slope model, the locus of a score on one axis is a plane which lies parallel to the plane fixed by the other two axes, and the locus of a pair of scores on two axes is a line which is parallel to the remaining axis. Three scores, including one on each axis, determine a point. The regression problem is solved without a regression line. For example, if $\mathbf{v}$ and $\mathbf{x}$ are given, the line which is the intersection of their loci has one point in the VX plane; $\mathbf{y'}$ is the direct projection of this point onto the Y axis. This presents a problem in solid geometry which has the following solution:

60] $$\mathbf{y'} = \beta_{VY \cdot X}\mathbf{v} + \beta_{YX \cdot V}\mathbf{x}$$

where

61] $$\beta_{VY \cdot X} = \frac{\cos \theta_{VY} - \cos \theta_{XY} \cos \theta_{VX}}{1 - \cos^2 \theta_{VX}}$$

and

$$\beta_{XY \cdot V} = \frac{\cos \theta_{XY} - \cos \theta_{VY} \cos \theta_{VX}}{1 - \cos^2 \theta_{VX}}$$

It is usually more convenient to define the *beta coefficients* by writing correlation coefficients in place of the cosines, since they have the same values. For example,

61a] $$\beta_{VY \cdot X} = \frac{r_{VY} - r_{XY}r_{VX}}{1 - r^2_{VX}}$$

Written in this form, they are called *standard partial regression coefficients*, and when they are so defined Formula 60 is also the formula for a regression plane in the slope model! However, to arrive at this formula in the slope model requires the solution of a least-squares problem which involves three equations based on the technique of partial differentiation in calculus.

A very important difference between the slope model and the cosine model is that although it is impossible to construct a physical slope model for more than three variables, it is sometimes possible to construct a cosine model for four or more variables. The dimensionality of the slope model is dependent on the number of variables in the problem, since each of these is represented as an axis at right angles to every other. The

---

* It can be expanded into a complete model by cutting three cardboard discs with the same radius which was used for the model of the first octant, and pasting one against each of its surfaces. Since the planes must intersect, it will be necessary to cut radial slices—one in the first disc, two in the second, and three in the third—but the task of assembly is a test of skill in handicraft rather than in mathematics.

dimensionality of the cosine model depends on the relationships among the variables, rather than their number. We shall illustrate this with a bit of fictional research, and we urge the reader to take the little trouble needed to actually construct the model which will be described. Suppose that the following correlation coefficients have been established in the feminine student body of a certain university:

	Beauty	Charm	Humor
Intelligence	.26	.71	.71
Beauty		.71	.02
Charm			.71

To construct the physical model, determine the angle which corresponds to each of these values regarded as a cosine, and then lay out a pattern by measuring sectors which have the required central angles. (Check your results with Figure 12.5.) Five of the six planes of this pattern can be folded into a three-dimensional structure, taking care that like-labeled axes coincide, and the sixth can be fitted into the same structure with the help of scissors and mucilage tape.* After constructing the model it will be useful, pedagogically speaking, to speculate about the points at which any young ladies of your acquaintance might be located in this space.

The fact that the relationships among n tests or variables can be represented in a space of m dimensions, where $m < n$, means that any point in this space can be located by reference to only m coordinates. This suggests the possibility of replacing a large number of descriptive traits with a smaller number which can serve just as well. We shall not follow this lead at the present moment, for we are reluctant to dispense with any of the four qualities which served as dimensions in this fictional example. Instead, we shall conclude this section with an interesting application of the qualities of the three-dimensional cosine model.

When r_{AB} and r_{AC} are known, we can set limits to the possible values of r_{BC}. Envisaging the problem within the framework of the cosine model, we reason as follows: Since three dimensions must always suffice to describe the relations among three variables, the sector which represents r_{BC} must have an arc such that it can complete a three-dimensional model, when it is joined to the sectors representing r_{AB} and r_{AC}. This means that θ_{BC} must lie within the limits $\theta_{AB} \pm \theta_{AC}$. Either of these limiting values would lead to a model in two dimensions, but a value outside these limits would call for an impossible construction. Hence,

$$\cos(\theta_{AB} - \theta_{AC}) < r_{BC} < \cos(\theta_{AB} + \theta_{AC})$$

* Only four of the six sectors form outside walls of the completed model. Two sectors form intersecting interior walls.

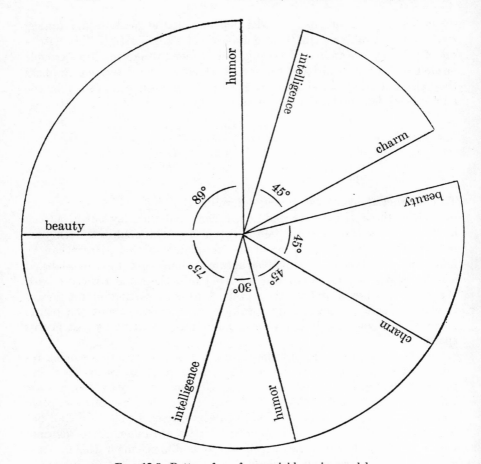

FIG. **12**.5. Pattern for a four-variable cosine model.

How much simpler this is, and how much more satisfying, than the algebraic solution:

$$r_{BC} = r_{AC}r_{AB} \pm \sqrt{1 - (r_{AB}^2 + r_{AC}^2) + r_{AB}^2 r_{AC}^2}$$

THE USE OF VECTORS IN THE COSINE MODEL

Up to this point we have thought of each variable as represented by an axis, that is, by a line having a stipulated direction but no stipulated length. To get the full advantages of the cosine model, we must think of variables as represented by *vectors*, that is, by lines which are specified both as to length and direction. (The letter h, with a single subscript to identify the variable, shall represent a vector. When written with two subscripts, thus: $h_{A:B}$, it shall represent the projection of one vector on another, or on an axis.)

Suppose that we want to represent a test, A, which has a validity coefficient of $r = .9$ with a criterion, C. Our interest in A is wholly concerned with the extent to which it coincides with the criterion. If measured along its own axis, the vector of Test A has unit length. Since $.9 = \cos 26°$, it follows that the axis of Test A forms this angle with the axis of Test C, the criterion, but this fact does not determine its direction fully. Therefore it is often convenient to represent A, or the available information about A, by means of a vector which has the same direction as C, and is of the same length as the projection. In symbols, $h_{A:C} = .9$. But what if we have two tests of C, and represent each of them in this manner? If our model is to be consistent with the facts, then the correlation between the two tests must be equal to the product of their vectors. Figure 12.6 depicts such a situation in terms of overlapping determinants. Test

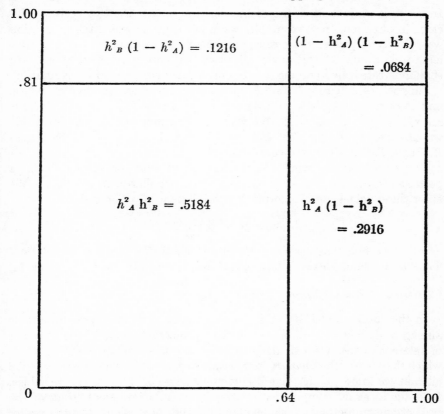

Fig. 12.6. Overlap of determinants in two otherwise independent tests of the same criterion. See text for explanation.

A has a validity coefficient of .9, and it therefore shares 81 per cent of the determinants of C; Test B has a validity coefficient of .8, and it therefore shares 64 per cent of the determinants of C. It is assumed that A and B are not related in any other way than by their association with C. This implies that if we divide the C-determinants into those-shared-with-B and those-not-shared-with-B, Test A would share 81 per cent of the determinants of either class. Likewise, if we divide the C-determinants into those-shared-with-A and those-not-shared-with-A, Test B shares 64 per cent of the elements in either class. Thus the proportion of C-determinants which A and B have in common equals $(.81)\ (.64) = .5184 = r^2_{AB}$, whence $r_{AB} = .72$. We might have found this directly as the product of their vectors.

The definition of a correlation in the cosine model may now be stated more fully than before:

62]
$$r_{AB} = h_A h_B \cos \theta_{AB}$$

In the case we just cited, the cosine was unity, since the two vectors coincided in direction. In the examples we used earlier, in which the correlation was directly equal to the cosine, the vectors were assumed to be of unit length. Formula 62 will cover all cases, without these restrictions. We shall illustrate it by applying it to the problem of correction for attenuation.

Suppose that Tests J and K are measuring different characteristics, and that $r_{JK} = .5$. It is also determined that the reliability coefficients are $r_{JJ} = .9$ and $r_{KK} = .8$. We wish to determine the correlation which would exist between perfect tests of the traits being measured by J and K. Since Test J has a self-correlation of .9, we represent it with a vector $h_J = \sqrt{.9}$, for this would be its correlation with, or projection on, a perfect measure of the same characteristic. Similarly, $h_K = \sqrt{.8}$. We enter these values, and the observed correlation, into Formula 62:

$$.5 = \sqrt{.9}\ \sqrt{.8}\ \cos \theta_{J_\infty K_\infty}$$

Solving, we find that $\cos \theta_{J_\infty K_\infty} = .59$, which is the corrected correlation. This is the same answer that results from Formula 58, in Chapter 11.

COMMON FACTOR SPACE

In the cosine model, it is always possible to reproduce the correlations among a number of variables from their projections on a smaller number of reference axes. We call the new reference axes *factors*, and the space which they define the *common factor space*, because it is adequate to describe all that we know about what is common to two or more of the variables. In order to avoid complicated forms of expression we shall speak of the projections on factor axes as "explaining" the correlations, but the reader will understand this to mean only that one can reproduce the correlations among the n variables from a knowledge of their projections on the m axes of the common factor space.

In this section we shall show how the correlations among three variables can be explained by projections on a single reference axis, or factor. In the next section we shall consider the four-variable case, which played an important part in the early history of factor analysis. Thereafter we shall consider the problem in more general terms, and shall describe a method of solution which can be applied to any correlation matrix.

For a three-variable problem, we take some correlations from an article by Holt[1] on the clinical assessment of therapeutic skill in psychiatric residents. Three independent evaluations were made for each resident— one by his supervisor, one by his peers, using a sociometric procedure, and one by a psychologist who based his ratings on blind analysis of test materials. In one phase of the study the following correlations were obtained:

$$\text{Psychologist—Peers} \quad r = .55$$
$$\text{Psychologist—Supervisor } r = .48$$

From elsewhere in the article we select the following as a representative value to complete the triad:

$$\text{Supervisor—Peers} \quad r = .73$$

Let S, P, and X stand, respectively, for evaluations by the Supervisor, the Peers, and the Psychologist, and let $h_{S:T}$, $h_{P:T}$, and $h_{X:T}$ stand for the projections of these variables on a single axis, which we optimistically label T for Therapeutic Skill. Then:

$$h_{X:T}h_{P:T} = .55, \quad h_{X:T}h_{S:T} = .48, \quad \text{and} \quad h_{S:T}h_{P:T} = .73$$

The solution of this system of three equations with three unknowns gives $h_{P:T} = .914$, $h_{S:T} = .798$, and $h_{X:T} = .602$. These vectors, measured along a common axis, suffice to explain the observed correlations in the sense stated earlier, that is, a knowledge of these projections enables us to reproduce the correlations by means of Formula 62. We might therefore reason (fallaciously) that since the three series of evaluations were all intended as measures of T, and since their intercorrelations can all be explained by projections on T, it can be assumed that what they have in common with T is the only important source of common variance among them. The fallacy in this argument lies in accepting the hypothesis of one common factor on inadequate evidence. For although the correlations *can* be explained mathematically in terms of one factor, it does not follow that they must be so explained. For example, the higher correlation between evaluations by supervisors and by peers may be due to the fact that both are being influenced by personal characteristics of the residents, say *likeableness* (L), whereas the psychologist, who sees only the test records, is free from this distracting influence. Then the correlations might be explained as resulting from projections on two factors, as follows:

	S	P	X
Projection on T	.680	.779	.705
Projection on L	.400	.500	.000

This hypothesis is suggested by a fact which Holt mentions, that when the psychologists were asked to rate the unseen residents according to how they *liked* them, as seen through the test records, the correlations with the criteria were improved! To reproduce the correlations from these projections, we shall have to amend Formula 62, as follows:

62a] $\qquad r_{AB} = \Sigma(h_A h_B \cos \theta_{AB})$

For example,

$$r_{SP} = h_{S:T} h_{P:T} + h_{S:L} h_{P:L}$$
$$= (.68)(.779) + (.40)(.50) = .73$$

Notice, as a practical consequence, that under this hypothesis the validity of the evaluation by the psychologist seems to be higher than that of the evaluation by the supervisor, whereas under the original hypothesis the evaluation by the psychologist seemed to be less valid. However, we cannot choose among hypotheses on the basis of our professional affiliations. It is possible to construct an unlimited number of such hypotheses, each of which is just as correct as any of the others from a purely mathematical point of view. And although science generally favors the simplest useful hypothesis, it is not possible to decide within the limits of the three-variable problem whether a one-factor hypothesis is really more useful than a two-factor hypothesis.

The Factors of Four Variables

· Factor analysis had its origin in the work of Charles Spearman on the nature of intelligence. He sought to demonstrate that all the common variance among many varied tests of mental abilities could be explained by a single general intellective factor, g. He attacked the problem ingeniously, by considering the correlations among different tests (number tests, memory tests, reasoning tests, etc.) in tetrads, or groups of four. Just as the relationship among three tests can always be explained by projections on one factor, so the relations among four tests can always be explained by projections on two factors. But Spearman reasoned that if it were shown that projections on one factor suffice to explain the correlations among four tests, then any hypothesis which invokes a second general factor can be rejected as nonparsimonious. The four-variable problem is different from the three-variable problem, because in the one case arbitrary or accidental values can be explained by projections on one factor, while in the other case arbitrary or accidental values will ordinarily require projections on two factors.

Spearman's[2] method was the *tetrad difference criterion*, an important step in the development of factor analysis. Consider four tests, J, K, L, and M. Let G be the only nonspecific factor which is present in these tests (that is, the only source of determinants of variance which are common to more than one of them), and let $h_{J;G}$, $h_{K;G}$, etc., represent the projections of these tests on the G axis. Now consider the equation,

$$r_{JK}r_{LM} - r_{JL}r_{KM} = D$$

This can be expanded into the form:

$$h_{J;G}h_{K;G}h_{L;G}h_{M;G} - h_{J;G}h_{L;G}h_{K;G}h_{M;G} = D$$

and it is seen that the two terms of the left-hand member are identical, and their difference, which is called the tetrad difference, is zero. However, this is the case only under the condition which we have assumed, namely, that there is no other nonspecific influence which results in an increment to these correlations. For example, if there is some factor F which contributes to the variance of both J and K, but not to the variance of L or M, then the expansion takes the following form:

$$(h_{J;G}h_{K;G} + h_{J;F}h_{K;F})h_{L;G}h_{M;G} - h_{J;G}h_{L;G}h_{K;G}h_{M;G} = D$$

and the tetrad difference will no longer be zero.

To summarize: the four-variable problem introduces a new aspect of the cosine model, which is the basis for the method of factor analysis: the possibility of "supersavings" in dimensionality, which point to the possibility of developing more parsimonious explanatory hypotheses.

REDUCTION OF DIMENSIONALITY

It is always possible to state in advance how many dimensions are needed for the exact solution of the dimensionality of any set of correlations which are based on empirical data, that is, correlations which include random error. If the n variables are arranged in a triangular pattern, thus:

$$
\begin{array}{cccc}
 & 1 & & \\
 & 2 & 3 & \\
 4 & 5 & 6 & \\
 7 & 8 & etc., &
\end{array}
$$

it is certain that $m = n - R$, where R is the number of completed rows in the pattern. However, it is possible that a still smaller number of dimensions may account for nearly all of the common variance, so that we may reasonably regard this smaller number as representing the number of dimensions which must be included in a general theory of the psychological domain being studied. It is this reduction in dimensionality beyond the assured savings which we refer to as "supersavings." This approach to the analysis of relationships among n variables was developed by Thurstone, as a generalization of the procedure which Spearman had introduced for dealing with four variables.

Before considering the n-dimensional problem, let us look again at the three-variable problem. There is a very simple device by which we might have solved this problem, instead of setting up a system of three simultaneous equations with three unknowns. First record the correlations in a square table, or matrix, in which only the entries in the principal diagonal (which henceforth will simply be called "the diagonal") are missing:

	P	S	X
P		.730	.550
S	.730		.480
X	.550	.480	

Each entry in this table is the product of two vectors, as yet unknown. To be consistent, the diagonal cells will have to be filled by squared values, h^2. When thus completed, the table will present the following pattern:

	P	S	X
P	$h_P\,h_P$	$h_P\,h_S$	$h_P\,h_X$
S	$h_S\,h_P$	$h_S\,h_S$	$h_S\,h_X$
X	$h_X\,h_P$	$h_X\,h_S$	$h_X\,h_X$

Notice that the same proportionality exists from row to row of every column, and from column to column of every row. Therefore the diagonal entries can be found as proportions of those already known. To specify:

$$\frac{h^2_P}{.730} = \frac{.730}{h^2_s} = \frac{.550}{.480} \quad \text{and} \quad \frac{.730}{.550} = \frac{.480}{h^2_x}$$

These diagonal entries, symbolized h^2, are called *communalities*, and the same name and symbol are also used for *sums* of squared projections of the same variable on several factors. Thus the communality represents the proportion of variance which one variable has "in common" with all other variables being studied. When the values of the communalities have been entered into the diagonal, the table is called a complete correlation matrix.

CENTROID ANALYSIS: FIRST CYCLE

If one attempts to apply this same method of solution to a matrix which is made up of the correlations among more than three variables, one will usually encounter the difficulty that the same proportionality does *not* exist from row to row, or from column to column, in such a table. Therefore, a theory which seeks to explain the correlations as due to the operation of a single factor must be associated with a null hypothesis which asserts that all of the nonproportionality is the consequence of error variance. The method of factor analysis which we shall now describe consists of the successive testing of a series of such hypotheses. It is Thurstone's[3] method of *centroid analysis*, although the steps are performed in a slightly altered sequence to facilitate a simplified statement of their rationale.

As the method is described, it will be illustrated step-by-step by application to a five-variable problem. The correlations are taken from an article by Henderson[4], on the prediction of grades among college freshmen. (A factor analysis did not enter into the plan of this investigation. For reasons which will become evident as we go along, many more variables would be needed for a useful factor analysis of this domain. However, considerations of clarity make it desirable to use an example with the smallest number of variables which can justify the extraction and interpretation of two factors.) In the following account, the separate parts of Table **12**.1 will be referred to as **12**.1(A), **12**.1(B), etc.

In **12**.1(A) each of the empirical correlations is entered twice, in a pattern which is symmetrical with respect to the principal diagonal. The matrix is completed by entering estimates of the communalities in the diagonal cells. This is done according to a rule of thumb suggested by Thurstone: that the communalities for each test will ordinarily be close to the highest correlation of that test with any other. Errors in such initial estimates are not a serious hazard, because (1) if the estimates are poor, this fact will show up later, and it will be possible to start over again with improved estimates which issue from this preliminary effort, and (2) when the number of variables is large, so that such a replication would be unduly onerous, errors in the communalities have relatively slight influence on the outcome of the analysis. The sum of each row of the complete matrix is recorded. The column sums are identical with the row sums, and therefore we do not bother to write them, although we shall refer to them from time to time.

The marginal sums of **12**.1(A) are used to set up a matrix of expected values, shown in **12**.1(B). This is done by the same method which is used to compute a table of expected frequencies, in the χ^2 technique: each entry in the new table is the product of the corresponding row sum and column sum, divided by the grand sum. These marginal sums are the same for both tables, except for errors due to rounding of numbers. The

TABLE 12.1

Computations in a Five-Variable Factor Analysis*

(A) *The original correlations, and assumed communalities*

	1	2	3	4	5	Check sums		Row sum	Loadings
1	*610*	610	400	410	360			2.390	
2	610	*610*	270	280	230			2.000	
3	400	270	*730*	730	530			2.660	
4	410	280	730	*730*	560			2.710	
5	360	230	530	560	*560*			2.240	
								12.000	

(B) *Expected values, first hypothesis* — h_I

	1	2	3	4	5			Row sum	h_I
1	476	398	530	540	446			2.390	.690
2	398	333	444	452	373			2.000	.577
3	530	544	589	600	496			2.659	.767
4	540	452	600	612	504			2.708	.782
5	446	373	496	504	418			2.237	.647
								11.994	3.463*

(C) *Residuals from first expected values*

	1	2	3	4	5			
1	134	212	−130	−130	−086	+346	−346	(−)0.692
2	212	277	−174	−172	−143	+489	−489	(−)0.978
3	−130	−174	141	130	034	+305	−304	0.609
4	−130	−172	130	118	054	+302	−302	0.604
5	−086	−143	034	054	142	+230	−229	0.459
								3.342

*Check:
3.463² =
11.992

(D) *Reflections of first residual signs*

	1	2	3	4	5
1 √	•	+−+	−+	−+	−+
2 √	+−+	•	−+	−+	−+
3	−+	−+	•	+	+
4	−+	−+	+	•	+
5	−+	−+	+	+	•

(E) *Expected values, second hypothesis* — h_{II}

	1	2	3	4	5				h_{II}
1	143	203	−106	−125	−095	+346	−346	(−)0.692	−.378
2	203	286	−178	−177	−134	+489	−491	(−)0.980	−.535
3	−126	−178	111	110	084	+305	−304	0.609	.333
4	−125	−177	110	109	083	+302	−302	0.604	.330
5	−095	−134	084	083	063	+230	−229	0.459	.251
								3.344	1.827**

(F) *Residuals from second expected values*

	1	2	3	4	5		
1	−009	009	−004	−005	009	+018	−019
2	009	−009	004	005	−009	+018	−018
3	−004	004	030	020	−050	+054	−054
4	−005	005	020	009	−029	+034	−034
5	009	−009	−050	−029	079	+088	−088

**Check:
1.827² =
3.338

*The correlations are taken from Henderson.[4] The variables are: (1) *A. C. E.*, (2) Cooperative Reading Test, (3) High school average grades, (4) Average grades on New York State Regents' examinations, English excepted, and (5) Grade on Regents' examination in English.

expected values represent a set of hypothetical correlations, based on the supposition that all of the common variance can be explained by projections on a single factor, plus random error. To the right, under the heading h_I, we list the square roots of the diagonal entries. These are the projections of the various tests on the assumed factor or, otherwise stated, the *loadings* of that factor in the various tests. Each expected value is the product of two of these loadings. They are directly proportional to the row sums, and their sum is the square root of the grand sum for either the original table or the table of expected values.

If the one-factor hypothesis is tenable, the expected values should agree fairly closely with the original correlations. We are prepared to tolerate a certain amount of discrepancy between the two tables as due to random error, but large discrepancies will compel us to reject the hypothesis. To facilitate this comparison, we prepare a table of residuals, **12.1(C)**. Each entry in this table is the difference between corresponding entries in the two preceding tables. Because the sum of entries on each row of **12.1(A)** has merely been redistributed in **12.1(B)**, it follows that the algebraic sum of the differences for each row, in **12.1(C)**, is zero, except for errors due to rounding. These subtotals are computed as a check. Looking over this table of residuals, we see that many of the entries have above-chance values, and therefore we reject the first hypothesis. (We shall not discuss the problem of a criterion to determine when a residual is greater than chance. More important than the criterion is this implication: the correlations which enter into a factor analysis should be very stable values, based on rather sizeable samples.)

CENTROID ANALYSIS: SECOND CYCLE

The fact that we are forced to reject the first hypothesis does not mean that we must throw out our work, but only that we must complicate the hypothesis with a supplement. We call this the second hypothesis, which states that all of the residual common variance can be explained by a second common factor, plus random error. We shall test this second hypothesis very much as we tested the first. The only difference arises from the fact that we cannot proceed immediately with the construction of a table of expected values, because the grand sum for the table of residuals is zero, or nearly so. We have contrived to make all the common variance in the table of residuals look like random error, at least in the sense that it is evenly divided into plus and minus values. To undo this effect, we *reflect* some of the variables, that is, we pretend that the scales for those variables had been reversed, which would also reverse the sign of any correlation in which such a variable was involved.

To minimize confusion, it is best to carry out the detail of reflecting the variables in a separate table. In each nondiagonal cell of **12.1(D)**, we enter first the algebraic sign of the entry which appears in the corresponding cell of **12.1**(C). Since the algebraic signs of diagonal entries will not be changed by any number of reflections, they are represented in **12.1**(D) only by dots. (They should in any case be positive, since each communality is the square of a real number. A negative residual in any of the diagonal cells implies that the original estimate for the communality was too low.) We pick a test to reflect, and change every sign on the row and in the column which represent that test. We do this for as many tests as necessary, and as often as necessary, until we are satisfied that we cannot further reduce the number of minus signs. The new signs are simply written alongside the old, and a check mark is made on the row reflected, as a memorandum. In this case it was only necessary to reflect Tests 1 and 2 in order to eliminate all minus signs from the table. We give effect to the result by making a circle around each value in the table of residuals which has a negative sign at the end of the process. (In the example, there are none.) This leaves the original signs undisturbed, and they will be needed to compute the second table of residuals. The new row sums are computed, ignoring the original signs but taking into account any minus signs which exist after the process of reflection. (If we are plagued with minus signs for any of the residual communalities, and do not want to start over again, these should be changed to plus signs. An alternative method is to replace all of the communalities, for each cycle of operations, with new estimates equal to the highest residual correlation of the given test with any other test. This would be recommended only when working with large matrices.)

The marginal sums of the first residuals, after reflection, are used to compute a new table of expected values for the second hypothesis, **12.1**(E). In this process, the sums for those variables which were reflected an odd number of times are used with a negative sign, thus in effect undoing the reflections after we have gained what we wanted from them. The square roots of the diagonal entries of these expected values are listed under the heading h_{11}, as hypothetical projections on the second factor. For those tests which were reflected an odd number of times, they are shown with a negative sign.

Again, we check the adequacy of the hypothesis by comparing the expected values, in **12.1**(E), with the residuals on which they were based, in **12.1**(C). The discrepancies are shown in **12.1**(F), the table of residuals for the test of the second hypothesis. Shall we stop the process of factoring at this point, or go on to test a third hypothesis? (In this case, the need to assume three factors would negate our hopes for the factor analysis, since we know in advance that correlations among five tests can always be explained by projections on three factors, and if we are forced to assume so many, it may well be that even more than three are involved.) The question of when to stop factoring is one of the major points of controversy in factor analysis, and the criticisms which one factorist may direct against the work of another quite commonly deal with charges of *overfactorization* and *underfactorization*. The principle is that one should stop when there are no significant residuals remaining—but there is still no really usable criterion of significance in this situation! We shall stop at this point because the extraction of the third factor would be repetitious, involving nothing different from what we have already done. It would be more useful to repeat the analysis with a new set of communalities, which would be obtained by subtracting the residuals in the diagonal cells of **12.1(F)** from the original estimates. We leave this as an exercise problem.

ROTATION OF FACTORS: ORTHOGONAL

Having determined that two factors suffice to explain most of the common variance among the five tests which we have been considering, the next problem is to find a psychologically meaningful interpretation for these two factors. This will be easier if we look at a geometric model of the test relationships, which is readily constructed from the discovered factor loadings, which appear in the final columns of **12.1(B)** and **12.1(D)**. Figure **12.7** shows the resulting configuration. In this figure, each test is represented by a point fixed by a pair of loadings. For example, the position of Test 1 is fixed by the intersection of perpendiculars to Axis I at .690 and to Axis II at −.378. The determination of the resulting configuration of all the tests is the first important outcome of the factor analysis. It is the basis for any interpretation of the psychological domain which is represented by the tests.

Once the configuration has been fixed, it may be described in many different ways. The projections on the original reference axes, I and II, do not necessarily constitute the most useful description. As a matter of fact, these projections are a more or less accidental outcome of the particular factoring procedure which we used, which always makes the second and all subsequent factors appear to be bipolar. Sometimes such bipolar factors may be psychologically meaningful, but more often they are not. Usually we prefer to use a new set of reference axes, which is so placed that all negative loadings are eliminated. If we can succeed in doing this, we say that the configuration has been transformed into a *positive manifold*. In Figure **12.7**, this has been achieved very simply, by rotating both axes 50° counterclockwise. The new reference axes are labelled I′ and II′. The projections on the new axes can be determined by direct measurement, or they can be computed by the following formulas:

63]
$$h_{I'} = h_I \cos \theta + h_{II} \sin \theta$$
and
$$h_{II'} = h_{II} \cos \theta - h_I \sin \theta$$

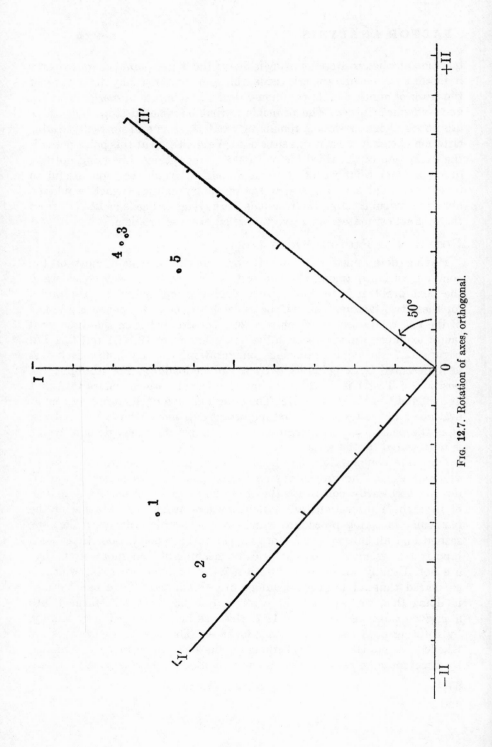

Fig. 12.7. Rotation of axes, orthogonal.

where θ represents a clockwise rotation. (If θ represents a counterclockwise rotation, reverse the sign of the last term in each equation.) We shall illustrate Formula 63 by showing the computation of one value in Table 12.2. First we take note that the axes were rotated 50° counterclockwise, and we determine, from trigonometric tables, that cos 50° = .643 and sin 50° = .766. The projection of Test 1 on Axis I' then becomes:

$$h_{\mathrm{I}}' = .690\,(.643) - (-.378)\,(.766)$$
$$= .444 + .289 = .733$$

TABLE 12.2

Loadings on Unrotated and Rotated Factors, and Communalities

| Test | Unrotated Factors | | Rotated Factors | | |
	I	II	I'	II'	h^2
1	.690	−.378	.733	.285	.618
2	.577	−.535	.781	.097	.619
3	.767	.333	.238	.801	.699
4	.782	.330	.250	.811	.720
5	.647	.251	.224	.656	.480

This changes nothing with regard to the configuration of the tests in the common factor space, but it gives a new set of projections which are so chosen that the two clusters are differentiated by their projections on either axis. Making use of what we know about the actual tests (see the heading of Table 12.1), we can now give names to the factors, calling Factor I' *Capacity*, and Factor II' *Achievement*. The high school grades and the Regents examinations are primarily tests of *Achievement*, but they also have moderate loadings on *Capacity*. (If these loadings seem too small, one must remember that they apply only to the sample of subjects in the study, that is, to a class of students from which the lower and even the middle parts of the range for both achievement and capacity have been excluded.)

It is easy to see as a whole the configuration of variables in a common factor space of only two dimensions, because this can be displayed in a single diagram, without distortion of perspective. When the common factor space has three dimensions, the configuration can be displayed in an approximate manner on the face of a globe, and the reference axes can be shown as great circles or "equators." The more usual method is to display the configuration of tests in three separate two-dimensional plots, each of which shows the configuration as it would appear from a line of sight which is parallel to the axis which has been omitted from that particular plot. Then the process of rotation may be likened to walking around and over and under the configuration, in order to select new viewpoints which will show the configuration with special clarity. After some practice, one learns to anticipate the sort of shifts in one plot which will occur as the result of a rotation of the axes in another plot. All such changes only involve the relationship between an invariant configuration of tests and an invariant set of axes which remain fixed at right angles to each other. The relationship of each test to all the others remains immutable.

When the common factor space has more than three dimensions, the task of rotation becomes more difficult, but it is not different in principle. Six two-dimensional plots are needed to display the configuration of tests in a common factor space of four dimensions, and ten are needed for a space of five dimensions. Patience and skill are needed to work one's way through this mass of details, in order to arrive at a final disposition of the axes which provides the most meaningful perspectives over the whole domain. The work of rotation is usually done graphically, although the final projections are computed by formula. The table of such projections constitutes the *factor structure*, which shows the factorial composition of all the tests. In this table, each column is a sort of profile of the entire configuration as seen from a certain point of view, and each row shows how much of the common variance of each test is explained by each of the factors, and by all together. (See the loadings on rotated factors in Table 12.2.)

Table **12**.3 presents (in abbreviated form) an orthogonal factor structure

TABLE 12.3

Rotated Factor Loadings for 8 of the 50 Adjective Pairs used by Osgood and Suci[5], in Their Factor Analysis of Meaning

Adjective Pair	I	II	III	IV	h^2
good-bad	.88	.05	−.09	.09	.79
large-small	.06	.62	.34	.04	.51
hard-soft	−.48	.55	.16	.21	.60
strong-weak	.19	.62	.20	−.03	.46
sharp-dull	.23	.07	.52	−.10	.34
rich-poor	.60	.10	.00	−.18	.40
healthy-sick	.69	.17	.09	.02	.59
fast-slow	.01	.00	.70	−.12	.50

which summarizes the results of an interesting investigation, a factor analysis of verbal meanings by Osgood and Suci.[5] Each of their 100 subjects rated 20 substantive concepts (such as *lady, boulder, patriot, fraud, sym-*

phony) on 50 bipolar dimensions. This provided 2450 correlations, each indicating the degree of association between two of the dimensions, across the whole range of concepts. For example, if objects called *sweet* rather than *bitter* were also called *good* rather than *bad*, this would lead to positive correlation; if objects called *sweet* rather than *bitter* were just as likely to be called *wide* as *narrow*, a nonsignificant correlation would result. Four factors were extracted, and the table shows projections on these factors after the rotations, for only a few of the 50 dimensions. From a study of all the loadings, the authors concluded that Factor I should be designated as *Evaluative*, Factor II as *Potency*, and Factor III as *Activity*, while Factor IV, which accounted for only a small proportion of the common variance, could not be interpreted. The last column of the table gives h^2, the communality, for each of the variables. This value is not changed by the rotations. It is extremely important, because it tells us what part of the test variance is explained as common variance. As h^2 is communality, so $1 - h^2$ is *uniqueness*. Furthermore, uniqueness represents a composite of variance from two sources: *specificity* and error. Since no factor analysis can explain more than the projections of the variables into the common factor space, a good research design should include variables which are so widely representative of the domain being studied that the communalities of the tests will be maximized, and their specificities minimized.

ROTATION OF AXES: OBLIQUE

But why should we be limited in the points of view which we select for viewing the configuration, as the official prison photographer is limited by regulations to taking full-face and profile views of those who pose for his art? Why not a one-quarter view, or a three-quarters view, when these are more revealing of the factorial composition? If m dimensions are needed to define a configuration, this does not mean that the m dimensions must be orthogonal to each other. Such factors as *Achievement* and *Capacity*, or *Beauty* and *Intelligence*, come correlated in our experience, and they should be allowed to remain so in our statistical analyses.

Once we get over our initial apprehension about oblique axes (that is, axes which are permitted to form oblique angles with respect to one another), we discover that in a well-organized factorial investigation it is easier to select advantageous positions for such axes than for orthogonal axes. Good factor studies generally involve large numbers of variables, since these are needed (*a*) to permit supersavings in dimensionality while allowing all important determinants of common variance to come to the fore, (*b*) to insure that a high proportion of the variance on most of the tests will be common variance, and (*c*) to define the positions of the factors with minimum error. In the design of such a study it is desirable to include several measures which can be expected to have relatively high projections on each of the factors which is expected to emerge in the analysis, and also to include a large number of measures which can be expected to have low or insignificant loadings of other factors. This facilitates rotation to *simple structure*, which was defined by Thurstone as a resolution of the rotational problem in which, to put it very simply, there is a good sprinkling of nonsignificant entries in every row and every column of the table of factor loadings. The usefulness of this criterion lies in the fact that on each two-dimensional plot of a hyperdimensional configuration, the tests having negligible projections on one of the factors tend to align themselves into what is called the *trace* of a *hyperplane*. A hyperplane is the $m - 1$ dimensional space which is the locus of a score on one of m dimensions, and its trace is a sort of foreshortened view, like the view of marbles on a table-top from a point which is level with the table. Instead of attempting to locate factors by means of tests which have high loadings, we look for the hyperplane, and place the factor axis perpendicular to it. After a number of such attempts, the hyperplanes begin to emerge more and more clearly, and experience with this method shows that two different workers, starting with the same unrotated factors, may go through two very different series of rotational manoeuvres, yet arrive at very similar final solutions. The accumulating evidence of this *invariance* of the rotational problem in well-designed factorial investigations has done much to dispel the skepticism about factor analysis which was formerly so general. Indeed, the mathematical definition of criteria for rotation has advanced to the point where it is now possible to give the task of rotation, like the preliminary computation of the correlations, into the care of an electronic computer, thus removing every suspicion of subjectivism in the result.

The loadings on oblique factors are not usually very different from those on orthogonal factors. One advantage is that they generally achieve a clearer resolution of the factor problem. Another is that their use in a primary factor analysis gives rise to the possibility of an analysis of these relationships, which may lead to the discovery of *second-order factors*. This has led to an interesting answer to the theoretical question which first gave rise to factor analysis, that is, whether intelligence is to be defined as a "general ability" or as a conglomerate of specific abilities. Thurstone showed clearly that Spearman's theory, which defined intelligence as g, must give way before the evidence of many *primary mental abilities*, but subsequent work showed that Spearman's g may reasonably be regarded as a general second-order factor. For example, in a recent study of the *Wechsler Adult Intelligence Scale*, Cohen[6] found evidence of five factors. Three of these could be rather clearly identified as Verbal Comprehension, Perceptual Organization, and Memory. All five factors were rather strongly correlated, and the second-order analysis showed a single second-order factor running through all of the subtests and all of the factors, and responsible for approximately half of the variance of the subtest scores. Cohen points to an interesting implication of his results: there is so little specificity left in the various subtests, that all attempts to use the scores of individual subtests for differential diagnosis, as has so often been done, are doomed to failure.

The methods of factor analysis form a bridge between the use of mathematics for purely analytic purposes, and the use of mathematics for the construction of theoretical models. The latter subject lies outside the scope of this book, but it is one to which the course in statistics should form a natural introduction.

PROBLEMS

1. *Show how r_{12}, in Table* **12**.1, *can be reconstructed from loadings of the unrotated factors on Tests 1 and 2 in Table* **12**.2. *Compare the error in these reconstructions with the residuals in Table* **12**.1 (F).

2. *Do the same, using loadings of the rotated factors.*

3. *Describe a recent research report including a factor analysis. Do you think that the "factors" defined by the author represent a meaningful simplification of the phenomena being studied?*

4. *What is the maximum number of dimensions required to explain the intercorrelations of 9 tests? of 22 tests? What is the maximum number of factors which can be given meaningful psychological interpretation, in each case?*

REFERENCES

1. Holt, R. R. Clinical *and* statistical prediction: a reformulation and some new data. *J. abn. soc. Psychol.*, 1958, **56**:1–12.

2. Spearman, C. E. *The abilities of man.* New York: Macmillan, 1927.

3. Thurstone, L. L. *Multiple factor analysis.* Chicago: University of Chicago Press, 1947.

4. Henderson, H. L. Predictors of freshman grades in a Long Island college. *Educ. psychol. Measmt.*, 1957, **17**:623–627.

5. Osgood, C. E., and Suci, G. J. Factor analysis of meaning. *J. exp. Psychol.*, 1955, 50:325–338.

6. Cohen, J. The factorial structure of the WAIS between early adulthood and old age, *J. cons. Psychol.*, 1957, **21**:283–290.

13

HANDLING NONNORMAL DATA

The probability distributions for both t and F are calculated on the assumption of random sampling from a normal universe. When we meet an "unlikely" value of t, for example, we are faced with the following possibilities: (1) that the sampling is not random, (2) that it is not from a normal universe, or (3) that the samples are not from the same universe. In the last case, it is possible that the universes differ with respect to (a) variance or (b) mean value. If we regard t as a test of significance of the difference between sample means, we are assuming that all the other possibilities may be disregarded, that is, that the sampling *is* random, that each sample *is* from a normal universe, and that the universes *do not* differ with respect to variance. When these assumptions are not valid, the conclusion that a low P reflects a difference between universe means includes elements of risk which are not assessed by the statistical procedure. And as a matter of fact, all three of these assumptions are violated in almost every practical application of a statistical test! It behooves us, therefore, to consider just how serious are the consequences of these irregularities, and also to consider what alternative methods are available.

This chapter will consider four possible ways to meet the situation. (1) We may elect to use F (or t) despite the doubts cast upon the accuracy of the resulting conclusions. (2) We may use some special probability distribution which is appropriate to the problem in hand. (3) We may attempt to transform the scores in a way which will produce normal distributions of homogeneous variance. (4) We may resort to the use of methods which are called *distribution-free* or *nonparametric*, because they make no assumptions about the form of distribution of scores in the universe being sampled, or at least none that cannot be readily satisfied. We shall consider the first three possibilities briefly, and devote the greater part of the chapter to distribution-free techniques.

THE CASE FOR A LENIENT APPROACH

It is reassuring to observe at the outset that the consequences of mathematical delinquency, while they are not to be disregarded, are less serious than they are often made to appear in the statements of statistical puritans. Published sampling experiments tend uniformly to support the view that the t test and the F test are rather satisfactory guides under the conditions which usually arise in practical work. The most extensive study of this kind was performed by D. W. Norton, and is reported at length by Lindquist.[1] The general conclusions stated by Lindquist are: (1) that "the F-distribution seems so insensitive to the form of the [parent] distribution . . . that it hardly seems worthwhile to apply any statistical test to the data to detect non-normality," and (2) that "unless the heterogeneity of form or variance is so extreme as to be readily apparent upon inspection of the data, the effect upon the F-distribution will probably be negligible." Lindquist recommends that even when marked heterogeneity does exist, it would generally be better to set a stricter level of significance, perhaps 2.5 per cent instead of 5 per cent and .1 per cent instead of 1 per cent, rather than to abandon use of the F test. Tending to the same conclusion is the fact that in numerous experimental reports, in which the treatment of data is by unimpeachable distribution-free methods, one finds a footnote or a parenthetic comment to the effect that the data were also treated by parametric methods, with essentially the same results.

In short, there is evidence that even conspicuous violations of the assumptions underlying the F test do not necessarily lead to grossly misleading results. This does not mean that alternative procedures are not often to be preferred. It does mean that we do not need to use a high-powered magnifying glass, as it were, to examine the conditions of its application. After we have looked at the other possibilities open to us, we shall take up again the question of when it may be the better part of wisdom to overlook minor irregularities, and just go on pretending that our data are really normal and the samples really are homogeneous in variance.

THE POISSON DISTRIBUTION

It is naive to suppose that all well-behaved data must conform to the normal pattern. Since a normal distribution results from the operation of many influences, none of which is predominant, it follows that any significant departure from normality deserves our attention, because it may provide a clue to the operation of a factor which is predominant in determining the behavior that is being studied. For example, Allport[2] pointed out that the J-curve (a distribution sharply truncated close to the median at one side, with a long tapered tail to the other side) is characteristic of "conforming" behavior. He demonstrated this in the behavior of factory workers punching a time-clock. It would doubtless also apply to the number of drinks consumed by each person at a cocktail party. The J-curve is a useful descriptive concept, but it has no precise statistical criteria.

A very useful type of nonnormal probability is described by the Poisson distribution. This may be said to define the long-term cumulative probability of improbable events. A classical application dealt with the annual number of deaths, in a cavalry division, from being kicked by a horse. Psychologists have used the Poisson distribution to analyze the concept of accident proneness. Suppose that in an industrial plant, employing 1000 men, there are 200 reported accidents during the year. Since some men are involved in two or more accidents, a psychological consultant is asked whether individual proneness to accidents is a factor of importance. His first step may be to determine how many men can be expected to have more than one accident, by chance. The nature of the exposure is indicated by the mean incidence of accidents, which is .2 per man, but this is not the value of p. The value of p is vanishingly small, for an accident occurs in an instant, and even on a man-hour basis p is about .000002. This makes it very difficult to compute a binomial probability distribution. The solution of the problem depends on solving the binomial expansion for the special case in which p is "almost zero" and q is "almost unity." The answer is:

64]
$$P\{X\} = \frac{e^{-\bar{X}}\bar{X}^X}{X!}$$

where e is the natural base of logarithms $(2.7183\cdots)$, X takes all positive integral values, including zero, and $P\{X\}$ stands for the probability of a given score. This formula is easily applied. The starting point for computing the probability distribution is the value of $e^{-\bar{X}}$, which can be taken from Table X. In this instance, $\bar{X} = .2$, and the table gives $e^{-.2} = .819$. Since any number to the zero power is unity, and zero factorial is also unity, this is also the proportional frequency of zero scores. That is, 819 men in a thousand should come through the year without accidents.

The proportional frequency of employees having just one accident equals

$$P\{1\} = \frac{.819\,(.2)}{1} = .164$$

The proportion having two accidents is

$$P\{2\} = \frac{.819\,(.2)^2}{2} = .016$$

and the proportion having three accidents is

$$P\{3\} = \frac{.819\,(.2)^3}{6} = .001$$

The proportion having four or more accidents is too small to concern us.

Slide-rule Hint

Notice that once the value of $P\{0\}$, which is taken from Table X, is marked on the slide-rule with the hairline, each successive computation merely involves dividing the previous answer by the next higher integer, and multiplying by $\overline{X}$. These two operations can usually be performed with one move of the slide. The fact that all of the proportions sum to unity constitutes a check on the series of computations.

The complete probability distribution therefore is:

X	0	1	2	3
P	.819	.164	.016	.001

Accordingly, one would expect 17 men to be involved in more than one accident, including one unlucky fellow, not necessarily accident-prone, who would be involved in three. Unless the number of individuals who are victims of more than one accident is significantly above this estimate (as shown by a test of goodness of fit) we cannot reject the null hypothesis. This implies that there is no evidence to support the theory of accident proneness in this situation.

It is an oddity of the Poisson distribution that the variance is always equal to the mean. Another important characteristic is that the merging of two Poisson distributions gives rise to a new Poisson distribution. Therefore the fact that we are dealing with many groups of workers, some of whom have more hazardous jobs than others, does not invalidate the method.

THE USE OF NONLINEAR TRANSFORMATIONS

The research worker often faces the dilemma that he wishes to exploit the advantages of a factorial design for his experiment, but the data which he gathers will not be in a form which meets the requirements for analysis of variance. If the violations of basic assumptions are not too extreme, he may decide to follow Lindquist's advice, quoted earlier, to perform an analysis of variance in the usual manner, and interpret the results with conservatism. But there is another possible escape from his dilemma. He may gather his data in whatever form is feasible, and then subject them to a nonlinear transformation, either to establish normality of distribution, or to reduce the heterogeneity of variance among the samples, or to effect both of these objectives. We have already described one such transformation, Fisher's z, which is used to normalize the chance distribution of r. The normalizing transformations to be described in this section are mathematically much simpler than z.

We should take note that heterogeneity of variance is the rule, rather than the exception, in experimental results, since any condition which effects a general rise in the level of the scores usually also increases their variance. Just as variance in the weight of tigers is greater than variance in the weight of kittens, so the variance of any set of scores tends to increase as the representative score increases. Whenever the experimental variable has a pronounced effect, it is as if the kittens were growing into tigers (or the tigers shrinking into kittens), so that the side-effect is to destroy the homogeneity of variance.

The most common way to correct this is by a *logarithmic transformation*. The portion of a logarithmic scale which represents the numbers from 1 to 10 occupies just as much space as the portion which represents the number from 10 to 100, or that which represents the numbers from 100 to 1000. Therefore, as each score is transformed into its logarithm the samples of wider range are compressed more than the samples of narrow range, and homogeneity of variance may be established sufficiently to meet the demands of an analysis of variance. Any conclusions based on the statistical analysis of the transformed scores can be applied to the original scores, because there is a one-to-one correspondence between points on both scales.

To illustrate: suppose that three samples have the following scores: *Sample A:* 1, 2, 3; *Sample B:* 4, 8, 12; *Sample C:* 20, 40 60. When these scores are transformed into logarithms (by Table XV), they become:

Sample A:	.00	.30	.48
Sample B:	.60	.90	1.08
Sample C:	1.30	1.60	1.78

The samples in this schematic example are now exactly matched in variance, and thus an obstacle to analysis of variance is removed.

Skewed distributions are often corrected by *reciprocal transformations*. This is a common treatment for latency scores, such as reaction times, and running times in animal experiments. To transform such scores into their reciprocals simply means that a measure of "slowness" has been transformed into a measure of "swiftness." Suppose that 5 rats take 2 seconds, 3 seconds, 4 seconds, 5 seconds, and 20 seconds to run from a starting chamber to a goal chamber, across an electric-shock obstruction. Rat 5 seems to be in a class by himself. The reciprocals of these scores are .50, .33, .25, .20, and .05. The separation between Rats 1 and 2 is greater than that between Rats 4 and 5!

Another useful device is the *inverse sine transformation*, which is used to normalize distributions of percentages. The tails of a per-cent distribution approach fixed limits (at 0 and 100) and therefore extreme values tend to be compressed, rather than tapering off. When each percentage value is transformed into the angle whose sine is the square root of the percentage, this condition is corrected. Values for this transformation are given in a portion of Table XI, where $p = \sin^2 \theta$. One important use of this transformation is that it enables us to establish confidence limits for an extreme percentage value, or to determine the significance of a difference between proportions when one or both are so extreme that the usual formula should not be used. If θ is the transformed value of the percentage, then

65] $$\sigma_\theta = \sqrt{\frac{821}{n}}$$

and

65a] $$\sigma_{\theta_1 - \theta_2} = \sqrt{\frac{821}{n_1} + \frac{821}{n_2}}$$

We shall illustrate Formula 65 by using it to obtain a more refined estimate of the confidence limits for the proportion in a problem which we have already treated by a less exact procedure. The problem (first stated on page 146) is to compute the confidence interval for the finding that 20 per cent of 65 persons interviewed stated that they dislike cottage cheese. By Formula 65,

$$\sigma_\theta = \sqrt{\frac{821}{65}} = 3.56$$

By Table XI, $\theta = 26.6°$, and therefore the 5 per cent confidence limits, stated in terms of θ, are 26.6 ± 1.96 (3.56). These limits are 19.6° and 33.6°. Transformed back again into percentage values, the limits are 11.2 per cent and 30.7 per cent. Rounding these values, we have 11 per cent and 31 per cent, in place of 10 per cent and 30 per cent by the other method. The effect here is slight; it would be much more marked if we were dealing with a value below 10 per cent, or above 90 per cent. The reader may recall that the other formula was not to be used beyond those limits.

When individual scores consist of percentage values, the use of this transformation will usually establish the necessary conditions for an analysis of variance.

Other commonly used transformations include the *square root* transformation and the *log log* transformation. It is permissible to use any transformation which is consistently applied to all the data in a problem, and then to apply any statistical technique which is suited to the distribution of transformed scores. These are not hocus-pocus procedures, to be viewed with distrust. When a set of scores which is not amenable to parametric statistical treatment is successfully transformed into a set which is amenable to such treatment, there is good reason to suppose that the scale of transformed scores is more meaningful than the scale of raw scores. The new scale has probably eliminated distortions due to the artifical nature of the units of measurement of the original scale.

THE SIGN TEST

We turn now to the consideration of distribution-free statistical techniques, and here we shall begin by re-examining two methods which have already been described in earlier chapters. In the context of distribution-free statistics, these are usually called the *sign test* and the *median test*.

The sign test consists in the application of binomial probabilities to any series of discrete events which can be classified dichotomously. For example: 7 rats were trained to jump a short distance from a platform to a single open window where food was available. Each day they were required to make 2 jumps, one soon after the other. One day they were confronted with the choice of 2 windows, and each timid beastie made his choice, right or left, after much hesitation. Immediately after, each rat had the same choice to make again. The responses on this crucial trial can be classified as "same" or "different," and they can be symbolized as "$+$" or "$-$." The experimental hypothesis stated that there would be an increased likelihood of "$+$" responses, while the null hypothesis stated that "$+$" and "$-$" responses would be equally likely. Reference to Table I shows that there are 128 possible combinations of "same" and "different" responses in this situation, where $n = 7$. Since, in fact, all 7 animals made "$+$" responses, the null hypothesis could be rejected at the 1 per cent level, by a one-tailed test.[3]

This use of the binomial distribution, in any situation in which the two outcomes are equally likely under the null hypothesis, is called the sign test. It can also be applied to a series of paired comparisons. For example, when we have "before" and "after" scores on the same subjects, the difference scores can be classified as either positive, negative, or zero. For purposes of the sign test, cases of "no difference" are discarded, reducing the number of pairs. Under the null hypothesis, positive and

negative differences have equal opportunity to occur, and the frequency
of occurrence of either sign among n non-zero pairs should vary according
to the expansion of $(.5 + .5)^n$. Let m stand for the number of occurrences
of the less frequent sign. For $n \leq 12$, the exact probability of obtaining
any m, or any equally extreme outcome, can be quickly determined with
the help of Table I. Critical values of m, for $n \leq 20$, are given in Table VII.

With $n > 20$, and $p = q$, the binomial distribution is very nearly normal,
and therefore beyond the limits of Table VII one can use the following
normal approximation, which includes a correction for continuity:

66]
$$z = \frac{n - (2m + 1)}{\sqrt{n}}$$

where m stands for the smaller number of signs among n non-zero differences.

We shall illustrate Formula 66 in connection with results reported by
Dember, Earl, and Paradise,[4] in an investigation of what might be called
the development of esthetic attitudes in rats. Each animal had its choice
of two paths, one of which had a more complex decor than the other.
It was predicted that animals which showed an initial preference for the
"complex" path would maintain that preference, while those which showed
an initial preference for the less complex path would tend to shift their
preference. A total of 13 shifts occurred, among 33 animals. Twelve shifts
were in the predicted direction. An exact treatment of this case calls for
extending Table I by one more column, and it leads to the conclusion
that P, for a one-tailed test, equals 14/8192, or $P = .0017$. Although
Formula 66 is not recommended for so small an n, it leads to much the
same conclusion:

$$z = \frac{13 - 3}{\sqrt{13}} = 2.77; \qquad P = .0028 \text{ (one-tailed)}$$

The sign test is delightfully easy to apply. Unfortunately, it is a relatively insensitive test. In the problem just cited, it made no use of the
fact that 19 rats which had showed initial preference for the complex
path maintained that preference. Nevertheless, the test was fully adequate
to the needs of the situation.

The Median Test

Tests of homogeneity by means of the χ^2 technique (or by the cognate
method for dealing with a difference in proportions) are also free from
any assumptions regarding the form of the parent distribution. The null
hypothesis states that a certain proportion of the universe is to be found
in each of the defined categories, but it does not assume anything about

distribution within those categories. This method can be used to compare two or more samples of any sort of numerical data, by classifying the scores within each sample into upper and lower groups on the basis of the common median of all the scores. When some scores coincide with the median, it is necessary to select a cutting point just above or just below it. The decision is guided by the rule that the marginal sums shall be as nearly equal as possible, for it is important that the frequencies, and not any preference of the investigator, shall determine the point of dichotomy.

When the median test is applied to the "hostility scores" of Table 2.3, the resulting fourfold table yields $\chi^2 = 2.69$. Hence, P < .05, agreeing with the t test of the same data on page 115.

However, the χ^2 procedure is not sufficiently exact for such small frequencies as those in this example. Fisher points out that the exact probability for any fourfold distribution can be computed thus:

$$P = (a + b)!\, (c + d)!\, (a + c)!\, (b + d)! \,/\, a!\, b!\, c!\, d!\, n!$$

In order to test the null hypothesis by this method, it is necessary to compute this probability, not only for the observed data, but also for each possible more extreme outcome that gives the same marginal totals. In this case, there would be four tables in all:

8	3		9	2		10	1		11	0
4	9		3	10		2	11		1	12

For the first of these tables, the computation takes this form:

$$P = 11!\, 13!\, 12!\, 12! \,/\, 8!\, 3!\, 4!\, 9!\, 24! = .044$$

It will be found that the aggregate probability of all four distributions is P < .05, indicating that the null hypothesis is to be rejected. Take note, however, that the t test and the median test, in this exact form, are not really in contradiction, since one test deals with the null hypothesis regarding universe means, and the other, with the null hypothesis regarding universe medians. (Page 249 gives another test of these data.)

Wilson's[5] "distribution-free test for analysis of variance hypotheses" seeks to extend the median test to factorial designs. Serious defects have been pointed out by McNemar[6] and Sheffield.[7] Therefore we omit Wilson's method, but mention it only to draw the reader's attention to the fact that there is as yet no satisfactory distribution-free treatment for factorial designs.

ORDER STATISTICS

Between the statistics which utilize equal-interval scores on theoretically continuous dimensions, on the one hand, and those which rely on classification into descriptive categories, on the other, there lies a third class of statistics, based on the use of ranks. These, too, are called distribution-free, because data which resist satisfactory normalization can almost always be readily transformed into a set of ranks. The exception is any set of data in which there is an excessive number of ties, so that a meaningful transformation into ranks is not possible. We shall see later that this restriction is to be interpreted liberally, although it would apply to data which consist of enumeration in only a few very broad categories.

Because of the relative ease of ranking procedures, they are frequently used in psychological measurement. For example, if we wish to study the relationship between intelligence and popularity in school children, it is difficult to devise a scale of measurement for popularity which is comparable to an intelligence test, but it is relatively easy, by sociometric methods, to rank the children in a class from the one who is "most popular" to the one who is "least popular."

A set of scores which consist of ranks, rather than measures, has distinctive mathematical properties. It consists of the first n integers, and therefore we know that*

$$\Sigma R = (n^2 + n)/2$$

and

$$\Sigma R^2 = (n^2 + n)(2n + 1)/6$$

When we substitute these expressions for ΣX and ΣX^2, in the formula for variance, and simplify, we discover that the variance of any set of ranks becomes:

67] $$\sigma^2_r = (n^2 - 1)/12$$

This is a component part of the formula for every one of the order statistics, although it is often disguised beyond easy recognition, in the process of simplifying the formula for computational purposes. These statistics are of two types. We shall consider first a group of three related methods for expressing the degree of correspondence between two or more sets of ranks, and later we shall consider methods which are based on random sampling from a single set of ranks.

RANK CORRELATION, r'

The product moment correlation can be used with ranks just as with interval scores. However, the computational work is simplified under these

---

* These formulas apply to true sets of ranks, which include no ties. When ties occur, each score is given the mean of the several ranks which would be assigned to the group of tied scores, if they could be differentiated. Thus, for the set 2, 4, 4, 7, the ranks are 1, 2.5, 2.5, 4. Using this convention, the sum of ranks is unchanged, but the sum of squares is reduced. (In the example, from 30 to 29.5.) The effect is usually negligible and therefore corrections for tied ranks, although available, are seldom used.

conditions. Since both sets of scores which enter into the correlation have the same n and the same σ^2, it follows from Formula 67 that

$$n\sigma_X\sigma_Y = n(n^2 - 1)/12$$

Furthermore, since $\Sigma X = \Sigma Y = (n^2 + n)/2$,

$$(\Sigma X)(\Sigma Y)/n = n(n + 1)^2/4$$

Making use of these identities, the formula for product moment correlation, between two sets of ranks, can be cast into this form:

$$r' = \frac{12 \Sigma XY - 3n(n + 1)^2}{n(n^2 - 1)}$$

We give this formula because its terms will reappear in the formulas for other order statistics. The exactly equivalent formula in general use, known as Spearman's coefficient of rank correlation, is:

$$68] \qquad\qquad r' = 1 - \frac{6 \Sigma D^2}{n(n^2 - 1)}$$

where D is the difference between the two ranks of a pair, which must be squared and then summed over all of the pairs.

This procedure is illustrated in Table 13.1, which is based on the same fictitious data which we have already used to illustrate computation of the differentiation ratios and r^2. The scores, it may be remembered, are ratings on the Timeless Scale of Love, and since it may well be doubted that intervals on this scale are really equal, although there is no reason to doubt that each higher score does indicate a greater intensity of amourous feeling, it is in order to express the relationship between the two sets of scores by a rank correlation rather than a product moment correlation. The first step is to transform the scores of each set into a series of ranks. These ranks are shown in the columns R_B and R_G. The manner in which tied scores have been treated should be studied. As it happens, all ties among the boys' scores were in sets of two, giving rise to such averaged ranks as 3.5 and 7.5, while all those among the girls' scores were in sets of three. Notice that the sum of ranks in each series is just what it would be if there had been no ties. The accuracy of the differences, in the next column, is partially checked by the fact that positive and negative differences are equal. All of this is merely preliminary to obtaining ΣD^2. The resulting value of r' is slightly higher than the value of r previously obtained for the same data (.615), but this small difference scarcely deserves attention in a problem based on such scant data.

The coefficient of rank correlation is virtually equivalent to the product moment correlation in large samples from a normal bivariate universe, in which regression is linear. Even when these assumptions are not tenable,

TABLE 13.1

Computation of the Coefficient of Rank Correlation, for Data First
Presented in Table 10.1*

Pair	(B) His Love	(G) Her Love	R_B	R_G	D	D^2
1	2	5	1.5	7	−5.5	30.25
2	8	6	12	10	2	4
3	7	5	10.5	7	3.5	12.25
4	5	5	7.5	7	0.5	0.25
5	4	6	5.5	10	−4.5	20.25
6	4	3	5.5	3	2.5	6.25
7	3	4	3.5	5	−1.5	2.25
8	2	3	1.5	3	−1.5	2.25
9	5	3	7.5	3	4.5	20.25
10	6	6	9	10	−1	1
11	7	7	10.5	12	−1.5	2.25
12	3	2	3.5	1	2.5	6.25
			78	78	15.5	
Check: $(12^2 + 12)/2 = 78$					−15.5	107.5

By Formula 68:

$$r' = 1 - \frac{6\,(107.5)}{12\,(143)} = 1 - \frac{107.5}{286} = .624$$

* Compare also the computation of the differentiation ratios, Table 10.2, and of r^2, Table 10.4.

it remains a useful measure of association in many situations where it is feasible to obtain rankings, although it would be well-nigh impossible to obtain valid interval scores. For example, in a content analysis of written fantasies about "a House and a Person" or about "a Tree and a Person," judges used a check-list of 50 adjectives to describe the "person-alities" of the inanimate characters.[8] The relative frequency of the adjectives was ranked for Trees and for Houses, in stories by men and by women, and the correlations between these rankings constituted measures of agreement in the way that the themes were handled. Thus, it was shown that men and women agree more in their handling of the Tree ($r' = .78$) than in their handling of the House ($r' = .35$), and also that the two themes were handled more similarly by men ($r' = .64$) than by women ($r' = .10$).

When an underlying normal distribution can be assumed, and n is not small, the significance of r' can be tested in the same manner as that of r, that is, by F computed according to Formula 45 (page 186). The method is inexact with small samples, because of the discontinuity of the r' distribution. With $n > 10$, Formula 47 gives a good approximation to 1 per cent critical values of r' if $(n - 2)$ is replaced by $(n - 3)$, and to 5 per cent critical values if it is replaced by $(n - 2.5)$, which necessitates interpolation in the table of F. These adjustments may be regarded as corrections for continuity. For $n \leq 10$, critical values are given in Table VII. Also, when n is not small, and underlying normal distribution of the measured trait can be assumed, the significance of a difference between two independent values of r' can be tested by means of the z transformation, using Formula 51.

COEFFICIENT OF CONCORDANCE, W

Just as it is possible to simplify the computations for the product moment correlation when it is based on ranks, so one can also simplify the computation of the differentiation ratio under like circumstances. Let us first describe a situation in which we would want to do this. Suppose that n subjects are ranked by k judges (or with respect to k different traits, or under k different conditions).* We arrange the ranks in a table in which each of the judges (or traits, or conditions) has his row, and each of the subjects his column. The sums of the rows will be identical, since each of the judges has the same ranks to give. The sums of the columns will differ, since all of the subjects do not receive the same ranks. Table **13.2** presents an example of this sort, in which the several judges have used different techniques for appraising personality rigidity. Three rankings are the work of clinical psychologists, one of whom based his judgments on content analysis of Rorschach protocols, one on the formal analysis of Rorschach psychograms, and one on examination of the subjects' drawings of a male figure, obtained under the standard procedure of the Draw-a-Person Test. The fourth judge was an art critic, who ranked the same drawings for "fluidity of style," these rankings being reversed in the table. The fifth "judge" was the California F-Scale, an attitude scale which is positively correlated with rigidity in a number of published reports.

The question of how well the judges agree in the ranks which they assign can be restated as the question of how well the subjects are differentiated by the ranks which they receive. An appropriate statistic to answer this question is the differentiation ratio for ranks or judgments as dependent

---

* Both Kendall and Friedman, whose work will be ·mentioned below, speak of "the problem of m rankings," using m where we use k. We vary from their practice in order to keep the notation within this book as consistent as possible. See definitions of m and k in the glossary.

TABLE 13.2

Rankings on Personality Rigidity*

				Subjects			
Basis of ranking	A	B	C	D	E	F	G
Rorschach protocol	6	5	3	1	2	7	4
Rorschach psychogram	5	4	2	1	7	6	3
DAP (clinical)	1	4	5	3	7	6	2
DAP (stylistic)	4	1	2	3	7	6	5
California F-Scale	5	6	4	1	7	3	2
Sums	21	20	16	9	30	28	16

By Formula 69:

$$W = \frac{12 \ (441 + 400 + 256 + 81 + 900 + 784 + 256)}{7 \ (25)(48)} - 3 \frac{8}{6}$$

$$= \frac{12 \ (3118)}{12 \ (700)} - 4 = .455.$$

* Based on Florence Diamond.[10]

on the subjects to whom they are assigned. But when we apply the usual formula for η^2 to rank scores, we discover that

$$\Sigma\Sigma X^2 = \frac{kn(n + 1)(2n + 1)}{6}$$

and

$$\frac{(\Sigma\Sigma X)^2}{N} = \frac{kn(n + 1)^2}{4} , \quad \text{where } N = kn$$

Making use of these identities, it is possible to rewrite the formula in the following equivalent form, which has been dubbed (by Kendall)[9] the *coefficient of concordance, W:*

69]
$$W = \frac{12 \ \Sigma(\Sigma R)^2}{nk^2(n^2 - 1)} - 3 \frac{n + 1}{n - 1}$$

where ΣR stands for the sum of the k ranks assigned to each subject by the different judges. The result depends, of course, on the differentiation of these sums, but it is a measure of concord or agreement among the judges in the ranks which they assign. This formula has been applied to the data of Table **13**.2, at the bottom of the table. A test of significance for W will be discussed in the next section.

FRIEDMAN'S TEST: χ^2_r

The coefficient of concordance is a versatile statistic, which can also be used when k subjects are tested under n treatments or conditions. In that case, the several performances of one subject are in effect so many judgments on the relative effectiveness of the treatments, and ranks are assigned accordingly. This procedure is called Friedman's two-way analysis of variance for ranks, or more simply *Friedman's test*. Instead of computing W, Friedman[11] computes a statistic which has approximately the distribution of χ^2 with $n - 1$ degrees of freedom, thus:

70]
$$\chi^2_r = \frac{12 \Sigma(\Sigma R)^2}{k(n^2 + n)} - 3k(n + 1)$$

Applying this formula to the data of Table **13**.2, we have:

$$\chi^2_r = \frac{12 (3118)}{5 (49 + 7)} - 3 (5)(8) = \frac{37416}{280} - 120 = 13.63$$

It is useful to note that

70a]
$$\chi^2_r = k(n - 1)W$$

This equation enables us to transform the values of one statistic into those of the other, which, we shall soon see, is often convenient in making a test of significance. The choice of one of these methods over the other is largely a matter of taste. The coefficient of concordance was developed with an eye to the problem of measuring agreement or common variance, and it is in effect a kind of averaged rank correlation for the k sets of rankings. Friedman's test was developed with an eye to the problem of discriminating the effects of different treatments. Basically the two methods are equivalent, and wherever one can be used, so can the other.

With n large, the distribution of χ^2_r approximates that of χ^2 with $n - 1$ degrees of freedom. The test will more often be used with n small, so that this approximation is unsatisfactory. Critical values tend to be lower than those for χ^2, and for $n > 3$ one can reject the null hypothesis whenever the tabled values of χ^2 have been exceeded. (In the example given, therefore, with $df = 6$, $P < .05$.) A more exact test requires relatively complex corrections for continuity and interpolations in the table of F. Table IX is based on this exact method. Beyond the limits of the table the same method is satisfactory without corrections for continuity, and it brings us into areas of the F table where linear interpolation will not be too grossly inaccurate. For this procedure,

71]
$$F = \frac{(k - 1)W}{1 - W}$$

with $df = (n - 1 - 2/k)$ for the numerator, and $(k - 1)(n - 1 - 2/k)$ for the denominator. Notice that the F ratio here is analogous to that for the test of η^2 (see Formula 44, page 186), but the degrees of freedom are different, because of the additional restraints imposed by the conventions of ranking.

ORDER STATISTICS OF COMPARISON

We now turn our attention to a variety of tests of homogeneity among samples, all of which are based on the principle of random sampling in a single set of ranks. Suppose you were asked to rank the following six authors, in an order which indicates the relative amount of pleasure which you have derived from reading their works:

> Arthur Conan Doyle
> T. S. Eliot
> Robert Frost
> Erle Stanley Gardner
> Ellery Queen
> Alfred Tennyson

If you rank Doyle, Gardner, and Queen ahead of Eliot, Frost, and Tennyson, it seems likely that you prefer reading mysteries to reading poetry. The mathematical test of this conclusion is based on a very simple idea: if six cards, numbered from 1 to 6, are shuffled into random order, what is the chance of dealing a sample of 3 cards which consists of numbers 1, 2, and 3? This is the basis for the methods to be presented in the next three sections. They all utilize a single series of ranks, and each is a test of the null hypothesis that two or more samples have been randomly drawn from the universe represented by that series.

We shall now look in some detail at an experiment whose results lend themselves to analysis by this approach. Wilson [12] reports an interesting study of cortical localization in rhesus monkeys, in which she demonstrated the functional differentiation of the parietal and inferotemporal regions. Eight animals were trained preoperatively in three tasks: an easy visual discrimination, an easy tactile discrimination, and then either a tactile or a visual problem of greater difficulty. Retention tests were given after an interval of 14 days, and then surgery was performed. Temporal lesions were inflicted on 4 animals, and parietal lesions on the others. One temporal operate succumbed, leaving only 7 survivors. After a period of convalescence, each animal was required to learn the task which had previously been omitted from its repertoire. Thus each monkey learned one of the more difficult tasks preoperatively, and the other postoperatively. It was predicted that only the parietal lesions would interfere with the learning of the tactile discrimination (Monkeys 227 and 240), and only the temporal lesions would interfere with the learning of the visual discrimination (Monkeys 218 and 219).

The results, in terms of trials to attain the criterion of learning, are shown in Table 13.3. The trend of the data conforms to both predictions.

TABLE 13.3

Trials Required to Meet a Learning Criterion, on Two Discrimination Tasks, Together with Rankings on Each Task*

Animal	Lesion	Tactile discrimination			Visual discrimination		
		Pre-op.	Post-op.	Rank	Pre-op.	Post-op.	Rank
216	Parietal	374		2		193	1
214	"	441		4		468	4
227	"		1000+	7	250		2
240	"		642	6	390		3
218	Temporal	240		1		1000+	6.5
219	"	579		5		1000+	6.5
238	"		439	3	518		5

* Based on Wilson.[12]

The evidence seems intuitively convincing, but can it support a statistical analysis? For this purpose the animals are ranked according to their scores on each task, regardless of the conditions under which the learning took place. This is the blind equalitarianism of the null hypothesis. In each case, the animals for whom poor performance was predicted are ranked behind the others, and we ask, what is the probability that this could occur by chance?

There are only 21 possible combinations of 2 ranks which can be drawn from a universe of 7 ranks. Taking them one by one $(1 + 2; 1 + 3; \cdots 1 + 7; 2 + 3; \cdots,$ etc.), it is not difficult to list the sums of ranks for these 21 possible samples. The distribution of their sums is as follows:

ΣR:	3	4	5	6	7	8	9	10	11	12	13
f:	1	1	2	2	3	3	3	2	2	1	1

Therefore, in a two-tailed test, the possibility of obtaining one of the extreme scores, 3 or 13, equals 2/21, or $P < .10$. In this case the precise formulation of the experimental hypothesis clearly justifies a one-tailed test, and the conclusion that $P < .05$.

MANN-WHITNEY TEST

The systematic application of this method, for the comparison of two independent groups which may be of unlike size, is known as the *Mann-*

Whitney U test.[13] When scores of both groups are merged in one ranking,

$$72] \qquad U = mn + \frac{m^2 + m}{2} - T$$

where m is the number of elements in the sample with the smaller sum of ranks, T is that sum, and n is the number in the other sample. The expected value of U under the null hypothesis is $mn/2$, and its sampling variance is

$$73] \qquad \sigma^2_U = \frac{mn(m + n + 1)}{12}$$

It is more convenient to combine these formulas into one formula for a normal deviate, which also includes a correction for continuity:

$$74] \qquad z = \frac{m(m + n + 1) - (2T \pm 1)}{\sqrt{mn(m + n + 1)/3}}$$

The correction must be taken in the sense needed to reduce the absolute size of the numerator. For example, in the preceding problem the smaller sum of ranks is either 3 or 13, depending on the direction of ranking. (These sums stand in the relationship: $T + T' = m\,[m + n + 1]$.) But

$$16 - (26 - 1) = -9, \qquad \text{whence} \qquad z = -1.74$$

and

$$16 - (6 + 1) = +9, \qquad \text{whence} \qquad z = +1.74$$

Either result implies, by the normal table, that $P = .041$, whereas the true value is $1/21 = .0475$. In practice, we use a table of critical values of T for small sample applications. Table VII shows that in this case the 5 per cent level of significance has been reached, for a one-tailed test. Formula 74 is trustworthy beyond the limits of Table VII.

Table 13.4 shows the application of the Mann-Whitney test to the data of Table 2.3. These same data were treated by the t test in Table 7.5, and by the median test on page 240 of this chapter. The Mann-Whitney test and the median test agree in their results; both are tests of the null hypothesis that the samples are drawn from universes with different *medians*.

WILCOXON SIGNED-RANKS TEST

Allied to the Mann-Whitney test (and historically its forerunner) is the Wilcoxon[14] *signed-ranks test*, which is designed to test the significance of a mean difference in matched pairs of scores. Find D within each pair, in terms of the original scores, and then rank these values according to their absolute size, ignoring the instances of zero difference and giving the smaller ranks to the smaller differences. Then find T, which is the

TABLE **13**.4

Application of the Mann-Whitney Test to the Data of Table **2**.3

X	f_M	f_W	Ranks	ΣR_M	ΣR_W
13	1		24	24	
10	3	1	20–23	64.5	21.5
9	4	2	14–19	66	33
8	1	2	11–13	12	24
7	1		10	10	
6	1	1	8–9	8.5	8.5
5		3	5–7		18
4		1	4		4
1		1	3		3
0	1	1	1–2	1.5	1.5
				186.5	113.5

By Formula 74:

$$z = \frac{12(12 + 12 + 1) - (227 \pm 1)}{\sqrt{144(12 + 12 + 1)/3}} = \frac{300 - 228}{12\sqrt{25/3}} = 2.08.$$

$$P < .05.$$

sum of the ranks *either* for those pairs which show positive differences *or* for those which show negative differences, whichever is smaller. In the absence of any systematic trend these sums should differ only by chance, and hence the extent of their difference is a measure of nonchance influences. For small samples, critical values of T are given in Table VII. For larger samples,

75]
$$z = \frac{2T + 1 - \dfrac{n^2 + n}{2}}{\sqrt{\dfrac{(2n + 1)(n^2 + n)}{6}}}$$

This test was used by Balvin,[15] in a study of decision-making. Subjects were required to guess at the outcome of an uncertain event, different groups receiving different patterns of cash rewards for successful guesses. In Group IV, for example, each successful guess of event A earned 5 cents, but each successful guess of event B earned 15 cents. A occurred, on the average, twice as often as B. Despite the unequal rewards, subjects tended, as the experiment went on, to increase the proportion of guesses for the more frequent event, rather than for the one which brought heavier gains. In Table **13**.5 the score for each subject (i.e., the number of guesses

TABLE **13**.5

Frequency of Guess of Event *A* Rather than *B*, When *A* Occurs About Twice as Often as *B*, but the Reward for Successful Guesses of *B* is Three Times as Great, in Early and Late Phases of a Decision-making Experiment, and Test of the Difference by Wilcoxon's Signed Ranks Test*

Sj	Trials 1–12	Trials 85–96	D	Rank of $\vert D \vert$	$\Sigma R_{(+)}$	$\Sigma R_{(-)}$
1	9	8	−1	3.5		3.5
2	2	5	3	14		
3	5	7	2	9.5		
4	4	3	−1	3.5		3.5
5	3	5	2	9.5		
6	4	12	8	17		
7	5	7	2	9.5		
8	3	2	−1	3.5	not needed	3.5
9	4	8	4	16		
10	6	8	2	9.5		
11	2	5	3	14		
12	6	7	1	3.5		
13	5	6	1	3.5		
14	4	7	3	14		
15	5	5	0			
16	1	3	2	9.5		
17	6	8	2	9.5		
18	7	6	−1	3.5		3.5
						——
						14

By Formula 75:

$$z = \frac{28 + 1 - \dfrac{289 + 17}{2}}{\sqrt{\dfrac{(34 + 1)(289 + 17)}{6}}} = -2.94; \quad P < .01.$$

* Data from Balvin.[15]

of the more frequent event) is given separately for early and late phases of the experiment, and the application of Formula 75 to these data is shown in detail. Note that in the computations *n* is taken as 17, because the case with zero difference has been dropped.

KRUSKAL-WALLIS H TEST

What we know about the relationship between t and F (see page 123f.) would lead us to suppose that the principle underlying the Mann-Whitney and the Wilcoxon tests can be generalized to deal with the situation in which there are three or more independent groups. That is the fact. In this form, the test is known as the *Kruskal-Wallis H test*.[16] Again, the first step is to transform all of the raw scores into a single series of ranks, without regard to their group affiliations. Then, letting m stand for the number of observations in any sample and letting $n = \Sigma m$,

$$76] \qquad H = \frac{12}{n^2 + n} \Sigma \frac{(\Sigma R)^2}{m} - 3(n + 1)$$

This, like Friedman's test, is an approximation of χ^2. When applied to only three samples, the approximation is not satisfactory unless the samples are large. Table VIII gives critical values of H for this situation. With $k > 3$, use χ^2 with $df = k - 1$. Critical values obtained by this rule will tend to be somewhat high, particularly at the 1 per cent level, unless k is large.

Although this test can be applied to comparisons of more than 2 samples, we shall illustrate it by applying it to the same "hostility scores" which have already been studied by several other methods. Referring to Table **13**.4, we see that $m_1 = m_2 = 12$, and that ΣR for one sample equals 186.5 and that for the other equals 113.5. Using these values in Formula 76,

$$H = \frac{12}{24^2 + 24} \left[\frac{186.5^2}{12} + \frac{113.5^2}{12} \right] - 3\,(25)$$

$$= \frac{47645}{600} - 75 = 4.41; \qquad df = 1; \qquad P < .05$$

Again we are led to reject the null hypothesis that the hostility scores of the men students and the women students can be regarded as two random samples from the same universe of ranks. The implication is that they are drawn from universes which have different medians.

THE POWER OF A TEST

We turn now to the question broached early in this chapter, and implicit throughout: when shall we use a distribution-free test rather than t or F? We can leave aside as of little consequence the fact that some of them are real time-savers, especially when they are used in conjunction with detailed tables of critical values. This is an important consideration in an industrial inspection procedure (and sometimes the hasty check we make on someone else's claims partakes of this character), but the psychologist who has put time and effort into gathering data will not begrudge the added time needed to extract all the information which they hold. Nor are we concerned here with those instances in which certain of these techniques are peculiarly appropriate, as the rank correlation and the coefficient of concordance may be appropriate to certain problems which arise with ranked data. Our question relates primarily to the situation in which we have scaled scores, but we are uncertain about the validity of the t tests or F tests, either because the sample distributions are not normal in form or because there are nonchance differences in variance. To what extent do these irregularities invalidate the parametric tests, or weaken them to the point that tests based on order statistics are superior, even though they do not use all the available information? In seeking an answer to this question we shall have to consider the nature of errors in statistical tests of null hypotheses more carefully than we have done previously, and define what is meant by the *power* of a test.

We shall approach the problem first in an empirical manner. We shall describe a small sampling experiment which provides an opportunity to compare the performance of the t test and the Mann-Whitney test under conditions which violate the parametric assumptions of the former. The experiment was performed by the Monte Carlo method, which was described in Chapter 6. Two universes were set up by arbitrarily assigning the 1000 three-place numbers to ten score classes for universe **A** and to seven score classes for universe **B**. The proportions in which the different scores were represented, as well as the universe parameters, are shown in Figure **13.1**. Notice that both distributions have deliberately been

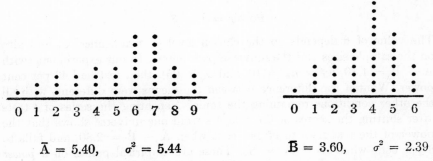

$$\bar{A} = 5.40, \qquad \sigma^2 = 5.44 \qquad\qquad \bar{B} = 3.60, \qquad \sigma^2 = 2.39$$

Fig. 13.1. Distribution of 1000 elements in each of two universes used for a sampling experiment. Each dot represents 25 elements.

skewed, and that the variance of one universe is more than twice that of the other. Ten samples, with $n = 10$, were drawn from each universe, entering the table of random numbers in a random manner for the start of each sample. Tests of goodness of fit showed that the 100 scores taken from each universe constituted a representative sample. (In each case, $P > .30$.)

The 90 intra-universe tests for the significance of the difference between sample means yielded only one t which reached the 5 per cent level of significance. A series of Mann-Whitney tests gave precisely the same result. Thus, both tests failed to yield the expected number of Type I errors—that is, rejections of a valid null hypothesis. However, we are more interested in the outcome of the 100 inter-universe comparisons, which test the null hypothesis that the two samples in each comparison are drawn from the same universe. Since we know that this is not the case, each instance of indicated significance must be scored as a success, and each instance of nonsignificance as a failure. These failures are called Type II errors, in which we fail to reject an invalid null hypothesis. By the t test, 40 comparisons were significant at the 5 per cent level, and 23 of these at the 1 per cent level. The Mann-Whitney test scored 37 successes, but only 16 at the 1 per cent level. It failed in 4 cases in which the t test succeeded, and succeeded once where the t test failed. (We note in passing that the relative superiority of the t test in this experiment is approximately what would theoretically be expected if the assumptions of the t test had been fulfilled.)

The experiment just described compared two statistical tests with respect to the proportion of successes in detecting the fact that two independent samples were drawn from different universes. This proportion is the measure of the test's *power*. If, as is customary, we designate the expected proportion of Type I errors as *alpha*, α, and the proportion of Type II errors as *beta*, β, then

$$\text{Power} = 1 - \beta$$

The value of β depends on the chosen level of significance, α, and also on the sample sizes and the universe parameters. In our experiment (with $\bar{A} - \bar{B} = 1.80$, $n_A = n_B = 10$, and $\alpha = .05$), the t test had 40 per cent power. What if the difference between the means were different, with all the other conditions remaining the same? Repeating the series of t tests after shifting the scores of the samples from one universe shows that the power of the test rises to 95 per cent when $\bar{A} - \bar{B} = 2.80$, and falls to 8 per cent when $\bar{A} - \bar{B} = .80$. These are empirical points on a *power curve*, or curve of *operating characteristics*, which tells what proportion of successes to expect under different conditions. Figure **13**.2 shows a series of theoretical power curves for the t test, when it is used to establish a confidence interval for the mean of a single sample drawn from a normal universe. Most power curves have the same general form.

THE ESTIMATE OF POWER

Let us see if we could have predicted the power of the t test in our sampling experiment, at least approximately. Since in this case we know the

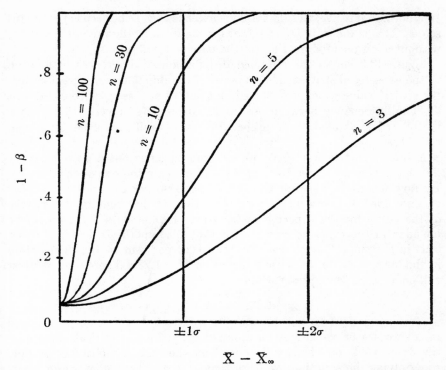

$$\bar{X} - \bar{X}_\infty$$

Fig. **13**.2. Operating characteristics of t, when used to establish confidence limits for a sample mean, as a function of n and $\bar{X} - \bar{X}_\infty$, when $\alpha = .05$. Based on Ferris, Grubbs, and Weaver.[17]

parameters of the parent universes, we can describe the universe of differences. Its mean is equal to the difference between the universe means, 1.80. Its standard deviation, the standard error of a difference, is:

$$\sigma_{\bar{A}-\bar{B}} = \sqrt{\frac{\sigma^2_A}{n_A} + \frac{\sigma^2_B}{n_B}} = \sqrt{\frac{5.44}{10} + \frac{2.39}{10}} = .885$$

With $df = 18$, $t = 2.101$ for the 5 per cent level, and therefore we shall not go far wrong if we assume that the proportion of successes will be about as great as the proportion of differences-between-means which reach the value of $\bar{A} - \bar{B}$ in the following equation:

$$\frac{\bar{A} - \bar{B}}{.885} = 2.101$$

This turns out to be 1.865. It will be more convenient to express this in standard units:

$$z = \frac{1.865 - 1.80}{.885} = .073$$

In a normal universe, this deviation is exceeded by 47 per cent of standard scores. This is the estimate of power for the t test in the present situation, without allowance for the skew of the parent distributions.

Figure **13**.3 shows the obtained distribution of differences in relation to the expected distribution. Forty-two of the differences are greater than the critical value which we selected, but not all of these yielded significant t's. The discrepancy between observed and predicted power (40 successes in 100 trials, as against 47 expected) is not significant even by a one-tailed test.

A statistical test with only 40 per cent power is not a good basis for decisions. The most effective remedy is to increase the size of the samples. By how much? If we want the test to have 90 per cent power—leaving us undecided 10 per cent of the time—then 90 per cent of the surface of the curve for the expected distribution of differences will have to be included in the *region of rejection* for the null hypothesis, leaving 10 per cent in a *region of indecision*. To cut off 10 per cent of the distribution in the lower tail, we must use a deviation of -1.28σ. Therefore the t test will have 90 per cent power when

$$t = \frac{1.8 - 1.28\sigma_{\bar{A}-\bar{B}}}{\sigma_{\bar{A}-\bar{B}}} = 2.00$$

where we are using 2.00 as an approximation for the critical value of t, the exact value of which will depend on the still undetermined sample size. Solving the equation, we learn that $\sigma_{\bar{A}-\bar{B}} = .548$. To learn the necessary sample size, we now solve

$$\frac{\sigma^2_A + \sigma^2_B}{n} = .548^2$$

and we discover that n must be 26.

Despite the fact that we do not ordinarily know the parameters of the universe, this method of forecasting the power of a test does have practical value. Something akin to this enters into the planning of every research. We usually know enough about the problem we are investigating so that we can state the practical difference which is of consequence. If the true difference should be less than this, we will not mind too much being left in a "region of indecision," but we would like to have a high probability of detecting larger differences. Past experience, or a pilot study, have probably also given us a fair idea of the expected variance of scores. Using these figures in place of the universe parameters, we can determine the necessary sample size to attain satisfactory power.

THE CHOICE OF A TEST

It is the relative power of two tests, in a given situation, which should be our main concern in choosing between them. The errors of Type I are

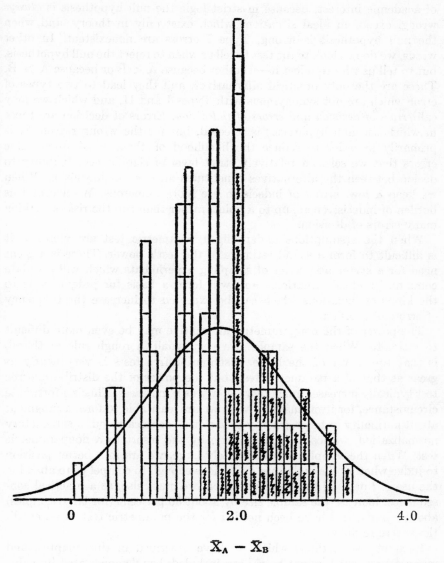

$$\bar{X}_A - \bar{X}_B$$

Fig. **13**.3. Obtained and expected distribution of differences, in the sampling experiment. Shaded cells represent instances which yielded significant t's.

of academic interest, because in strict logic the null hypothesis is *always* wrong, except in ideal situations which exist only in theory, and when the null hypothesis is wrong, Type I errors are nonexistent. In other words, we do not look to the test to tell us when to reject the null hypothesis, but to tell us why to reject it—whether because $\bar{A} < \bar{B}$ or because $\bar{A} > \bar{B}$. These are the only practical alternatives, and they lead to two types of error which are not synonymous with Types I and II, and which we may call *errors of decision* and *errors of indecision*. Errors of decision are those in which the null hypothesis is rejected, but for the wrong reason. It is primarily in order to reduce the likelihood of these most undesirable errors that we select a relatively strict level of significance. Inability to decide between the alternatives constitutes an error of indecision. When we keep α low, errors of indecision are more numerous. We accept this burden of indecisiveness, up to a point, rather than run the risk of making many errors of decision.

When the assumptions underlying a parametric test are violated, it is difficult to form a sound estimate of the test's power. There is a great need for a systematic series of sampling experiments which will simulate common practical situations, and will form a basis for judgment as to the kinds of violations which can be expected to increase the frequency of errors of decision.

The power of the nonparametric alternative may be even more difficult to estimate. When the samples are very small, a rough rule of thumb is that the power of the better distribution-free tests is very nearly as great as that of a parametric test, but the power of the distribution-free test typically increases much more slowly as n increases. This is a fortunate circumstance, for it means that when we are least able to form a judgment about normality or heterogeneity of variance, or to carry out a satisfactory normalization, we lose relatively little by the resort to a nonparametric test. When the samples are moderately large, we are in a better position to judge whether the violations are serious enough to compel us to abandon the use of t or F. If that is our decision, we must also, as a practical consequence, increase the sample size by about 50 per cent (for large samples) above what would have been needed for the parametric test, if its conditions were fulfilled.

Each of the methods which we have described in this chapter, and many others which might have been included, has demonstrated its value for some applications in psychological research. A general familiarity with them has therefore become a necessity for anyone who wishes to read the current research reports with understanding. Furthermore, the availability of these methods is influencing the choice of experimental design, tending to encourage greater reliance on rankings and classificatory schemes in place of scaled scores, and to some extent also the use of smaller populations of subjects. Therefore research workers will want to have a more thorough mastery of their potential than can be gained from this brief discussion. (See Siegel,[18] and Tate and Clelland.[19]) However, an appreciation of the advantages of distribution-free methods should not lead us to overlook the fact that progress in psychological research calls, in many fields, for increasingly complex experimental designs, and there is little basis for optimism that the near future will bring us satisfactory distribution-free methods for the analysis of interactions among several variables. Distribution-free tests will become increasingly useful, but they are not likely to displace parametric methods as the major tools of statistical analysis.

PROBLEMS

1. *Does the distribution of accidents among the 88 workers in Table* **10**.8 *conform to a chance expectation?*

2. *Use a logarithmic transformation to equalize variances of the score distributions in Problem 3, Chapter 3 (page 57). Perform a one-dimensional analysis of variance and compare the result with that shown in Table* **8**.1.

3. *Use both the sign test and the signed-ranks test on the data of Table* **7**.7. *If there is an important difference in the results, how can it be explained?*

4. *Find the coefficient of rank correlation for each possible set of paired ratings in Table* **2**.4. *Compare the results with those obtained in Problem 1, Chapter 10 (page 190).*

5. *A class was organized into discussion groups, each with 5 members. Following half an hour of discussion on an assigned problem, each student was asked to rank the members of his own group according to their contribution to the group discussion. The rankings obtained in two of the groups are shown herewith.*

	Ranks in Group I						Ranks in Group II			
	A	B	C	D	E		F	G	H	I	J
A	3	2	4	5	1	F	5	1	2	4	3
B	2	3	4	1	5	G	2	3	5	1	4
C	3	4	5	2	1	H	4	2	3	5	1
D	4	5	3	2	1	I	3	1	5	2	4
E	4	5	3	1	2	J	3	1	5	2	4

In each case, does the distribution of ranks indicate better than chance agreement? Use the concordance ratio for one set of rankings, and Friedman's test for the other.

6. *Use the Mann-Whitney test to determine whether the grades of women*

are significantly better than those of men, in the data at the top of Table **1**.1.

7. *Use the Kruskal-Wallis method to test the null hypothesis in* (*a*) *Problem* 6, *Chapter* 8, *page* 141, *and* (*b*) *Problem* 7, *same chapter.*

REFERENCES

1. Lindquist, E. F. *Design and analysis of experiments in psychology and education.* Boston: Houghton Mifflin, 1953.

2. Allport, F. H. The *J*-curve hypothesis of conforming behavior. *J. soc. Psychol.*, 1934, **5**:141–183.

3. Diamond, S. Habit-formation under non-selective conditions. *J. comp. Psychol.*, 1934, **17**:109–122.

4. Dember, W. N., Earl, R. W., and Paradise, N. Response by rats to differential stimulus complexity. *J. comp. physiol. Psychol.*, 1957, **50**:514–518.

5. Wilson, K. V. A distribution-free test of analysis of variance hypotheses. *Psychol. Bull.*, 1956, **53**:96–101.

6. McNemar, Q. On Wilson's distribution-free test of analysis of variance hypotheses. *Psychol. Bull.*, 1957, **54**:361–362.

7. Sheffield, F. D. Comment on a distribution-free factorial-design analysis. *Psychol. Bull.* 1957, **54**:426–428.

8. Diamond, S. The house and tree in verbal fantasy, II. Their different roles. *J. proj. Techniques*, 1954, **18**:414–417.

9. Kendall, M. G. *Rank correlation methods*, 2nd ed. London: Griffin, 1955.

10. Diamond, Florence. *Style and content in personality rigidity.* Unpublished doctoral dissertation, Claremont Graduate School, 1958.

11. Friedman, M. The use of ranks to avoid the assumption of normality implicit in the analysis of variance. *J. Amer. Statist. Assoc.*, 1937, **32**:675–701.

12. Wilson, Martha. Effects of circumscribed cortical lesions upon somesthetic and visual discrimination in the monkey. *J. comp. physiol. Psychol.*, 1957, **50**:630–635.

13. Mann, H. B., and Whitney, D. R. On a test of whether one of two random variables is stochastically larger than the other. *Ann. Math. Stat.*, 1947, **18**:50–60.

14. Wilcoxon, F. Individual comparisons by ranking methods. *Biometrics Bull.*, 1945, **1**:80–83.

15. Balvin, R. S. *Decision-making in a situation involving stationary probabilities.* Unpublished doctoral dissertation, Univ. of California at Los Angeles, 1956.

16. Kruskal, W. H., and Wallis, W. A. Use of ranks in one-criterion variance analysis. *J. Amer. Statist. Ass.*, 1952, **47**:583–621.

17. Ferris, C. D., Grubbs, F. E., and Weaver, C. L. Operating characteristics for the common statistical tests of significance. *Ann. Math. Stat.*, 1946, **17**:178–197.

18. Siegel, S. *Nonparametric statistics for the behavioral sciences.* New York: McGraw-Hill, 1956.

19. Tate, M. W. and Clelland, R. C. *Nonparametric and shortcut statistics.* Danville, Ill.: Interstate, 1957.

LIST OF APPENDICES

GLOSSARY OF SYMBOLS

The Glossary includes all symbols which occur in formulas, excepting subscripts which serve only to identify variables. It omits some symbols which appear only in discussion material and which are defined in the context of the discussion. Nonliteral symbols are listed first, followed by letters of the English alphabet, and then letters of the Greek alphabet. It is assumed that the reader is already familiar with the common symbols for sums, differences, products, quotients, squares, and square roots, as well as with the use of parentheses and brackets to indicate the proper sequence of these operations. Parenthetic numbers give the page on which the symbol first appears.

$\neq$ Does not equal. (Useful for blackboard discussions.)

$\doteq$ Tends to equal; includes the implication that more extensive sampling will usually give a better approximation. (127)

$\pm$ Plus or minus; used to indicate the limits of a range of values. Thus, $a \pm b$ indicates the entire range of values from $(a - b)$ to $(a + b)$. (30)

$<$ Is less than; sometimes used in this book where an exact statement would call for $\leq$. (43)

$\leq$ Is equal to or less than; hence $a \leq b$ is equivalent to the statement that a approaches b as a limit, from below. (24)

$>$ Is greater than. (54)

$\geq$ Is equal to or greater than; hence $a \geq b$ is equivalent to the statement that a approaches b as a limit, from above. (54)

!   Factorial; indicates that the preceding number is multiplied by every smaller positive integer. For example, $3! = (3)(2)(1) = 6$. (31)

$|a|$ Absolute; the numerical value of the symbol or expression enclosed by the two vertical lines is to be taken as a positive magnitude, even if it has a negative sign. (24)

∞   Infinity; used in this book as a subscript to identify "true" values or parameters, which are defined as the values which would result from exhaustive sampling. (91)

A ··· *Z*

       Any capital letter in italics may be used to identify a variable· However, many of the capital letters also have other special uses, which will be defined below. When a letter identifies a variable, then the use of the many variants of this letter (A, *A*, **A**, Ā, A′, *a*, **a**, and *a′*) follow certain conventions which are set forth in the discussion of *X* and *Y*, the preferred letters for this purpose.

A   A fixed or constant value in certain formulas; specifically, in the raw-score form of a regression equation. (84, 194)

a   The upper-left cell in a fourfold table, or the value therein. (150)

b   The upper-right cell in a fourfold table, or the value therein. (150)

b   *As subscript:* below, in the formula for the median. (24)

b   *As subscript:* between, in symbols for variance, sums of squares, etc. (56)

b   The regression coefficient. (194)

C   Centile; a score expressed as the per cent of scores in its distribution which it equals or surpasses. (19)

C   The number of columns in a contingency table, or the number of treatments on one of the variables in an experiment of factorial design. (135)

c   The lower-left cell in a fourfold table, or the value therein. (150)

c   *As subscript:* of columns, to identify subsums, etc. (134)

D   Difference score; the difference between two paired scores, such as the two scores of the same individual under different conditions. (103)

d   The lower-right cell of a fourfold table, or the value therein. (150)

df   Degrees of freedom; the number of observations available for the computation of a statistic, less the number of restraints imposed upon the outcome. (97)

e   A mathematical constant, the natural base of logarithms, approximately 2.718, which appears in the exact statement of many probability distributions. (81, 234)

e   *As subscript:* expected. (148)

F   Variance ratio; the ratio of two independent estimates of the same universe variance. (105, 124)

f Frequency; the number of scores in a class. (16)

H In defining the range, the highest score of a sample. (29)

H In the Kruskal-Wallis test, a statistic which is an approximation of χ^2. (252)

h In the cosine model of correlation, the length of a vector. (From *hypothenuse*.) (214)

h^2 Communality. (220)

i Interval; the difference between the mid-values of successive classes in a distribution by classes. (16)

j *As subscript:* used to represent the individual case, in general. See the definition of the summation sign, Σ. (63)

k The number of cells or categories in a one-dimensional schema of classification; the number of categories on the major dimension in a $2 \times k$ classification; the number of parallel sets of ranks; the number of cells in an $R \times C$ classification. (From the German, *Klasse*.) (126)

k Coefficient of alienation. (197)

k *As subscript:* of the cell. (57)

L In defining the range, the lowest score of a sample. (29)

LL In computing the median, the lower theoretical limit of the class in which the median falls. (24)

M' Assumed mean, chosen for convenience in computations. (49)

m The number of scores or elements in a sample or subset, or in a cell, row, or column, as specified in the context or by appropriate subscripts; in the sign test, the frequency of the less frequent sign. (31, 239)

N The number of elements in a set; an alternative symbol to n; specifically, the number of elements in a universe, when n is the number in a sample. (72)

n The number of scores or elements in a set or sample; the total number whenever subtotals have been specified as m's. (14)

$\binom{n}{m}$ The number of ways in which subsets, each consisting of m elements, can be formed from a set of n elements. (31)

o *As subscript:* obtained or observed. (149)

P Probability. (71)

p Proportion. (71)

p *As subscript:* of the proportion. (146)

Q Quartile; specifically, Q_1 and Q_3 stand for the first quartile and the third quartile, respectively. (30)

q Proportion of non-occurrences: $1 - p$. (72)

R Range. (29)

R Rank, ranks. (241)

R	Number of rows; compare C. (135)
r	Product moment correlation. (177, 181)
r	*As subscript:* of the correlation; of rows; of ranks. (134)
r'	Coefficient of rank correlation. (241)
s	Estimate of standard deviation. (Does not appear in this book without a subscript; compare s^2 and σ.)
s_D	Standard error of the difference. (103)
s_p	Standard error of the proportion. (146)
$s_{p_1 - p_2}$	Standard error of the difference in proportions. (146)
s_r	Standard error of the correlation. (188)
$s_{\bar{x}}$	Standard error of the mean. (91)
$s_{\bar{x}_1 - \bar{x}_2}$	Standard error of the difference between means. (110)
s_z	Standard error of z, which is a certain transformation of the product moment correlation. (189)
s^2	Estimate of variance. This symbol may be used with any of the subscripts listed for s, the estimate of the standard deviation. Other common subscripts follow. (69)
s^2_b	The between-estimate of variance. (127)
s^2_w	The within-estimate of variance. (127)
T	In the Mann-Whitney test, and in the Wilcoxon signed-ranks test, the sum of ranks in the group which has the smaller sum. (249)
t	The ratio of any statistic to an unbiased estimate of its standard error; the family of probability distributions for such ratios, called *Student's distribution.* (96)
t	*As subscript:* total. (56)
U	A statistic in the Mann-Whitney test. (249)
W	Coefficient of concordance. (186)
w	*As subscript:* within. (24)
X	The most commonly used symbol for a variable, or score dimension. The special meanings which are attached to the following variants of X also apply to any other letter of the English alphabet, when used for the same purpose. The large letter, in *italics*, stands for the variable or dimension as such. (166)
X	The large letter, in Roman type, stands for an original or raw score on the dimension. (14)
X	The boldface capital stands for the set of scores on the dimension. (64)
$\bar{\text{X}}$	The overlined capital stands for the arithmetic mean of a set of scores. (22)
X'	The large letter, prime, stands for a regressed score in the original scale units. (173)
x	The small letter, in *italics*, stands for a deviation from the mean. (22)

x' The small letter prime, in *italics*, stands for a deviation from an assumed mean. (49)

x   The small boldface letter stands for a standard score, which is more commonly represented as z_x. This device is used in Chapters 10, 11, and 12 in order to avoid excessive use of subscripts, which strain the attention of the reader. (177)

Y Another letter which is frequently used to represent a variable; variants of Y have meanings similar to those of variants of X, as already defined. In a scatter diagram or in a graph, X usually designates the horizontal axis or dimension, and Y the vertical axis or dimension. (166)

y The height of an ordinate, especially of a curve which defines a probability distribution. (81)

z Standard score, that is, a score which is stated in standard deviation units; $z = x/\sigma$. Hence, also, the ratio of a normally distributed statistic to its standard error. (85)

$z_{Y'}$ A regressed standard score; the regressed score in standard units of the original distribution. (193)

z A mathematical function which is used to provide a nearly-normal transformation of r. Usually called Fisher's z. (189)

z *As subscript:* refers to transformations of r. (189)

α Alpha: the level of significance of a statistical test, that is, the expected proportion of Type I errors. (254)

β Beta: the expected proportion of Type II errors in the operation of a statistical test under a given set of circumstances. (254)

β Beta-coefficient. (212)

ϵ^2 Epsilon-square. The differentiation ratio without bias. (130)

η Eta. The correlation ratio. (55)

η^2 Eta-square. The differentiation ratio—a neologism; usually called the squared correlation ratio. (55)

θ Theta. The angle included between two vectors or axes, or the angle of rotation of a factor axis from one position to another. (209)

π Pi. A mathematical constant, equal to the ratio of the circumference of a circle to its diameter. (40)

σ Standard deviation. For common subscripts, see s. (85)

σ^2 Variance. For common subscripts, see s^2. (62)

Σ Summation; indicates that the following symbol, or term, is to be evaluated as the sum of all the possible values which it can have in the defined situation. In this book the subscripts and superscripts which would define the limits of summation are usually omitted. An exception is the use of the summation $\sum_{m=0}^{n}$ in the formula for the binomial expansion. This means that the summation is for all integral values of m, starting with $m = 0$ and ending with $m = n$. Such limits are "understood" in relation to every use of the summation sign. For example, although we give the formula for the mean as $\bar{X} = \dfrac{\Sigma X}{n}$, it would be more correctly stated thus:

$$\bar{X} = \frac{\sum\limits_{i=1}^{n} X_i}{n},$$

that is, as based on the sum of n individual values of X. (22)

Double summation signs ($\Sigma\Sigma$) and triple summation signs ($\Sigma\Sigma\Sigma$) stand for "sums of sums," which are not logically different from simple sums. (134)

χ^2 Chi-square. A measure of discrepancy between two frequency distributions, or a sum of such measures. (150)

χ_r^2 Friedman's statistic. (246)

SELECTED FORMULAS FOR REVIEW AND REFERENCE

To describe the sample

$$\bar{X} = \frac{\Sigma X}{n} = M' + \frac{\Sigma x'}{n} i$$

$$\sigma^2 = \frac{\Sigma x^2}{n} = \frac{\Sigma X^2}{n} - \left(\frac{\Sigma X}{n}\right)^2 = \left[\frac{\Sigma x'^2}{n} - \left(\frac{\Sigma x'}{n}\right)^2\right] i^2$$

$$s^2 = \frac{\Sigma x^2}{n-1} = \frac{n\sigma^2}{n-1}$$

$$s^2_{\bar{X}} = \frac{s^2}{n} = \frac{\sigma^2}{n-1} = \frac{\Sigma x^2}{n^2 - n}$$

$$\bar{X}_\infty = \bar{X} \pm ts_{\bar{X}}$$

To compare paired samples

$$t_D = \frac{\bar{D}}{s_D} \; ; \qquad t^2 = \frac{(n-1)(\Sigma D)^2}{n \Sigma D^2 - (\Sigma D)^2}$$

To compare two independent samples

$$t = \frac{\bar{X}_1 - \bar{X}_2}{s_{\bar{X}_1 - \bar{X}_2}} \quad \text{where either} \quad s_{\bar{X}_1 - \bar{X}_2} = \sqrt{s^2_{\bar{X}_1} + s^2_{\bar{X}_2}}$$

$$\text{or} \quad s_{\bar{X}_1 - \bar{X}_2} = \sqrt{\frac{s^2}{n_1} + \frac{s^2}{n_2}}$$

$$\text{and} \quad s^2 = \frac{\Sigma x^2_1 + \Sigma x^2_2}{n_1 + n_2 - 2}$$

$$t^2 = \frac{n_1 n_2 (\bar{X}_1 - \bar{X}_2)^2}{\Sigma x^2_1 + \Sigma x^2_2} \cdot \frac{n_1 + n_2 - 2}{n_1 + n_2}$$

To compare k independent samples

$$F = \frac{s^2_b}{s^2_w} = \frac{\Sigma x^2_b/(k-1)}{\Sigma x^2_w/(n-k)} \quad \text{where} \quad \Sigma x^2_b = \Sigma \frac{(\Sigma X)^2}{m} - \frac{(\Sigma\Sigma X)^2}{n}$$

$$\text{and} \quad \Sigma x^2_w = \Sigma\Sigma X^2 - \Sigma \frac{(\Sigma X)^2}{m}$$

$$\eta^2 = 1 - \frac{\Sigma x^2_w}{\Sigma x^2_t} \; ; \qquad F = \frac{\eta^2/(k-1)}{(1 - \eta^2)/(n-k)}$$

WHEN THE DATA ARE SCORES ON TWO VARIABLES

$$r = \frac{\Sigma xy}{n\sigma_X\sigma_Y} = \frac{\Sigma XY - (\Sigma X)(\Sigma Y)/n}{\sqrt{\Sigma X^2 - (\Sigma X)^2/n}\ \sqrt{\Sigma Y^2 - (\Sigma Y)^2/n}}$$

To test significance: $\quad F = \dfrac{r^2}{(1 - r^2)/(n - 2)}$

To test linearity: $\quad F = \dfrac{(\eta^2 - r^2)/(k - 2)}{(1 - \eta^2)/(n - k)}$

$z_{Y'} = rz_X \quad$ where $\quad z_{Y'} = \dfrac{(Y' - \bar{Y})}{\sigma_Y}$

$Y' = \bar{Y} + b(X - \bar{X}) \quad$ where $\quad b = r\dfrac{\sigma_Y}{\sigma_X}$

$\quad = A + bX \quad$ where $\quad A = \bar{Y} - b\bar{X}$

$\sigma_{Y \cdot X} = \sigma_Y\sqrt{1 - r^2}$

WHEN THE DATA ARE CLASSIFICATIONS

$$s_p = \sqrt{pq/n}$$

$$s_{p_1-p_2} = \sqrt{\frac{pq}{n_1} + \frac{pq}{n_2}}$$

$$\chi^2 = \frac{(f_o - f_e)^2}{f_e}, \quad \text{or, in fourfold table,} \quad \frac{(|f_o - f_e| - .5)^2}{f_e}$$

For tests of independence, $\qquad f_e = \dfrac{n_r n_c}{n}$

and $\quad df = (R - 1)(C - 1)$

For tests of fit, f_e is fixed by theory
and $df = k$ less restrictions

WHEN THE DATA ARE RANKS

$$r' = 1 - \frac{6\,\Sigma D^2}{n(n^2 - 1)}$$

$$W = \frac{12\,\Sigma(\Sigma R)^2}{nk^2(n^2 - 1)} - 3\frac{n + 1}{n - 1}$$

$$\chi^2_r = k(n - 1)W = \frac{12\,\Sigma(\Sigma R)^2}{k(n^2 + n)} - 3k(n + 1); \qquad df = n - 1$$

DISTRIBUTION-FREE TESTS

For paired samples: Wilcoxon signed ranks

$$z = \frac{2T + 1 - \frac{n^2 + n}{2}}{\sqrt{\frac{(2n + 1)(n^2 + n)}{6}}}$$

For two independent samples: Mann-Whitney

$$z = \frac{m(m + n + 1) - (2T \pm 1)}{\sqrt{mn(m + n + 1)/3}}$$

For k independent samples: Kruskal-Wallis

$$H = \frac{12}{n^2 + n} \Sigma \frac{(\Sigma R)^2}{m} - 3(n + 1)$$

where H approximates χ^2 with $df = k - 1$

For paired samples: the sign test

$$z = \frac{n - (2m + 1)}{\sqrt{n}}$$ where m signs, of n, have the less frequent sign

Median tests: applications of χ^2, with classes fixed by medial cuts

PROBABILITY DISTRIBUTIONS

Binomial

$$(p + q)^n = 1 = \sum_{m=0}^{n} \left[\binom{n}{m} p^m q^{n-m} \right]$$

where $\binom{n}{m} = \frac{n!}{m!(n - m)!}$

Normal (approximate):

$$\log y = -.217 \frac{x^2}{\sigma^2}$$ where y is a proportion of the frequency at the mean of the distribution

Poisson

$$P\{X\} = \frac{e^{-\bar{X}} \bar{X}^X}{X!}.$$

APPENDIX OF TABLES

TABLE I.

Binomial coefficients: Values of $\binom{n}{m}$

m \ n	0	1	2	3	4	5	6	7	8	9	10	11	12
0	1	1	1	1	1	1	1	1	1	1	1	1	1
1		1	2	3	4	5	6	7	8	9	10	11	12
2			1	3	6	10	15	21	28	36	45	55	66
3				1	4	10	20	35	56	84	120	165	220
4					1	5	15	35	70	126	210	330	495
5						1	6	21	56	126	252	462	792
6							1	7	28	84	210	462	924
7								1	8	36	120	330	792
8									1	9	45	165	495
9										1	10	55	220
10											1	11	66
11												1	12
12													1
2^n	1	2	4	8	16	32	64	128	256	512	1024	2048	4096

$$\binom{n}{m} = \frac{n!}{m!(n-m)!}$$

TABLE II.

The Normal Probability Area

(A). Per cent of area in the smaller portion (i.e., in one tail) cut off by $\pm z$, a deviation expressed in standard units.

$\pm z$	%	$\pm z$	%
.00	50.0	1.05	14.7
.05	48.0	1.10	13.6
.10	46.0	1.15	12.5
.15	44.0	1.20	11.5
.20	42.1	1.25	10.6
.25	40.1	1.30	9.7
.30	38.2	1.35	8.9
.35	36.3	1.40	8.1
.40	34.5	1.45	7.4
.45	32.6	1.50	6.7
.50	30.9	1.60	5.5
.55	29.1	1.70	4.5
.60	27.4	1.80	3.6
.65	25.8	1.90	2.9
.70	24.2	2.00	2.3
.75	22.7	2.10	1.8
.80	21.2	2.20	1.4
.85	19.8	2.30	1.1
.90	18.4	2.40	0.8
.95	17.1	2.50	0.6
1.00	15.9	2.75	0.3
		3.00	0.135

TABLE II—*Continued*

The Normal Probability Area

(B). The deviation, in standard units, which divides the normal distribution into given portions, stated as percentages.

Critical portions	±z	Centile portions	±z
0.005 : 99.995	3.891	21 : 79	.81
0.05 : 99.95	3.291	22 : 78	.77
0.10 : 99.90	3.090	23 : 77	.74
0.50 : 99.50	2.576	24 : 76	.71
2.50 : 97.50	1.960	25 : 75	.6745
		26 : 74	.64
Centile portions		27 : 73	.61
1 : 99	2.33	28 : 72	.58
2 : 98	2.05	29 : 71	.55
3 : 97	1.88	30 : 70	.52
4 : 96	1.75	31 : 69	.50
5 : 95	1.64	32 : 68	.47
6 : 94	1.55	33 : 67	.44
7 : 93	1.48	34 : 66	.41
8 : 92	1.41	35 : 65	.39
9 : 91	1.34	36 : 64	.36
10 : 90	1.28	37 : 63	.33
11 : 89	1.23	38 : 62	.31
12 : 88	1.18	39 : 61	.28
13 : 87	1.13	40 : 60	.25
14 : 86	1.08	41 : 59	.23
15 : 85	1.04	42 : 58	.20
16 : 84	.99	43 : 57	.18
17 : 83	.95	44 : 56	.15
18 : 82	.92	45 : 55	.13
19 : 81	.88	46 : 54	.10
20 : 80	.84	47 : 53	.08
		48 : 52	.05
		49 : 51	.03
		50 : 50	.00

TABLE III. t

P df	.10	.05	.02	.01
1	6.314	12.706	31.821	63.657
2	2.920	4.303	6.965	9.925
3	2.353	3.182	4.541	5.841
4	2.132	2.776	3.747	4.604
5	2.015	2.571	3.365	4.032
6	1.943	2.447	3.143	3.707
7	1.895	2.365	2.998	3.499
8	1.860	2.306	2.896	3.355
9	1.833	2.262	2.821	3.250
10	1.812	2.228	2.764	3.169
11	1.796	2.201	2.718	3.106
12	1.782	2.179	2.681	3.055
13	1.771	2.160	2.650	3.012
14	1.761	2.145	2.624	2.977
15	1.753	2.131	2.602	2.947
16	1.746	2.120	2.583	2.921
17	1.740	2.110	2.567	2.898
18	1.734	2.101	2.552	2.878
19	1.729	2.093	2.539	2.861
20	1.725	2.086	2.528	2.845
21	1.721	2.080	2.518	2.831
22	1.717	2.074	2.508	2.819
23	1.714	2.069	2.500	2.807
24	1.711	2.064	2.492	2.797
25	1.708	2.060	2.485	2.787
26	1.706	2.056	2.479	2.779
27	1.703	2.052	2.473	2.771
28	1.701	2.048	2.467	2.763
29	1.699	2.045	2.462	2.756
30	1.697	2.042	2.457	2.750
∞	1.64485	1.95996	2.32635	2.57583

The major portion of Table III is abridged from Table III of Fisher and Yates: *Statistical Tables for Biological, Agricultural, and Medical Research*, published by Oliver and Boyd, Ltd., Edinburgh, by permission of the authors and publishers.

The additional values on the following page are taken from Table 2.7.1 of Snedecor: *Statistical Methods*, 5th edition, 1956, Iowa State College Press, Ames, Iowa, with permission of the author and publisher.

TABLE IV.
Critical Values of χ^2

df \ P	.50	.10	.05	.02	.01
1	.455	2.706	3.841	5.412	6.635
2	1.386	4.605	5.991	7.824	9.210
3	2.366	6.251	7.815	9.837	11.345
4	3.357	7.779	9.488	11.668	13.277
5	4.351	9.236	11.070	13.388	15.086
6	5.348	10.645	12.592	15.033	16.812
7	6.346	12.017	14.067	16.622	18.475
8	7.344	13.362	15.507	18.168	20.090
9	8.343	14.684	16.919	19.679	21.666
10	9.342	15.987	18.307	21.161	23.209
11	10.341	17.275	19.675	22.618	24.725
12	11.340	18.549	21.026	24.054	26.217
13	12.340	19.812	22.362	25.472	27.688
14	13.339	21.064	23.685	26.873	29.141
15	14.339	22.307	24.996	28.259	30.578
16	15.338	23.542	26.296	29.633	32.000
17	16.338	24.769	27.587	30.995	33.409
18	17.338	25.989	28.869	32.346	34.805
19	18.338	27.204	30.144	33.687	36.191
20	19.337	28.412	31.410	35.020	37.566
21	20.337	29.615	32.671	36.343	38.932
22	21.337	30.813	33.924	37.659	40.289
23	22.337	32.007	35.172	38.968	41.638
24	23.337	33.196	36.415	40.270	42.980
25	24.337	34.382	37.652	41.566	44.314
26	25.336	35.563	38.885	42.856	45.642
27	26.336	36.741	40.113	44.140	46.963
28	27.336	37.916	41.337	45.419	48.278
29	28.336	39.087	42.557	46.693	49.588
30	29.336	40.256	43.773	47.962	50.892

Table IV is abridged from Table IV of Fisher and Yates: *Statistical Tables for Biological, Agricultural, and Medical Research*, Oliver and Boyd, Ltd., Edinburgh, by permission of the authors and publishers.

TABLE III—*Continued*
Additional values of t

df \ P	.05	.01	df \ P	.05	.01
35	2.030	2.724	70	1.994	2.648
40	2.021	2.704	80	1.989	2.638
45	2.014	2.690	90	1.986	2.631
50	2.008	2.678	100	1.982	2.625
55	2.004	2.669	120	1.980	2.617
60	2.000	2.660			

TABLE V.

5 per cent (Roman) and 1 per cent (Boldface) critical values of F

df_2 \ df_1	1	2	3	4	5	6	7	8	10	14	20	40	100	∞
3	10.13	9.55	9.28	9.12	9.01	8.94	8.88	8.84	8.78	8.71	8.66	8.60	8.56	8.53
	34.12	**30.82**	**29.46**	**28.71**	**28.24**	**27.91**	**27.67**	**27.49**	**27.23**	**26.92**	**26.69**	**26.41**	**26.23**	**26.12**
4	7.71	6.94	6.59	6.39	6.26	6.16	6.09	6.04	5.96	5.87	5.80	5.71	5.66	5.63
	21.20	**18.00**	**16.69**	**15.98**	**15.52**	**15.21**	**14.98**	**14.80**	**14.54**	**14.24**	**14.02**	**13.74**	**13.57**	**13.46**
5	6.61	5.79	5.41	5.19	5.05	4.95	4.88	4.82	4.74	4.64	4.56	4.46	4.40	4.36
	16.26	**13.27**	**12.06**	**11.39**	**10.97**	**10.67**	**10.45**	**10.27**	**10.05**	**9.77**	**9.55**	**9.29**	**9.13**	**9.02**
6	5.99	5.14	4.76	4.53	4.39	4.28	4.21	4.15	4.06	3.96	3.87	3.77	3.71	3.67
	13.74	**10.92**	**9.78**	**9.15**	**8.75**	**8.47**	**8.26**	**8.10**	**7.87**	**7.60**	**7.39**	**7.14**	**6.99**	**6.88**
7	5.59	4.74	4.35	4.12	3.97	3.87	3.79	3.73	3.63	3.52	3.44	3.34	3.28	3.23
	12.25	**9.55**	**8.45**	**7.85**	**7.46**	**7.19**	**7.00**	**6.84**	**6.62**	**6.35**	**6.15**	**5.90**	**5.75**	**5.65**
8	5.32	4.46	4.07	3.84	3.69	3.58	3.50	3.44	3.34	3.23	3.15	3.05	2.98	2.93
	11.26	**8.65**	**7.59**	**7.01**	**6.63**	**6.37**	**6.19**	**6.03**	**5.82**	**5.56**	**5.36**	**5.11**	**4.96**	**4.86**
9	5.12	4.26	3.86	3.63	3.48	3.37	3.29	3.23	3.13	3.02	2.93	2.82	2.76	2.71
	10.56	**8.02**	**6.99**	**6.42**	**6.06**	**5.80**	**5.62**	**5.47**	**5.26**	**5.00**	**4.80**	**4.56**	**4.41**	**4.31**
10	4.96	4.10	3.71	3.48	3.33	3.22	3.14	3.07	2.97	2.86	2.77	2.67	2.59	2.54
	10.04	**7.56**	**6.55**	**5.99**	**5.64**	**5.39**	**5.21**	**5.06**	**4.85**	**4.60**	**4.41**	**4.17**	**4.01**	**3.91**
11	4.84	3.98	3.59	3.36	3.20	3.09	3.01	2.95	2.86	2.74	2.65	2.53	2.45	2.40
	9.65	**7.20**	**6.22**	**5.67**	**5.32**	**5.07**	**4.88**	**4.74**	**4.54**	**4.29**	**4.10**	**3.86**	**3.70**	**3.60**
12	4.75	3.88	3.49	3.26	3.11	3.00	2.92	2.85	2.76	2.64	2.54	2.42	2.35	2.30
	9.33	**6.93**	**5.95**	**5.41**	**5.06**	**4.82**	**4.65**	**4.50**	**4.30**	**4.05**	**3.86**	**3.61**	**3.46**	**3.36**
13	4.67	3.80	3.41	3.18	3.02	2.92	2.84	2.77	2.67	2.55	2.46	2.34	2.26	2.21
	9.07	**6.70**	**5.74**	**5.20**	**4.86**	**4.62**	**4.44**	**4.30**	**4.10**	**3.85**	**3.67**	**3.42**	**3.27**	**3.16**
14	4.60	3.74	3.34	3.11	2.96	2.85	2.77	2.70	2.60	2.48	2.39	2.27	2.19	2.13
	8.86	**6.51**	**5.56**	**5.03**	**4.69**	**4.46**	**4.28**	**4.14**	**3.94**	**3.70**	**3.51**	**3.26**	**3.11**	**3.00**
15	4.54	3.68	3.29	3.06	2.90	2.79	2.70	2.64	2.55	2.43	2.33	2.21	2.12	2.07
	8.68	**6.36**	**5.42**	**4.89**	**4.56**	**4.32**	**4.14**	**4.00**	**3.80**	**3.56**	**3.36**	**3.12**	**2.97**	**2.87**
16	4.49	3.63	3.24	3.01	2.85	2.74	2.66	2.59	2.49	2.37	2.28	2.16	2.07	2.01
	8.53	**6.23**	**5.29**	**4.77**	**4.44**	**4.20**	**4.03**	**3.89**	**3.69**	**3.45**	**3.25**	**3.01**	**2.86**	**2.75**
17	4.45	3.59	3.20	2.96	2.81	2.70	2.62	2.55	2.45	2.33	2.23	2.11	2.02	1.96
	8.40	**6.11**	**5.18**	**4.67**	**4.34**	**4.10**	**3.93**	**3.79**	**3.59**	**3.35**	**3.16**	**2.92**	**2.76**	**2.65**
18	4.41	3.55	3.16	2.93	2.77	2.66	2.58	2.51	2.41	2.29	2.19	2.07	1.98	1.92
	8.28	**6.01**	**5.09**	**4.58**	**4.25**	**4.01**	**3.85**	**3.71**	**3.51**	**3.27**	**3.07**	**2.83**	**2.68**	**2.57**

Table V is abridged from Table 10.5.3 of Snedecor: *Statistical Methods*, 5th edition 1956, Iowa State College Press, Ames, Iowa, by permission of the author and publisher

TABLE V—*Continued*

5 per cent (Roman) and 1 per cent (Boldface) critical values of F

df_2 \ df_1	1	2	3	4	5	6	7	8	10	14	20	40	100	∞
19	4.38	3.52	3.13	2.90	2.74	2.63	2.55	2.48	2.38	2.26	2.15	2.02	1.94	1.88
	8.18	**5.93**	**5.01**	**4.50**	**4.17**	**3.94**	**3.77**	**3.63**	**3.43**	**3.19**	**3.00**	**2.76**	**2.60**	**2.49**
20	4.35	3.49	3.10	2.87	2.71	2.60	2.52	2.45	2.35	2.23	2.12	1.99	1.90	1.84
	8.10	**5.85**	**4.94**	**4.43**	**4.10**	**3.87**	**3.71**	**3.56**	**3.37**	**3.13**	**2.94**	**2.69**	**2.53**	**2.42**
21	4.32	3.47	3.07	2.84	2.68	2.57	2.49	2.42	2.32	2.20	2.09	1.96	1.87	1.81
	8.02	**5.78**	**4.87**	**4.37**	**4.04**	**3.81**	**3.65**	**3.51**	**3.31**	**3.07**	**2.88**	**2.63**	**2.47**	**2.36**
22	4.30	3.44	3.05	2.82	2.66	2.55	2.47	2.40	2.30	2.18	2.07	1.93	1.84	1.78
	7.94	**5.72**	**4.82**	**4.31**	**3.99**	**3.76**	**3.59**	**3.45**	**3.26**	**3.02**	**2.83**	**2.58**	**2.42**	**2.31**
23	4.28	3.42	3.03	2.80	2.64	2.53	2.45	2.38	2.28	2.14	2.04	1.91	1.82	1.76
	7.88	**5.66**	**4.76**	**4.26**	**3.94**	**3.71**	**3.54**	**3.41**	**3.21**	**2.97**	**2.78**	**2.53**	**2.37**	**2.26**
24	4.26	3.40	3.01	2.78	2.62	2.51	2.43	2.36	2.26	2.13	2.02	1.89	1.80	1.73
	7.82	**5.61**	**4.72**	**4.22**	**3.90**	**3.67**	**3.50**	**3.36**	**3.17**	**2.93**	**2.74**	**2.49**	**2.33**	**2.21**
25	4.24	3.38	2.99	2.76	2.60	2.49	2.41	2.34	2.24	2.11	2.00	1.87	1.77	1.71
	7.77	**5.57**	**4.68**	**4.18**	**3.86**	**3.63**	**3.46**	**3.32**	**3.13**	**2.89**	**2.70**	**2.45**	**2.29**	**2.17**
26	4.22	3.37	2.98	2.74	2.59	2.47	2.39	2.32	2.22	2.10	1.99	1.85	1.76	1.69
	7.72	**5.53**	**4.64**	**4.14**	**3.82**	**3.59**	**3.42**	**3.29**	**3.09**	**2.86**	**2.66**	**2.41**	**2.25**	**2.13**
27	4.21	3.35	2.96	2.73	2.57	2.46	2.37	2.30	2.20	2.08	1.97	1.84	1.74	1.67
	7.68	**5.49**	**4.60**	**4.11**	**3.79**	**3.56**	**3.39**	**3.26**	**3.06**	**2.83**	**2.63**	**2.38**	**2.21**	**2.10**
28	4.20	3.34	2.95	2.71	2.56	2.44	2.36	2.29	2.19	2.06	1.96	1.81	1.72	1.65
	7.64	**5.45**	**4.57**	**4.07**	**3.76**	**3.53**	**3.36**	**3.23**	**3.03**	**2.80**	**2.60**	**2.35**	**2.18**	**2.06**
29	4.18	3.33	2.93	2.70	2.54	2.43	2.35	2.28	2.18	2.05	1.94	1.80	1.71	1.64
	7.60	**5.42**	**4.54**	**4.04**	**3.73**	**3.50**	**3.33**	**3.20**	**3.00**	**2.77**	**2.57**	**2.32**	**2.15**	**2.03**
30	4.17	3.32	2.92	2.69	2.53	2.42	2.34	2.27	2.16	2.04	1.93	1.79	1.69	1.62
	7.56	**5.39**	**4.51**	**4.02**	**3.70**	**3.47**	**3.30**	**3.17**	**2.98**	**2.74**	**2.55**	**2.29**	**2.13**	**2.01**
32	4.15	3.30	2.90	2.67	2.51	2.40	2.32	2.25	2.14	2.02	1.91	1.76	1.67	1.59
	7.50	**5.34**	**4.46**	**3.97**	**3.66**	**3.42**	**3.25**	**3.12**	**2.94**	**2.70**	**2.51**	**2.25**	**2.08**	**1.96**
34	4.13	3.28	2.88	2.65	2.49	2.38	2.30	2.23	2.12	2.00	1.89	1.74	1.64	1.57
	7.44	**5.29**	**4.42**	**3.93**	**3.61**	**3.38**	**3.21**	**3.08**	**2.89**	**2.66**	**2.47**	**2.21**	**2.04**	**1.91**
36	4.11	3.26	2.86	2.63	2.48	2.36	2.28	2.21	2.10	1.98	1.87	1.72	1.62	1.55
	7.39	**5.25**	**4.38**	**3.89**	**3.58**	**3.35**	**3.18**	**3.04**	**2.86**	**2.62**	**2.43**	**2.17**	**2.00**	**1.87**
38	4.10	3.25	2.85	2.62	2.46	2.35	2.26	2.19	2.09	1.96	1.85	1.71	1.60	1.53
	7.35	**5.21**	**4.34**	**3.86**	**3.54**	**3.32**	**3.15**	**3.02**	**2.82**	**2.59**	**2.40**	**2.14**	**1.97**	**1.84**

TABLE V—*Continued*

5 per cent (Roman) and 1 per cent (Boldface) critical values of F

df_2 \ df_1	1	2	3	4	5	6	7	8	10	14	20	40	100	∞
40	4.08	3.23	2.84	2.61	2.45	2.34	2.25	2.18	2.07	1.95	1.84	1.69	1.59	1.51
	7.31	**5.18**	**4.31**	**3.83**	**3.51**	**3.29**	**3.12**	**2.99**	**2.80**	**2.56**	**2.37**	**2.11**	**1.94**	**1.81**
42	4.07	3.22	2.83	2.59	2.44	2.32	2.24	2.17	2.06	1.94	1.82	1.68	1.57	1.49
	7.27	**5.15**	**4.29**	**3.80**	**3.49**	**3.26**	**3.10**	**2.96**	**2.77**	**2.54**	**2.35**	**2.08**	**1.91**	**1.78**
44	4.06	3.21	2.82	2.58	2.43	2.31	2.23	2.16	2.05	1.92	1.81	1.66	1.56	1.48
	7.24	**5.12**	**4.26**	**3.78**	**3.46**	**3.24**	**3.07**	**2.94**	**2.75**	**2.52**	**2.32**	**2.06**	**1.88**	**1.75**
46	4.05	3.20	2.81	2.57	2.42	2.30	2.22	2.14	2.04	1.91	1.80	1.65	1.54	1.46
	7.21	**5.10**	**4.24**	**3.76**	**3.44**	**3.22**	**3.05**	**2.92**	**2.73**	**2.50**	**2.30**	**2.04**	**1.86**	**1.72**
48	4.04	3.19	2.80	2.56	2.41	2.30	2.21	2.14	2.03	1.90	1.79	1.64	1.53	1.45
	7.19	**5.08**	**4.22**	**3.74**	**3.42**	**3.20**	**3.04**	**2.90**	**2.71**	**2.48**	**2.28**	**2.02**	**1.84**	**1.70**
50	4.03	3.18	2.79	2.56	2.40	2.29	2.20	2.13	2.02	1.90	1.78	1.63	1.52	1.44
	7.17	**5.06**	**4.20**	**3.72**	**3.41**	**3.18**	**3.02**	**2.88**	**2.70**	**2.46**	**2.26**	**2.00**	**1.82**	**1.68**
55	4.02	3.17	2.78	2.54	2.38	2.27	2.18	2.11	2.00	1.88	1.76	1.61	1.50	1.41
	7.12	**5.01**	**4.16**	**3.68**	**3.37**	**3.15**	**2.98**	**2.85**	**2.66**	**2.43**	**2.23**	**1.96**	**1.78**	**1.64**
60	4.00	3.15	2.76	2.52	2.37	2.25	2.17	2.10	1.99	1.86	1.75	1.59	1.48	1.39
	7.08	**4.98**	**4.13**	**3.65**	**3.34**	**3.12**	**2.95**	**2.82**	**2.63**	**2.40**	**2.20**	**1.93**	**1.74**	**1.60**
65	3.99	3.14	2.75	2.51	2.36	2.24	2.15	2.08	1.98	1.85	1.73	1.57	1.46	1.37
	7.04	**4.95**	**4.10**	**3.62**	**3.31**	**3.09**	**2.93**	**2.79**	**2.61**	**2.37**	**2.18**	**1.90**	**1.71**	**1.56**
70	3.98	3.13	2.74	2.50	2.35	2.23	2.14	2.07	1.97	1.84	1.72	1.56	1.45	1.35
	7.01	**4.92**	**4.08**	**3.60**	**3.29**	**3.07**	**2.91**	**2.77**	**2.59**	**2.35**	**2.15**	**1.88**	**1.69**	**1.53**
80	3.96	3.11	2.72	2.48	2.33	2.21	2.12	2.05	1.95	1.82	1.70	1.54	1.42	1.32
	6.96	**4.88**	**4.04**	**3.56**	**3.25**	**3.04**	**2.87**	**2.74**	**2.55**	**2.32**	**2.11**	**1.84**	**1.65**	**1.49**
100	3.94	3.09	2.70	2.46	2.30	2.19	2.10	2.03	1.92	1.79	1.68	1.51	1.39	1.28
	6.90	**4.82**	**3.98**	**3.51**	**3.20**	**2.99**	**2.82**	**2.69**	**2.51**	**2.26**	**2.06**	**1.79**	**1.59**	**1.43**
125	3.92	3.07	2.68	2.44	2.29	2.17	2.08	2.01	1.90	1.77	1.65	1.49	1.36	1.25
	6.84	**478**	**3.94**	**3.47**	**3.17**	**2.95**	**2.79**	**2.65**	**2.47**	**2.23**	**2.03**	**1.75**	**1.54**	**1.37**
150	3.91	3.06	2.67	2.43	2.27	2.16	2.07	2.00	1.89	1.76	1.64	1.47	1.34	1.22
	6.81	**4.75**	**3.91**	**3.44**	**3.14**	**2.92**	**2.76**	**2.62**	**2.44**	**2.20**	**2.00**	**1.72**	**1.51**	**1.33**
200	3.89	3.04	2.65	2.41	2.26	2.14	2.05	1.98	1.87	1.74	1.62	1.45	1.32	1.19
	6.76	**4.71**	**3.88**	**3.41**	**3.11**	**2.90**	**2.73**	**2.60**	**2.41**	**2.17**	**1.97**	**1.69**	**1.48**	**1.28**
400	3.86	3.02	2.62	2.39	2.23	2.12	2.03	1.96	1.85	1.72	1.60	1.42	1.28	1.13
	6.70	**4.66**	**3.83**	**3.36**	**3.06**	**2.85**	**2.69**	**2.55**	**2.37**	**2.12**	**1.92**	**1.64**	**1.42**	**1.19**
∞	3.84	2.99	2.60	2.37	2.21	2.09	2.01	1.94	1.83	1.69	1.57	1.40	1.24	1.00
	6.64	**4.60**	**3.78**	**3.32**	**3.02**	**2.80**	**2.64**	**2.51**	**2.32**	**2.07**	**1.87**	**1.59**	**1.36**	**1.00**

TABLE VI.

Some 5 per cent values of F, t, r^2, ϵ^2, and χ^2, arranged to display the relationships among the principal continuous probability distributions

df_1 df_2	1				2	5		10	40	∞
	t	F	r^2	ϵ^2	F	F	ϵ^2	F	F	F
5	2.57	6.61	.569	.483	.579	4.95	.669	4.74	4.46	4.36
10	2.23	4.96	.332	.264	4.10	3.22	.437	2.97	2.67	2.54
40	2.02	4.08	.093	.069	3.23	2.34	.139	2.07	1.69	1.51
∞	1.96	3.84			2.99	2.21		1.83	1.40	1.00
χ^2	3.84				5.99	11.07		18.31	55.76	∞

When $df_1 = 1$, $t = \sqrt{F}$, $r^2 = F/(df_2 + F)$, and $\epsilon^2 = (F - 1)/(df_2 + F)$.
Whenever $df_1 \leqq df_2$, $\epsilon^2 = (df_1 F - df_1)/(df_1 F + df_2)$.
$\chi^2 = df_1 F$, where F is selected for $df_2 = \infty$.

TABLE VII.

Critical scores for certain small-sample tests (two-tailed)

	Signs Count of the less frequent sign among n non-zero pairs			Signed ranks The smaller sum of ranks among n non-zero pairs			Mann-Whitney ΣR for m objects of one sample, ranked together with n objects of another sample, when the direction of ranking is chosen to minimize ΣR.														Rank Correlation.	
							$m = 2$			$m = 3$			$m = 4$			$m = 5$						
P n	.10	.05	.01	.10	.05	.01	.10	.05	.01	.10	.05	.01	.10	.05	.01	.10	.05	.01	.10	.02
3										6										
4										6			11	10					1.00	
5	0			0			3			7	6		12	11		19	17	15	.90	1.00
6	0	0		2	0		3			8	7		13	12	10	20	18	16	.83	.94
7	0	0		3	2		3			8	7		14	13	10	21	20	16	.71	.89
8	1	0	0	5	3	0	4	3		9	8		15	14	11	23	21	17	.64	.83
9	1	1	0	8	5	1	4	3		9	8	6	16	14	11	24	22	18	.60	.78
10	1	1	0	10	8	3	4	3		10	9	6	17	15	12	26	23	19	.56	.73
11	2	1	0	14	10	5	4	3		11	9	6	18	16	12	27	24	20		
12	2	2	1	17	13	7	5	4		11	10	7	19	17	13	28	26	21		
13	3	2	1	21	17	9	5	4		12	10	7	20	18	14	30	27	22		
14	3	2	1	25	21	12	5	4		13	11	7	21	19	14	31	28	22		
15	3	3	2	30	25	16	6	4		13	11	8	22	20	15	33	29	23		
16	4	3	2	35	29	19	6	4		14	12	8	24	21	15	34	30	24		
17	4	4	2	41	34	23	6	5		15	12	8	25	21	16	35	32	25		
18	5	4	3	47	40	27	7	5		15	13	8	26	22	16	37	33	26		
19	5	4	3	53	46	32	7	5	3	16	13	9	27	23	17	38	34	27		
20	5	5	3	60	52	37	7	5	3	17	14	9	28	24	18	40	35	28		

Table VII is abridged from Tables O, P, L and G of Tate and Clelland: *Nonparametric and Shortcut Statistics*, 1957, Danville, Ill.: Interstate, with permission of the authors and the publisher.

TABLE VIII.

Critical values of *H*, in the Kruskal-Wallis test applied to three samples, for specified combinations of sample *m*'s

m_1	m_2	m_3	$P \leq .05$	$P \leq .01$	m_1	m_2	m_3	$P \leq .05$	$P \leq .01$
1	2	5	5.00		2	4	4	5.45	7.04
1	3	3	5.14		2	4	5	5.27	7.12
1	3	4	5.21		2	5	5	5.34	7.27
1	3	5	4.96		3	3	3	5.60	7.20
1	4	4	4.97	6.67	3	3	4	5.73	6.75
1	4	5	4.99	6.95	3	3	5	5.65	7.08
1	5	5	5.13	7.31	3	4	4	5.60	7.14
2	2	3	4.71		3	4	5	5.63	7.44
2	2	4	5.33		3	5	5	5.71	7.54
2	2	5	5.16	6.53	4	4	4	5.69	7.65
2	3	3	5.36		4	4	5	5.62	7.76
2	3	4	5.44	6.44	4	5	5	5.64	7.79
2	3	5	5.25	6.82	5	5	5	5.78	7.98

Table VIII is abridged and re-arranged from Kruskal, W. H., and Wallis, W. A., Use of ranks in one-criterion variance analysis. *J. Amer. Statist. Assoc.*, 1952, 47:614–617 (with a note of errata, *ibid.*, 48:910), by permission of the authors and the publisher.

TABLE IX.

Critical values of χ^2_r, at 5 per cent (Roman type) and 1 per cent (boldface) levels of significance

k \ n	3	4	5	6	7
3			8.59	9.90	11.24
			10.08	**11.69**	**13.26**
4		7.43	8.84	10.24	11.62
		9.21	**10.93**	**12.59**	**14.19**
5		7.52	8.98	10.42	11.84
		9.66	**11.42**	**13.11**	**14.74**
6		7.57	9.08	10.54	11.97
		9.95	**11.74**	**13.45**	**15.09**
8	6.012	7.63	9.18	10.68	12.14
	8.35	**10.31**	**12.13**	**13.87**	**15.53**
10	5.999	7.67	9.25	10.76	12.23
	8.51	**10.52**	**12.37**	**14.11**	**15.79**
15	5.985	7.72	9.33	10.87	12.36
	8.74	**10.79**	**12.67**	**14.44**	**16.14**
20	5.983	7.74	9.37	10.92	12.42
	8.85	**10.93**	**12.82**	**14.60**	**16.31**

Table IX is abridged from Table II of M. Friedman, A comparison of alternative tests of significance for the problem of *m* rankings, *Annals of math. Statistics*, 1940, 11:86–92, with permission of the author and the publisher. The computations were based on the method of M. G. Kendall and B. B. Smith, The problem of *m* rankings, *Annals of math. Stat.*, 1939, 10:275–287.

TABLE X.

Values of $e^{-\bar{X}}$

$\bar{X}$	$e^{-\bar{X}}$	$\bar{X}$	$e^{-\bar{X}}$	$\bar{X}$	$e^{-\bar{X}}$
0	1.0000				
1	.3679	0.1	.905	.01	.990
2	.1353	0.2	.819	.02	.980
3	.0498	0.3	.741	.03	.970
4	.0183	0.4	.670	.04	.961
5	.0067	0.5	.607	.05	.951
6	.0025	0.6	.549	.06	.942
7	.0009	0.7	.497	.07	.932
8	.00034	0.8	.449	.08	.923
9	.00012	0.9	.407	.09	.914

For values not shown in the table, use the relationship

$$e^{-(A+B+C)} = e^{-A}e^{-B}e^{-C}.$$

Thus, $e^{-2.37} = (.1353)(.741)(.932) = .0934$.

The table facilitates calculation of Poisson probability distributions by the formula

$$\Sigma \frac{e^{-\bar{X}}\bar{X}^X}{X!} = 1.$$

For detailed instructions, see pages 234f.

TABLE XI.

Three Transformations

I. $r = \tanh z$ II. $r = \cos \theta_1$ III. $p = \sin^2 \theta_2$

p or r	(I) z	(II) θ_1	(III) θ_2	p or r	(I) z	(II) θ_1	(III) θ_2
.00	.000	90.0	00.0	.25	.255	75.5	30.0
.01	.010	89.4	05.7	.26	.266	74.9	30.7
.02	.020	88.9	08.1	.27	.277	74.3	31.3
.03	.030	88.3	10.0	.28	.288	73.7	32.0
.04	.040	87.7	11.5	.29	.299	73.1	32.6
.05	.050	87.1	12.9	.30	.309	72.5	33.2
.06	.060	86.6	14.2	.31	.321	71.9	33.8
.07	·070	86.0	15.3	.32	.332	71.3	34.4
.08	.080	85.4	16.4	.33	.343	70.7	35.1
.09	.090	84.8	17.5	.34	.354	70.1	35.7
.10	.100	84.3	18.4	.35	.365	69.5	36.3
.11	.110	83.7	19.4	.36	.377	68.9	36.9
.12	.121	83.1	20.3	.37	.388	68.3	37.5
.13	.131	82.5	21.2	.38	.400	67.7	38.0
.14	.141	82.0	22.0	.39	.412	67.0	38.6
.15	.151	81.4	22.8	.40	.424	66.4	39.2
.16	.161	80.8	23.6	.41	.436	65.8	39.8
.17	.172	80.2	24.4	.42	.448	65.2	40.4
.18	.182	79.6	25.1	.43	.460	64.5	41.0
.19	.192	79.0	25.8	.44	.472	63.9	41.5
.20	.203	78.5	26.6	.45	.485	63.3	42.1
.21	.213	77.9	27.3	.46	.497	62.6	42.8
.22	.224	77.3	28.0	.47	.510	62.0	43.3
.23	.234	76.7	28.7	.48	.523	61.3	43.9
.24	.245	76.1	29.3	.49	.536	60.7	44.5

TABLE XI—*Continued*

Three Transformations

I. $r = \tanh z$ II. $r = \cos \theta_1$ III. $p = \sin^2 \theta_2$

p or r	(I) z	(II) θ_1	(III) θ_2	p or r	(I) z	(II) θ_1	(III) θ_2
.50	.549	60.0	45.0	.75	.973	41.4	60.0
.51	.563	59.3	45.5	.76	.996	40.5	60.7
.52	.576	58.7	46.1	.77	1.020	39.6	61.3
.53	.590	58.0	46.7	.78	1.045	38.7	62.0
.54	.604	57.3	47.2	.79	1.071	37.8	62.7
.55	.618	56.6	47.9	.80	1.099	36.9	63.4
.56	.633	55.9	48.5	.81	1.127	35.9	64.2
.57	.648	55.2	49.0	.82	1.157	34.9	64.9
.58	.663	54.5	49.6	.83	1.188	33.9	65.6
.59	.678	53.8	50.2	.84	1.221	32.9	66.4
.60	.693	53.1	50.8	.85	1.256	31.8	67.2
.61	.709	52.4	51.4	.86	1.293	30.7	68.0
.62	.725	51.7	52.0	.87	1.333	29.5	68.8
.63	.741	50.9	52.5	.88	1.376	28.4	69.7
.64	.758	50.2	53.1	.89	1.422	27.1	70.6
.65	.775	49.5	53.7	.90	1.472	25.8	71.6
.66	.793	48.7	54.3	.91	1.528	24.5	72.5
.67	.811	47.9	54.9	.92	1.589	23.1	73.6
.68	.829	47.2	55.6	.93	1.658	21.6	74.7
.69	.848	46.4	56.2	.94	1.738	19.9	75.8
.70	.867	45.6	56.8	.95	1.832	18.2	77.1
.71	.887	44.8	57.4	.96	1.946	16.3	78.5
.72	.908	43.9	58.0	.97	2.092	14.1	80.0
.73	.929	43.1	58.7	.98	2.298	11.5	81.9
.74	.950	42.3	59.3	.99	2.647	8.1	84.3
				1.00		0.0	90.0

TABLE XII

10,000 Random Digits

C / R	0 01234	56789	1 01234	56789	2 01234	56789	3 01234	56789	4 01234	56789
00	19612	78430	11661	94770	77603	65669	86868	12665	30012	75989
01	39141	77400	28000	64238	73258	71794	31340	26256	66453	37016
02	64756	80457	08747	12836	03469	50678	03274	43423	66677	82556
03	92901	51878	56441	22998	29718	38447	06453	25311	07565	53771
04	03551	90070	09483	94050	45938	18135	36908	43321	11073	51803
05	98884	66209	06830	53656	14663	56346	71430	04909	19818	05707
06	27369	86882	53473	07541	53633	70863	03748	12822	19360	49088
07	59066	75974	63335	20483	43514	37481	58278	26967	49325	43951
08	91647	93783	64169	49022	98588	09495	49829	59068	38831	04838
09	83605	92419	39542	07772	71568	75673	35185	89759	44901	74291
10	24895	88530	70774	35439	46758	70472	70207	92675	91623	61275
11	35720	26556	95596	20094	73750	85788	34264	01703	46833	65248
12	14141	53410	38649	06343	57256	61342	72709	75318	90379	37562
13	27416	75670	92176	72535	93119	56077	06886	18244	92344	31374
14	82071	07429	81007	47749	40744	56974	23336	88821	53841	10536
15	21445	82793	24831	93241	14199	76268	70883	68002	03829	17443
16	72513	76400	52225	92348	62308	98481	29744	33165	33141	61020
17	71479	45027	76160	57411	13780	13632	52308	77762	88874	33697
18	83210	51466	09088	50395	26743	05306	21706	70001	99439	80767
19	68749	95148	94897	78636	96750	09024	94538	91143	96693	61886
20	05184	75763	47075	88158	05313	53439	14908	08830	60096	21551
21	13651	62546	96892	25240	47511	58483	87342	78818	07855	39269
22	00566	21220	00292	24069	25072	29519	52548	54091	21282	21296
23	50958	17695	58072	68990	60329	95955	71586	63417	35947	67807
24	57621	64547	46850	37981	38527	09037	64756	03324	04986	83666
25	09282	25844	79139	78435	35428	43561	69799	63314	12991	93516
26	23394	94206	93432	37836	94919	26846	02555	74410	94915	48199
27	05280	37470	93622	04345	15092	19510	18094	16613	78234	50001
28	95491	97976	38306	32192	82639	54624	72434	92606	23191	74693
29	78521	00104	18248	75583	90326	50785	54034	66251	35774	14692
30	96345	44579	85932	44053	75704	20840	86583	83944	52456	73766
31	77963	31151	32364	91691	47357	40338	23435	24065	08458	95366
32	07520	11294	23238	01748	41690	67328	54814	37777	10057	42332
33	38423	02309	70703	85736	46148	14258	29236	12152	05088	65825
34	02463	65533	21199	60555	33928	01817	07396	89215	30722	22102
35	15880	92261	17292	88190	61781	48898	92525	21283	88581	60098
36	71926	00819	59144	00224	30570	90194	18329	06999	26857	19238
37	64425	28108	16554	16016	00042	83229	10333	36168	65617	94834
38	79782	23924	49440	30432	81077	31543	95216	64865	13658	51081
39	35337	74538	44553	64672	90960	41849	93865	44608	93176	34851
40	05249	29329	19715	94082	14738	86667	43708	66354	93692	25527
41	56463	99380	38793	85774	19056	13939	46062	27647	66146	63210
42	96296	33121	54196	34108	75814	85986	71171	15102	28992	63165
43	98380	36269	60014	07201	62448	46385	42175	88350	46182	49126
44	52567	64350	16315	53969	80395	81114	54358	64578	47269	15747
45	78498	90830	25955	99236	43286	91064	99969	95144	64424	77377
46	49553	24241	08150	89535	08703	91041	77323	81079	45127	93686
47	32151	07075	83155	10252	73100	88618	23891	87418	45417	20268
48	11314	50363	26860	27799	49416	83534	19187	08059	76677	02110
49	12364	71210	87052	50241	90785	97889	81399	58130	64439	05614

Table XII includes digits 10,001 to 20,000, from *A Million Random Digits with 100,000 Normal Deviates,* The RAND Corporation, Free Press, Glencoe, Ill., 1955, reprinted by permission of The RAND Corporation and the publishers.

TABLE XII—*Continued*

Random Digits

C R	0 01234	56789	1 01234	56789	2 01234	56789	3 01234	56789	4 01234	56789
50	59467	58309	87834	57213	37510	33689	01259	62486	56320	46265
51	73452	17619	56421	40725	23439	41701	93223	41682	45026	47505
52	27635	56293	91700	04391	67317	89604	73020	69853	61517	51207
53	86040	02596	01655	09918	45161	00222	54577	74821	47334	08582
54	52403	94255	26351	46527	68224	90183	85057	72310	34963	83462
55	49465	46581	61499	04844	94626	02963	41482	83879	44942	63915
56	94365	92560	12363	30246	02086	75036	88620	91088	67691	67762
57	34261	08769	91830	23313	18256	28850	37639	92748	57791	71328
58	37110	66538	39318	15626	44324	82827	08782	65960	58167	01305
59	83950	45424	72453	19444	68219	64733	94088	62006	89985	36936
60	61630	97966	76537	46467	30942	07479	67971	14558	22458	35148
61	01929	17165	12037	74558	16250	71750	55546	29693	94984	37782
62	41659	39098	23982	29899	71594	77979	54477	13764	17315	72893
63	32031	39608	75992	73445	01317	50525	87313	45191	30214	19769
64	90043	93478	58044	06949	31176	88370	50274	83987	45316	38551
65	79418	14322	91065	07841	36130	86602	10659	40859	00964	71577
66	85447	61079	96910	72906	07361	84338	34114	52096	66715	51091
67	86219	81115	49625	48799	89485	24855	13684	68433	70595	70102
68	71712	88559	92476	32903	68009	58417	87962	11787	16644	72964
69	29776	63075	13270	84758	49560	10317	28778	23006	31036	84906
70	81488	17340	75154	42801	27917	89792	62604	62234	13124	76471
71	51667	37589	87147	24743	48023	06325	79794	35889	13255	04925
72	99004	70322	60832	76636	56907	56534	72615	46288	36788	93196
73	68656	66492	35933	52293	47953	95495	95304	50009	83464	28608
74	38074	74083	09337	07965	65047	36871	59015	21769	30398	44855
75	01020	80680	59328	08712	48190	45332	27284	31287	66011	09376
76	86379	74508	33579	77114	92955	23085	92824	03054	25242	16322
77	48498	09938	44420	13484	52319	58875	02012	88591	52500	95795
78	41800	95362	54142	17482	32705	60564	12505	40954	46174	64130
79	63026	96712	79883	39225	52653	69549	36693	59822	22684	31661
80	88298	15489	16030	42480	15372	38781	71995	77438	91161	10192
81	07839	62735	99218	25624	02547	27445	69187	55749	32322	15504
82	73298	51108	48717	92926	75705	89787	96114	99902	37749	96305
83	12829	70474	00838	50385	91711	80370	56504	56857	80906	09018
84	76569	61072	48568	36491	22587	44363	39592	61546	90181	37348
85	41665	41339	62106	44203	06732	76111	79840	67999	32231	76869
86	58652	49983	01669	27464	79553	52855	25988	18087	38052	17529
87	13607	00657	76173	43357	77334	24140	53860	02906	89863	44651
88	55715	26203	65933	51087	98234	40625	45545	63563	89148	82581
89	04110	66683	99001	09796	47349	65003	66524	81970	71262	14479
90	31300	08681	58068	44115	40064	77879	23965	69019	73985	19453
91	26225	97543	37044	07494	85778	35345	61115	92498	49737	64599
92	07158	82763	25072	38478	57782	75291	62155	52056	04786	11585
93	71251	25572	79771	93328	66927	54069	58752	26624	50463	77361
94	29991	96526	02820	91659	12818	96356	49499	01507	40223	09171
95	83642	21057	02677	09367	38097	16100	19355	06120	15378	56559
96	69167	30235	06767	66323	78294	14916	19124	88044	16673	66102
97	86018	29406	75415	22038	27056	26906	25867	14751	92380	30434
98	44114	06026	79553	55091	95385	41212	37882	46864	54717	97038
99	53805	64150	70915	63127	63695	41288	38192	72437	75075	18570

TABLE XII—*Continued*

Random Digits

C R	5 01234	56789	6 01234	56789	7 01234	56789	8 01234	56789	9 01234	56789
00	52065	08853	30104	79937	66913	53200	84570	78079	28970	53859
01	37632	80274	35240	32960	74859	07359	55176	03930	38984	35151
02	82576	82805	94031	12779	90879	24109	25367	77861	09541	85739
03	69023	64971	99321	07521	95909	43897	71724	92581	05471	64337
04	98949	03606	78236	78985	29212	57369	34857	67757	58019	58872
05	96526	28749	56592	37871	72905	70198	57319	54116	47014	18285
06	33692	72111	60958	96848	17893	40993	50445	14186	76877	87867
07	50335	09513	44346	26439	55293	06449	44301	63740	40158	72703
08	88321	85062	57345	66231	15409	03451	95261	43561	15673	28956
09	90303	62469	82517	43035	36850	15592	64098	59022	31752	04370
10	50486	11885	23085	41712	80692	48492	16495	99721	36912	28267
11	27882	16269	64483	11273	02680	01616	46138	54606	14761	05134
12	45144	63213	49666	27441	86989	29884	54334	06740	08368	80051
13	81020	17882	74973	74531	94994	24927	64894	22667	20466	82948
14	66831	47427	76033	31197	59817	20064	61135	28556	29695	80179
15	74058	18293	09963	35278	13062	83094	23373	90287	33477	48865
16	30348	70174	11468	25994	25343	22317	01587	30682	00001	67814
17	59557	23362	13746	82244	42093	24671	79458	93730	45488	60234
18	67098	09899	25775	00332	36636	57594	19958	85564	58977	12247
19	60774	66371	69442	20385	14486	91330	50332	46023	75768	59877
20	60081	92936	72302	75064	85727	52987	05750	19384	33684	78859
21	80458	69902	34870	88684	49762	40801	86291	18194	90366	82639
22	53844	96326	65728	48563	26027	52692	62406	76294	41848	63010
23	69841	29451	36170	21529	16525	64326	22086	24469	57407	96033
24	37771	31002	18311	93285	31948	14331	58335	15977	80336	81667
25	27286	24361	61638	57580	95270	46180	76990	53031	94366	02727
26	49944	19278	05756	51875	53445	33342	01965	07937	10054	97712
27	87693	58124	46064	39133	77385	09605	65359	70113	90563	86637
28	94282	12025	31926	24541	23854	58407	32131	92845	20714	27898
29	26917	50326	35145	50859	72119	95094	29441	42301	62460	75252
30	94267	38422	73047	24200	85349	72049	91723	97802	98496	12734
31	73432	10371	57213	53300	80847	46229	07099	72961	13767	65654
32	31102	82119	96946	65919	81083	03819	57888	57908	16849	77111
33	41429	92261	45263	01172	55926	78835	27697	48420	58865	41207
34	21406	08582	10785	36233	12237	07866	13706	92551	11021	63813
35	71512	65206	37768	94325	14721	20990	54235	71986	05345	56239
36	52028	01419	07215	55067	11669	21738	66605	69621	69827	08537
37	18638	60982	28151	98885	76431	25566	03085	23639	30849	63986
38	73287	26201	36174	14106	54102	57041	16141	64174	03591	90024
39	73332	31254	17288	59809	25061	51612	47951	16570	43330	79213
40	11354	55585	19646	99246	37564	32660	20632	21124	60597	69315
41	31312	57741	85108	21615	24365	27684	16124	33888	14966	35303
42	69921	15795	04020	67672	86816	63027	84470	45605	44887	26222
43	79888	58982	22466	98844	48353	60666	58256	31140	93507	69561
44	06256	88526	18655	00865	75247	00264	65957	98261	72706	36396
45	46065	85700	32121	99975	73627	78812	89638	86602	96758	65099
46	52777	46792	13790	55240	52002	10313	91933	71231	10053	78416
47	54563	96004	42215	30094	45958	48437	49591	50483	13422	69108
48	59952	27896	40450	79327	31962	46456	39260	51479	61882	48181
49	50691	64709	32902	10676	12083	35771	79656	56667	76783	03937

TABLE XII—*Continued*

Random Digits

| C | 5 | | 6 | | 7 | | 8 | | 9 | |
R	01234	56789	01234	56789	01234	56789	01234	56789	01234	56789
50	99859	10362	57411	40986	35045	02838	29255	64230	84418	34988
51	77644	39892	77327	74129	53444	35487	95803	38640	20383	55402
52	25793	14213	87082	42837	95030	97198	61608	97723	79390	35290
53	34683	81419	87133	70447	53127	97146	28299	56763	12868	01145
54	12147	58158	92124	60934	18414	97510	07056	54488	20719	53743
55	91037	44797	52110	08512	18991	20129	31441	51449	14661	71126
56	23180	68124	18807	70997	21913	19594	70355	73637	68266	60775
57	43164	52643	96363	77989	79332	39890	65379	20405	52935	43816
58	92740	95319	04538	60660	28982	15328	80475	34690	02293	19646
59	46524	96627	33159	42081	08816	74931	20674	08697	66169	46460
60	46326	39923	60625	28386	22919	19415	75766	43668	31626	70301
61	67053	03949	70082	02303	48642	38429	94053	38770	68137	68441
62	52928	70244	91954	17401	92693	98342	21451	84988	80487	33807
63	73797	49494	41878	76635	83227	77618	11946	13451	87591	78381
64	21407	90038	72638	69692	51599	86413	32019	64856	74730	41531
65	11064	01790	58817	86400	66213	92599	70905	78324	54326	43659
66	34206	63132	38837	40210	96346	16967	81619	96503	14881	89405
67	32205	49508	98425	02451	35423	56072	36810	30332	85998	49358
68	92748	84147	79835	94867	41224	61794	35066	82220	66684	20096
69	02754	41731	37068	32753	91059	13407	05607	69384	53329	95909
70	44968	11397	92973	50014	92997	80968	93761	57598	74703	07768
71	37978	73873	33475	09720	97852	98449	48722	84977	11271	11728
72	68318	22312	78792	87508	88466	72976	47099	84126	38595	85124
73	64405	90020	07492	52413	95111	34455	86311	68892	01074	60274
74	28136	19328	38161	57475	13771	63562	84207	94121	18901	52768
75	33801	82087	86091	59969	90398	56870	55756	78841	98450	54165
76	55106	50343	70519	14567	36780	55450	19606	83749	67562	64765
77	38543	16585	86841	73742	08766	39252	75678	75379	78760	37279
78	15280	13558	95916	89759	76686	76467	67147	63110	94008	08037
79	35263	53710	16667	79008	11231	29397	67136	18601	64502	90228
80	89109	72849	22711	65547	34542	26686	81678	87765	77654	23664
81	96352	14106	32938	28083	18633	80286	65507	46197	52722	75476
82	77816	47204	34876	45963	79262	90181	84041	03745	90041	30780
83	27226	92847	85572	15308	80688	05761	82638	13464	23683	81015
84	54214	64175	43701	86845	15569	50687	52679	87696	08285	97444
85	47599	94472	64150	87753	68652	60726	26213	17320	64553	81285
86	98126	12158	52095	64833	00492	35817	55571	91300	97812	37507
87	04209	53515	64342	21223	16662	43265	68219	03529	43636	68417
88	53640	95326	93381	37113	80751	76469	96677	43054	22937	31954
89	13266	34140	27253	02734	99070	60077	57988	93211	92795	83795
90	57477	03941	39007	14619	38320	93449	31336	25279	97030	26245
91	47394	39475	90621	23820	29344	94859	91604	14033	41868	14816
92	04075	66644	87803	97815	99552	78666	03942	08175	22345	19983
93	76783	99044	20851	84981	59052	77178	72109	76475	21619	73017
94	06812	56633	50612	55289	04671	84419	94072	94446	80603	32188
95	93415	23464	43947	43728	74284	67177	57105	31059	10642	13803
96	69602	46961	66567	19359	84676	63918	40650	12923	15974	79732
97	20225	92525	71179	04859	91208	60430	05239	61458	24089	68852
98	60171	29603	42535	86365	93905	28237	45317	60718	82001	41679
99	20679	56304	70043	87568	21386	59049	78353	48696	77379	55309

TABLE XIII

Squares

10.0² to 54.9²

N •	.0	.1	.2	.3	.4	.5	.6	.7	.8	.9
	••		••			••			••	
10	100	102.0	104.0	106.1	108.2	110.3	112.4	114.5	116.6	118.8
11	121	123.2	125.4	127.7	130.0	132.3	134.6	136.9	139.2	141.6
12	144	146.4	148.8	151.3	153.8	156.3	158.8	161.3	163.8	166.4
13	169	171.6	174.2	176.9	179.6	182.3	185.0	187.7	190.4	193.2
14	196	198.8	201.6	204.5	207.4	210.3	213.2	216.1	219.0	220.0
15	225	228.0	231.0	234.1	237.2	240.3	243.4	246.5	249.6	252.8
16	256	259.2	262.4	265.7	269.0	272.3	275.6	278.9	282.2	285.6
17	289	292.4	295.8	299.3	302.8	306.3	309.8	313.3	316.8	320.4
18	324	327.6	331.2	334.9	338.6	342.3	346.0	349.7	353.4	357.2
19	361	364.8	368.6	372.5	376.4	380.3	384.2	388.1	392.0	396.0
20	400	404.0	408.0	412.1	416.2	420.3	424.4	428.5	432.6	436.8
21	441	445.2	449.4	453.7	458.0	462.3	466.6	470.9	475.2	479.6
22	484	488.4	492.8	497.3	501.8	506.3	510.8	515.3	519.8	524.4
23	529	533.6	538.2	542.9	547.6	552.3	557.0	561.7	566.4	571.2
24	576	580.8	585.6	590.5	595.4	600.3	605.2	610.1	615.0	620.0
25	625	630.0	635.0	640.1	645.2	650.3	655.4	660.5	665.6	670.8
26	676	681.2	686.4	691.7	697.0	702.3	707.6	712.9	718.2	723.6
27	729	734.4	739.8	745.3	750.8	756.3	761.8	767.3	772.8	778.4
28	784	789.6	795.2	800.9	806.6	812.3	818.0	823.7	829.4	835.2
29	841	846.8	852.6	858.5	864.4	870.3	876.2	882.1	888.0	894.0
30	900	906.0	912.0	918.1	924.2	930.3	936.4	942.5	948.6	954.8
31	961	967.2	973.4	979.7	986.0	992.3	998.6	1005	1011	1018
32	1024	1030	1037	1043	1050	1056	1063	1069	1076	1082
33	1089	1096	1102	1109	1116	1122	1129	1136	1142	1149
34	1156	1163	1170	1176	1183	1190	1197	1204	1211	1218
35	1225	1232	1239	1246	1253	1260	1267	1274	1282	1289
36	1296	1303	1310	1318	1325	1332	1340	1347	1354	1362
37	1369	1376	1384	1391	1399	1406	1414	1421	1429	1436
38	1444	1452	1459	1467	1475	1482	1490	1498	1505	1513
39	1521	1529	1537	1544	1552	1560	1568	1576	1584	1592
40	1600	1608	1616	1624	1632	1640	1648	1656	1665	1673
41	1681	1689	1697	1706	1714	1722	1731	1739	1747	1756
42	1764	1772	1781	1789	1798	1806	1815	1823	1832	1840
43	1849	1858	1866	1875	1884	1892	1901	1910	1918	1927
44	1936	1945	1954	1962	1971	1980	1989	1998	2007	2016
45	2025	2034	2043	2052	2061	2070	2079	2088	2098	2107
46	2116	2125	2134	2144	2153	2162	2172	2181	2190	2200
47	2209	2218	2228	2237	2247	2256	2266	2275	2285	2294
48	2304	2314	2323	2333	2343	2352	2362	2372	2381	2391
49	2401	2411	2421	2430	2440	2450	2460	2470	2480	2490
50	2500	2510	2520	2530	2540	2550	2560	2570	2581	2591
51	2601	2611	2621	2632	2642	2652	2663	2673	2683	2694
52	2704	2714	2725	2735	2746	2756	2767	2777	2788	2798
53	2809	2820	2830	2841	2852	2862	2873	2884	2894	2905
54	2916	2927	2938	2948	2959	2970	2981	2992	3003	3014

• Shift decimal *two* places in N^2 for *one* place in N.

TABLE XIII—*Continued*

Squares

55.0^2 to 99.9^2

N •	.0	.1	.2	.3	.4	.5	.6	.7	.8	.9
	••		••			••			••	
55	3025	3036	3047	3058	3069	3080	3091	3102	3114	3125
56	3136	3147	3158	3170	3181	3192	3204	3215	3226	3238
57	3249	3260	3272	3283	3295	3306	3318	3329	3341	3352
58	3364	3376	3387	3399	3411	3422	3434	3446	3457	3469
59	3481	3493	3505	3516	3528	3540	3552	3564	3576	3588
60	3600	3612	3624	3636	3648	3660	3672	3684	3697	3709
61	3721	3733	3745	3758	3770	3782	3795	3807	3819	3832
62	3844	3856	3869	3881	3894	3906	3919	3931	3944	3956
63	3969	3982	3994	4007	4020	4032	4045	4058	4070	4083
64	4096	4109	4122	4134	4147	4160	4173	4186	4199	4212
65	4225	4238	4251	4264	4277	4290	4303	4316	4330	4343
66	4356	4369	4382	4396	4409	4422	4436	4449	4462	4476
67	4489	4502	4516	4529	4543	4556	4570	4583	4597	4610
68	4624	4638	4651	4665	4679	4692	4706	4720	4733	4747
69	4761	4775	4789	4802	4816	4830	4844	4858	4872	4886
70	4900	4914	4928	4942	4956	4970	4984	4998	5013	5027
71	5041	5055	5069	5084	5098	5112	5127	5141	5155	5170
72	5184	5198	5213	5227	5242	5256	5271	5285	5300	5314
73	5329	5344	5358	5373	5388	5402	5417	5432	5446	5461
74	5476	5491	5506	5520	5535	5550	5565	5580	5595	5610
75	5625	5640	5655	5670	5685	5700	5715	5730	5746	5761
76	5776	5791	5806	5822	5937	5852	5968	5883	5898	5914
77	5929	5944	5960	5975	5991	6006	6022	6037	6053	6068
78	6084	6100	6115	6131	6147	6162	6178	6194	6209	6225
79	6241	6257	6273	6288	6304	6320	6336	6352	6368	6384
80	6400	6416	6432	6448	6464	6480	6496	6512	6529	6545
81	6561	6577	6593	6610	6626	6642	6659	6675	6691	6708
82	6724	6740	6757	6773	6790	6806	6823	6839	6856	6872
83	6889	6906	6922	6939	6956	6972	6989	7006	7022	7039
84	7056	7073	7090	7106	7123	7140	7157	7174	7191	7208
85	7225	7242	7259	7276	7293	7310	7327	7344	7362	7379
86	7396	7413	7430	7448	7465	7482	7500	7517	7534	7552
87	7569	7586	7604	7621	7639	7656	7674	7691	7708	7726
88	7744	7762	7779	7797	7815	7832	7850	7868	7885	7903
89	7921	7939	7957	7974	7992	8010	8028	8046	8064	8082
90	8100	8118	8136	8154	8172	8190	8208	8226	8245	8263
91	8281	8299	8317	8336	8354	8372	8391	8409	8427	8446
92	8464	8482	8501	8519	8538	8556	8575	8593	8612	8630
93	8649	8668	8686	8705	8724	8742	8761	8780	8798	8817
94	8836	8855	8874	8892	8911	8930	8949	8968	8987	9006
95	9025	9044	9063	9082	9101	9120	9139	9158	9178	9197
96	9216	9235	9254	9274	9293	9312	9332	9351	9370	9390
97	9409	9428	9448	9467	9487	9506	9526	9545	9565	9584
98	9604	9624	9643	9663	9683	9702	9722	9742	9761	9781
99	9801	9821	9841	9860	9880	9900	9920	9940	9960	9980

• Shift decimal *two* places in N^2 for *one* place in N.

TABLE XIV

Square roots

$\sqrt{1.00}$ to $\sqrt{5.49}$

N ••	.00	.01	.02	.03	.04	.05	.06	.07	.08	.09
1.0	1.000	.005	.010	.015	.020	.025	.030	.034	.039	0.44
1.1	.049	.054	.058	.063	.068	.072	.077	.082	.086	.091
1.2	.095	.100	.105	.109	.114	.118	.122	.127	.131	.136
1.3	.140	.145	.149	.153	.158	.162	.166	.170	.175	.179
1.4	.183	.187	.192	.196	.200	.204	.208	.212	.217	.221
1.5	1.225	.229	.233	.237	.241	.245	.249	.253	.257	.261
1.6	.265	.269	.273	.277	.281	.285	.288	.292	.296	.300
1.7	.304	.308	.311	.315	.319	.323	.327	.330	.334	.338
1.8	.342	.345	.349	.353	.356	.360	.364	.367	.371	.375
1.9	.378	.382	.386	.389	.393	.396	.400	.404	.407	.411
2.0	1.414	.418	.421	.425	.428	.432	.435	.439	.442	.446
2.1	.449	.453	.456	.459	.463	.466	.470	.473	.476	.480
2.2	.483	.487	.490	.493	.497	.500	.503	.507	.510	.513
2.3	.517	.520	.523	.526	.530	.533	.536	.539	.543	.546
2.4	.549	.552	.556	.559	.562	.565	.568	.572	.575	.578
2.5	1.581	.584	.587	.591	.594	.597	.600	.603	.606	.609
2.6	.612	.616	.619	.622	.625	.628	.631	.634	.637	.640
2.7	.643	.646	.649	.652	.655	.658	.661	.664	.667	.670
2.8	.673	.676	.679	.682	.685	.688	.691	.694	.697	.700
2.9	.703	.706	.709	.712	.715	.718	.720	.723	.726	.729
3.0	1.732	.735	.738	.741	.744	.746	.749	.752	.755	.758
3.1	.761	.764	.766	.769	.772	.775	.778	.780	.783	.786
3.2	.789	.792	.794	.797	.800	.803	.806	.808	.811	.814
3.3	.817	.819	.822	.825	.828	.830	.833	.836	.838	.841
3.4	.844	.847	.849	.852	.855	.857	.860	.863	.865	.868
3.5	1.871	.874	.876	.879	.881	.884	.887	.889	.892	.895
3.6	.897	.900	.903	.905	.908	.911	.913	.916	.918	.921
3.7	.924	.926	.929	.931	.934	.936	.939	.942	.944	.947
3.8	.949	.952	.954	.957	.960	.962	.965	.967	.970	.972
3.9	.975	.977	.980	.982	.985	.987	.990	.992	.995	.997
4.0	2.000	.002	.005	.007	.010	.012	.015	.017	.020	.022
4.1	.025	.027	.030	.032	.035	.037	.040	.042	.044	.047
4.2	.049	.052	.054	.057	.059	.062	.064	.066	.069	.071
4.3	.074	.076	.078	.081	.083	.086	.088	.090	.093	.095
4.4	.098	.100	.102	.105	.107	.110	.112	.114	.117	.119
4.5	2.121	.124	.126	.128	.131	.133	.135	.138	.140	.142
4.6	.145	.147	.149	.152	.154	.156	.159	.161	.163	.166
4.7	.168	.170	.173	.175	.177	.179	.182	.184	.186	.189
4.8	.191	.193	.195	.198	.200	.202	.205	.207	.209	.211
4.9	.214	.216	.218	.220	.223	.225	.227	.229	.232	.234
5.0	2.236	.238	.241	.243	.245	.247	.249	.252	.254	.256
5.1	.258	.261	.263	.265	.267	.269	.272	.274	.176	.278
5.2	.280	.283	.285	.287	.289	.291	.293	.296	.298	.300
5.3	.302	.304	.307	.309	.311	.313	.315	.317	.319	.322
5.4	.324	.326	.328	.330	.332	.335	.337	.339	.341	.343

•• Shift decimal *two* places in N for *one* place in $\sqrt{N}$.

TABLE XIV—*Continued*

Square roots $\sqrt{5.50}$ to $\sqrt{9.99}$

N ••	.00	.01	.02	.03	.04	.05	.06	.07	.08	.09
	•		•			•			•	
5.5	2.345	.347	.349	.352	.354	.356	.358	.360	.362	.364
5.6	.366	.369	.371	.373	.375	.377	.379	.381	.383	.385
5.7	.387	.390	.392	.394	.396	.398	.400	.402	.404	.406
5.8	.408	.410	.412	.415	.417	.419	.421	.423	.425	.427
5.9	.429	.431	.433	.435	.437	.439	.441	.443	.445	.447
6.0	2.449	.452	.454	.456	.458	.460	.462	.464	.466	.468
6.1	.470	.472	.474	.476	.478	.480	.482	.484	.486	.488
6.2	.490	.492	.494	.496	.498	.500	.502	.504	.506	.508
6.3	.510	.512	.514	.516	.518	.520	.522	.524	.526	.528
6.4	.530	.532	.534	.536	.538	.540	.542	.544	.546	.548
6.5	2.550	.551	.553	.555	.557	.559	.561	.563	.565	.567
6.6	.569	.571	.573	.575	.577	.579	.581	.583	.585	.587
6.7	.588	.590	.592	.594	.596	.598	.600	.602	.604	.606
6.8	.608	.610	.612	.613	.615	.617	.619	.621	.623	.625
6.9	.627	.629	.631	.632	.634	.636	.638	.640	.642	.644
7.0	2.646	.648	.650	.651	.653	.655	.657	.659	.661	.663
7.1	.665	.666	.668	.670	.672	.674	.676	.678	.680	.681
7.2	.683	.685	.687	.689	.691	.693	.694	.696	.698	.700
7.3	.702	.704	.706	.707	.709	.711	.713	.715	.717	.718
7.4	.720	.722	.724	.726	.728	.729	.731	.733	.735	.737
7.5	2.739	.740	.742	.744	.746	.748	.750	.751	.753	.755
7.6	.757	.759	.760	.762	.764	.766	.768	.769	.771	.773
7.7	.775	.777	.778	.780	.782	.784	.786	.787	.789	.791
7.8	.793	.795	.796	.798	.800	.802	.804	.805	.807	.809
7.9	.811	.812	.814	.816	.818	.820	.821	.823	.825	.827
8.0	2.828	.830	.832	.834	.836	.837	.839	.841	.843	.844
8.1	.846	.848	.850	.851	.853	.855	.857	.858	.860	.862
8.2	.864	.865	.867	.869	.871	.872	.874	.876	.878	.879
8.3	.881	.883	.884	.886	.888	.890	.891	.893	.895	.897
8.4	.898	.900	.902	.903	.905	.907	.909	.910	.912	.914
8.5	2.915	.917	.919	.921	.922	.924	.926	.927	.929	.931
8.6	.933	.934	.936	.938	.939	.941	.943	.944	.946	.948
8.7	.950	.951	.953	.955	.956	.958	.960	.961	.963	.965
8.8	.966	.968	.970	.972	.973	.975	.977	.978	.980	.982
8.9	.983	.985	.987	.988	.990	.992	.993	.995	.997	.998
9.0	3.000	.002	.003	.005	.007	.008	.010	.012	.013	.015
9.1	.017	.018	.020	.022	.023	.025	.027	.028	.030	.031
9.2	.033	.035	.036	.038	.040	.041	.043	.045	.046	.048
9.3	.050	.051	.053	.055	.056	.058	.059	.061	.063	.064
9.4	.066	.068	.069	.071	.072	.074	.076	.077	.079	.081
9.5	3.082	.084	.085	.087	.089	.090	.092	.094	.095	.097
9.6	.098	.100	.102	.103	.105	.106	.108	.110	.111	.113
9.7	.114	.116	.118	.119	.121	.122	.124	.126	.127	.129
9.8	.130	.132	.134	.135	.137	.138	.140	.142	.143	.145
9.9	.146	.148	.150	.151	.153	.154	.156	.158	.159	.161

•• Shift decimal *two* places in N for *one* place in $\sqrt{N}$.

TABLE XIV—*Continued*

Square roots

$\sqrt{10.0}$ to $\sqrt{54.9}$

N ••	.0	.1	.2	.3	.4	.5	.6	.7	.8	.9
10	3.162	.178	.194	.209	.225	.240	.256	.271	.286	.302
11	.317	.332	.347	.362	.376	.391	.406	.421	.435	.450
12	.464	.479	.493	.507	.521	.536	.550	.564	.578	.592
13	.606	.619	.633	.647	.661	.674	.688	.701	.715	.728
14	.742	.755	.768	.782	.795	.808	.821	.834	.847	.860
15	3.873	.886	.899	.912	.924	.937	.950	.962	.975	.987
16	4.000	.012	.025	.037	.050	.062	.074	.087	.099	.111
17	.123	.135	.147	.159	.171	.183	.195	.207	.219	.231
18	.243	.254	.266	.278	.290	.301	.313	.324	.336	.347
19	.359	.370	.382	.393	.405	.416	.427	.438	.450	.461
20	4.472	.483	.494	.506	.517	.528	.539	.550	.561	.572
21	.583	.593	.604	.615	.626	.637	.648	.658	.669	.680
22	.690	.701	.712	.722	.733	.743	.754	.764	.775	.785
23	.796	.806	.817	.827	.837	.848	.858	.868	.879	.889
24	.899	.909	.919	.929	.940	.950	.960	.970	.980	.990
25	5.000	.010	.020	.030	.040	.050	.060	.070	.079	.089
26	.099	.109	.119	.128	.138	.148	.158	.167	.177	.187
27	.196	.206	.215	.225	.235	.244	.254	.263	.273	.282
28	.292	.301	.310	.320	.329	.339	.348	.357	.367	.376
29	.385	.394	.404	.413	.422	.431	.441	.450	.459	.468
30	5.477	.486	.495	.505	.514	.523	.532	.541	.550	.559
31	.568	.577	.586	.595	.604	.612	.621	.630	.639	.648
32	.657	.666	.675	.683	.692	.701	.710	.718	.727	.736
33	.745	.753	.762	.771	.779	.788	.797	.805	.814	.822
34	.831	.840	.848	.857	.865	.874	.882	.891	.799	.908
35	5.916	.925	.933	.941	.950	.958	.967	.975	.983	.992
36	6.000	.008	.017	.025	.033	.041	.050	.058	.066	.075
37	.083	.091	.099	.017	.116	.124	.132	.140	.148	.156
38	.164	.173	.181	.189	.197	.205	.213	.221	.229	.237
39	.245	.253	.261	.269	.277	.285	.293	.301	.309	.317
40	6.325	.332	.349	.348	.356	.364	.372	.380	.387	.395
41	.403	.411	.419	.427	.434	.442	.450	.458	.465	.472
42	.481	.488	.496	.504	.512	.519	.527	.535	.542	.550
43	.557	.565	.573	.580	.588	.595	.603	.611	.618	.626
44	.633	.641	.648	.656	.663	.671	.678	.686	.693	.701
45	6.708	.716	.723	.731	.738	.745	.753	.760	.768	.775
46	.782	.790	.797	.804	.812	.819	.826	.834	.841	.848
47	.856	.863	.870	.877	.885	.892	.899	.907	.914	.921
48	.928	.935	.943	.950	.957	.964	.971	.979	.986	.993
49	7.000	.007	.014	.021	.029	.036	.043	.050	.057	.064
50	7.071	.078	.085	.092	.099	.106	.113	.120	.127	.134
51	.141	.148	.155	.162	.169	.176	.183	.190	.197	.204
52	.211	.218	.225	.232	.239	.246	.253	.259	.266	.273
53	.280	.287	.294	.301	.308	.314	.321	.328	.335	.342
54	.348	.355	.362	.369	.376	.382	.389	.396	.403	.409

•• Shift decimal *two* places in N for *one* place in $\sqrt{N}$.

TABLE XIV—*Continued*

Square roots $\sqrt{55.0}$ to $\sqrt{99.9}$

N ••	.0	.1	.2	.3	.4	.5	.6	.7	.8	.9
	•		•			•			•	
55	7.416	.423	.430	.436	.443	.450	.457	.463	.470	.470
56	.483	.490	.497	.503	.510	.517	.523	.530	.537	.543
57	.550	.556	.563	.570	.576	.583	.589	.596	.603	.609
58	.616	.622	.629	.635	.642	.649	.655	.662	.668	.675
59	.681	.688	.694	.701	.707	.714	.720	.727	.733	.740
60	7.746	.752	.759	.765	.772	.778	.785	.791	.797	.804
61	.810	.817	.823	.830	.836	.842	.849	.855	.861	.868
62	.874	.880	.887	.893	.899	.906	.912	.918	.925	.931
63	.937	.944	.950	.956	.962	.969	.975	.981	.987	.994
64	8.000	.006	.012	.019	.025	.031	.037	.044	.050	.056
65	8.062	.068	.075	.081	.087	.093	.099	.106	.112	.118
66	.124	.130	.136	.142	.149	.155	.161	.167	.173	.179
67	.185	.191	.198	.204	.210	.216	.222	.228	.234	.240
68	.246	.252	.258	.264	.270	.276	.283	.289	.295	.301
69	.307	.313	.319	.325	.331	.337	.343	.349	.355	.361
70	8.367	.373	.379	.385	.390	.396	.402	.408	.414	.420
71	.426	.432	.438	.444	.450	.456	.462	.468	.473	.479
72	.485	.491	.497	.503	.509	.515	.521	.526	.532	.538
73	.544	.550	.556	.562	.567	.573	.579	.585	.591	.597
74	.602	.608	.614	.620	.626	.631	.637	.643	.649	.654
75	8.660	.666	.672	.678	.683	.689	.695	.701	.706	.712
76	.718	.724	.729	.735	.741	.746	.752	.758	.764	.769
77	.775	.781	.786	.792	.798	.803	.809	.815	.820	.826
78	.832	.837	.843	.849	.854	.860	.866	.871	.877	.883
79	.888	.894	.899	.905	.911	.916	.922	.927	.933	.939
80	8.944	.950	.955	.961	.967	.972	.978	.983	.989	.994
81	9.000	.006	.011	.017	.022	.028	.033	.039	.044	.050
82	.055	.061	.066	.072	.077	.083	.088	.094	.099	.105
83	.110	.116	.121	.127	.132	.138	.143	.149	.154	.160
84	.165	.171	.176	.182	.187	.192	.198	.203	.209	.214
85	9.220	.225	.230	.236	.241	.247	.252	.257	.263	.268
86	.274	.279	.284	.290	.295	.301	.306	.311	.317	.322
87	.327	.333	.338	.343	.349	.354	.359	.365	.370	.375
88	.381	.386	.391	.397	.402	.407	.413	.418	.423	.429
89	.434	.439	.445	.450	.455	.460	.466	.471	.476	.482
90	9.487	.492	.497	.503	.508	.513	.518	.524	.529	.534
91	.539	.545	.550	.555	.560	.566	.571	.576	.581	.586
92	.592	.597	.602	.607	.612	.618	.623	.628	.633	.638
93	.644	.649	.654	.659	.664	.670	.675	.680	.685	.690
94	.695	.701	.706	.711	.716	.721	.726	.731	.737	.742
95	9.747	.752	.757	.762	.767	.772	.778	.783	.788	.793
96	.798	.803	.808	.813	.818	.823	.828	.834	.839	.844
97	.849	.854	.859	.864	.869	.874	.879	.884	.889	.894
98	.899	.905	.910	.915	.920	.925	.930	.935	.940	.945
99	.950	.955	.960	.965	.970	.975	.980	.985	.990	.995

•• Shift decimal *two* places in N for *one* place in $\sqrt{N}$.

TABLE XV
Common logarithms

N	0	1	2	3	4	5	6	7	8	9
10	0000	0043	0086	0128	0170	0212	0253	0294	0334	0374
11	0414	0453	0492	0531	0569	0607	0645	0682	0719	0755
12	0792	0828	0864	0899	0934	0969	1004	1038	1072	1106
13	1139	1173	1206	1239	1271	1303	1335	1367	1399	1430
14	1461	1492	1523	1553	1584	1614	1644	1673	1703	1732
15	1761	1790	1818	1847	1875	1903	1931	1959	1987	2014
16	2041	2068	2095	2122	2148	2175	2201	2227	2253	2279
17	2304	2330	2355	2380	2405	2430	2455	2480	2504	2529
18	2553	2577	2601	2625	2648	2672	2695	2718	2742	2765
19	2788	2810	2833	2856	2878	2900	2923	2945	2967	2989
20	3010	3032	3054	3075	3096	3118	3139	3160	3181	3201
21	3222	3243	3263	3284	3304	3324	3345	3365	3385	3404
22	3424	3444	3464	3483	3502	3522	3541	3560	3579	3598
23	3617	3636	3655	3674	3692	3711	3729	3747	3766	3784
24	3802	3820	3838	3856	3874	3892	3909	3927	3945	3962
25	3979	3997	4014	4031	4048	4065	4082	4099	4116	4133
26	4150	4166	4183	4200	4216	4232	4249	4265	4281	4298
27	4314	4330	4346	4362	4378	4393	4409	4425	4440	4456
28	4472	4487	4502	4518	4533	4548	4564	4579	4594	4609
29	4624	4639	4654	4669	4683	4698	4713	4728	4742	4757
30	4771	4786	4800	4814	4829	4843	4857	4871	4886	4900
31	4914	4928	4942	4955	4969	4983	4997	5011	5024	5038
32	5051	5065	5079	5092	5105	5119	5132	5145	5159	5172
33	5185	5198	5211	5224	5237	5250	5263	5276	5289	5302
34	5315	5328	5340	5353	5366	5378	5391	5403	5416	5428
35	5441	5453	5465	5478	5490	5502	5514	5527	5539	5551
36	5563	5575	5587	5599	5611	5623	5635	5647	5658	5670
37	5682	5694	5705	5717	5729	5740	5752	5763	5775	5786
38	5798	5809	5821	5832	5843	5855	5866	5877	5888	5899
39	5911	5922	5933	5944	5955	5966	5977	5988	5999	6010
40	6021	6031	6042	6053	6064	6075	6085	6096	6107	6117
41	6128	6138	6149	6160	6170	6180	6191	6201	6212	6222
42	6232	6243	6253	6263	6274	6284	6294	6304	6314	6325
43	6335	6345	6355	6365	6375	6385	6395	6405	6415	6425
44	6435	6444	6454	6464	6474	6484	6493	6503	6513	6522
45	6532	6542	6551	6561	6571	6580	6590	6599	6609	6618
46	6628	6637	6646	6656	6665	6675	6684	6693	6702	6712
47	6721	6730	6739	6749	6758	6767	6776	6785	6794	6803
48	6812	6821	6830	6839	6848	6857	6866	6875	6884	6893
49	6902	6911	6920	6928	6937	6946	6955	6964	6972	6981
50	6990	6998	7007	7016	7024	7033	7042	7050	7059	7067
51	7076	7084	7093	7101	7110	7118	7126	7135	7143	7152
52	7160	7168	7177	7185	7193	7202	7210	7218	7226	7235
53	7243	7251	7259	7267	7275	7284	7292	7300	7308	7316
54	7324	7332	7340	7348	7356	7364	7372	7380	7388	7396
N	0	1	2	3	4	5	6	7	8	9

TABLE XV—*Continued*

Common logarithms

N	0	1	2	3	4	5	6	7	8	9
55	7404	7412	7419	7427	7435	7443	7451	7459	7466	7474
56	7482	7490	7497	7505	7513	7520	7528	7536	7543	7551
57	7559	7566	7574	7582	7589	7597	7604	7612	7619	7627
58	7634	7642	7649	7657	7664	7672	7679	7686	7694	7701
59	7709	7716	7723	7731	7738	7745	7752	7760	7767	7774
60	7782	7789	7796	7803	7810	7818	7825	7832	7839	7846
61	7853	7860	7868	7875	7882	7889	7896	7903	7910	7917
62	7924	7931	7938	7945	7952	7959	7966	7973	7980	7987
63	7993	8000	8007	8014	8021	8028	8035	8041	8048	8055
64	8062	8069	8075	8082	8089	8096	8102	8109	8116	8122
65	8129	8136	8142	8149	8156	8162	8169	8176	8182	8189
66	8195	8202	8209	8215	8222	8228	8235	8241	8248	8254
67	8261	8267	8274	8280	8287	8293	8299	8306	8312	8319
68	8325	8331	8338	8344	8351	8357	8363	8370	8376	8382
69	8388	8395	8401	8407	8414	8420	8426	8432	8439	8445
70	8451	8457	8463	8470	8476	8482	8488	8494	8500	8506
71	8513	8519	8525	8531	8537	8543	8549	8555	8561	8567
72	8573	8579	8585	8591	8597	8603	8609	8615	8621	8627
73	8633	8639	8645	8651	8657	8663	8669	8675	8681	8686
74	8692	8698	8704	8710	8716	8722	8727	8733	8739	8745
75	8751	8756	8762	8768	8774	8779	8785	8791	8797	8802
76	8808	8814	8820	8825	8831	8837	8842	8848	8854	8859
77	8865	8871	8876	8882	8887	8893	8899	8904	8910	8915
78	8921	8927	8932	8938	8943	8949	8954	8960	8965	8971
79	8976	8982	8987	8993	8998	9004	9009	9015	9020	9025
80	9031	9036	9042	9047	9053	9058	9063	9069	9074	9079
81	9085	9090	9096	9101	9106	9112	9117	9122	9128	9133
82	9138	9143	9149	9154	9159	9165	9170	9175	9180	9186
83	9191	9196	9201	9206	9212	9217	9222	9227	9232	9238
84	9243	9248	9253	9258	9263	9269	9274	9279	9284	9289
85	9294	9299	9304	9309	9315	9320	9325	9330	9335	9340
86	9345	9350	9355	9360	9365	9370	9375	9380	9385	9390
87	9395	9400	9405	9410	9415	9420	9425	9430	9435	9440
88	9445	9450	9455	9460	9465	9469	9474	9479	9484	9489
89	9494	9499	9504	9509	9513	9518	9523	9528	9533	9538
90	9542	9547	9552	9557	9562	9566	9571	9576	9581	9586
91	9590	9595	9600	9605	9609	9614	9619	9624	9628	9633
92	9638	9643	9647	9652	9657	9661	9666	9671	9675	9680
93	9685	9689	9694	9699	9703	9708	9713	9717	9722	9727
94	9731	9736	9741	9745	9750	9754	9759	9763	9768	9773
95	9777	9782	9786	9791	9795	9800	9805	9809	9814	9818
96	9823	9827	9832	9836	9841	9845	9850	9854	9859	9863
97	9868	9872	9877	9881	9886	9890	9894	9899	9903	9908
98	9912	9917	9921	9926	9930	9934	9939	9943	9948	9952
99	9956	9961	9965	9969	9974	9978	9983	9987	9991	9996
N	0	1	2	3	4	5	6	7	8	9

INDEX

Note: Mathematical symbols do not appear in the index. They are defined in the Glossary of Symbols, page 263.

A

abscissa, 17
absolute value, 24
Adelson, J., 163
alienation, coefficient of, 197, 201
Allport, F. H., 234
alpha error, 254
analysis of variance, 125–130, 132–139
  of interaction, 133–135, 137–139
  multi-dimensional, 138 f.
  one-dimensional, 125–130
  two-dimensional, 132–138
  see also variance ratio
angular transformation, 237
Armsen, P., 151n.
assumed mean, 49
assumptions, of parametric methods, 97, 232 f., 258
  of regression formulas, 202
attenuation, correction for, 202–204, 216
attribute scores, 144
average, arithmetic, 22
  see also mean
average deviation, 29

B

Baldwin, R. R., 12
Balvin, R. S., 250 f.
Bartlett's test, 132
Bennett, G. K., 107
Bernstein, A., 162 f.
best fit, *see* line of best fit
beta coefficient, 212
beta error, 254
between-estimate of variance, 127
bias, in differentiation ratio, 130
  due to grouping, 50 f.
  in small samples, 95 f.
  in variance estimate, 69
bimodal distribution, 25, 149
binomial coefficients, 72, 76
  table, 273
binomial distribution, 73 f.
  and fourfold table, 148
  and sign tests, 238
  variance of, 145
bivariate distribution, 166 f.
  quadrants of, 175 f.
Blodgett, H. C., 7, 12
Bush, R. R., 159

ANSWERS TO COMPUTATIONAL PROBLEMS

NOTE: Where there are more than two problems of the same pattern, later answers are omitted.

Chapter 2: *(4)* $\bar{A} = 3.76$, mdn $= 3.9$; $\bar{B} = 3.23$, mdn $= 3.3$

Chapter 3: *(2)* With $i_A = 0.2$, $\bar{A} = 3.76$, $\Sigma a^2 = 13.55$; with $i_B = 0.3$, $\bar{B} = 3.22$, $\Sigma b^2 = 16.06$ *(3)* $\eta^2 = .408$

Chapter 4: *(1)* 60.4; 62.5 *(2)* .387, .398; .459, .472

Chapter 5: *(2)* Proportions for successive scores, 0 to 8, are: .004, .031, .109, .219, .273, .219, .109, .031, .004 *(3)* Similarly, .100, .267, .312, .208, .086, .023, .004, .000, .000 *(5)* Dick; Tom; Harry *(6)* Using 70.0, 90.0, etc., as theoretical class limits, proportions are: .030, .244, .452, .244, .030 *(7)* 62 and below, 63 to 87, 88 to 112, 113 to 137, 138 and above

Chapter 6: *(1)* 39.44 to 43.42 *(2)* 26.20 to 29.76; 25.62 to 30.34

Chapter 7: *(1)* First three t's $= .35$, 1.13, 1.45 *(2)* For publications-religious comparisons, first three t's $= 2.5$, .40, 1.99 *(3)* $t = 2.17$

Chapter 8: *(1)* For Hs, $F = 7.05$; for D, $F = 1.13$ *(2)* For first three scales, F's $= 1.25$, 1.07, 1.50; for the last of these, $P < .10$ *(4)* $F = 10.3$ *(5)* $F = 1.84$ *(6)* $F = 9.75$ *(7)* $F = 11.2$

Chapter 9: A corrected χ^2 cannot be computed for "collecting," because χ^2 vanishes with the correction; for negativistic-cooperative, $\chi^2 = 2.96$ *(2)* $\chi^2 = 13.14$ *(3)* For dating, $\chi^2 = 5.67$; for humor, 7.20; for punishment, 25.06, with $df = 2$ *(5)* 21 *(7)* $z = 4.7$, $\chi^2 = 21.17$

Chapter 10: *(1)* $r_{AB} = .03$; $r_{AC} = .52$ *(3)* $r = .11$, $\eta_{V \cdot A} = .279$; for test of linearity, $F = 2.89$ *(5)* $r = -.505$, $\eta_{A \cdot S} = .555$; for test of linearity, $F = 2.16$

Chapter 11: *(1)* 17, 20 *(2)* $C' = 31$; $C' = 92$ *(3)* In first case, $-2.07\sigma < Y' < 1.06\sigma$, and $2 < C' < 86$ *(4)* .45 *(5)* .93; .64; .80; .78 *(6)* .824; .95

Chapter 12: *(4)* 6, 16; 5, 15

Chapter 13: *(1)* $\chi^2 = 2.31$, $df = 3$ *(2)* $F = 4.00$ *(3)* $P > .05$ by sign test, $P < .05$ by signed-ranks test *(4)* $r'_{AB} = .06$; $r'_{AC} = .45$ *(5)* $W = .296$; $\chi^2_r = 6.4$ *(6)* $z = 2.11$ *(7)* $H = 9.78$